THE EXTRUSION OF METALS

THE EXTRUSION
OF METALS

CLAUDE E. PEARSON

M.Met. (Sheffield), F.I.M.

Lately Professor of Metallurgy
in the University of Durham

and

REDVERS N. PARKINS

B.Sc., Ph.D., A.I.M.

Lecturer in Metallurgy
Kings College
University of Durham

SECOND EDITION
REVISED

NEW YORK

JOHN WILEY & SONS INC.

440 FOURTH AVENUE

1960

First published *1944*
Reprinted with revisions *1953*
Second edition (revised) *1960*

© CLAUDE E. PEARSON
AND REDVERS N. PARKINS 1960

Printed in Great Britain by Butler & Tanner Ltd., Frome and London

Preface to Second Edition

THE advances in the technology and science of extrusion can no longer be accommodated by revisions of the original edition. For example, notable progress has been made in our understanding of the complex deformation which metals undergo during extrusion. Experimental work, coupled with mathematical treatment, have enabled a theory of flow to be evolved which serves as a most valuable guide to industrial practice. This has merited the introduction of a special chapter to deal with it.

From the industrial aspect, the modern trend to fully automatic operation of presses is leading to increased efficiency, partly by reducing the time occupied by idle motions. The very powerful rapid-acting units now available in some countries permit not only much larger sections to be made but, more important, bring into the scope of the process many high-performance alloys which on account of their stiffness were previously marginal but are now processed as a routine. The introduction of glass as a high-temperature lubricant has overcome many of the earlier obstacles to the economic extrusion of steel and other alloys, giving rise to the possibility of a vast field of application.

The unique quality which the process offers of deformation under predominantly compressive forces has proved attractive for the working of the new metals which metallurgy has recently brought into service. The advent of stepped extrusions and growing use of composite billets for making cladded products, such as nuclear fuel elements, are further examples of extended applications. Exciting as some of these are by reason of their novelty, the basic principles involved are those which are well established, and the treatment given in the present edition has aimed at keeping these developments in their correct perspective.

Besides the acknowledgments made in the earlier edition, much of the new material introduced in the present one, especially in the form of diagrams and illustrations, is due to the valuable help which has been received from many individuals and organizations, in particular from:

Dr. J. F. W. Bishop
Mr. R. M. L. Elkan
Dr. A. P. Green
Mr. C. Smith
Aluminium Development Association
British Iron and Steel Research Association
British Non-Ferrous Metals Research Association
Department of Scientific and Industrial Research
Dow Chemical Co., Ltd.
Felton and Guillaeume Carlswerk A. G.
Fielding and Platt Ltd.
General Cable Corporation
G.W.B. Furnaces Ltd.
Hackbridge Cable Co., Ltd.
Hadfields Ltd.
Hydraulik G.M.B.H.
Loewy Engineering Co., Ltd.
Magnesium Elektron Ltd.
Ministry of Supply
Mond Nickel Co., Ltd.
Northern Aluminium Co., Ltd.
Pirelli-General Cable Works Ltd.
Schloemann A.G.
Stein and Atkinson Ltd.

Diagrams or photographs from:

Journal of the Institute of Metals
Journal of the Iron and Steel Institute
Journal of the Mechanics and Physics of Solids
Metal Industry
Metallurgia
Metallurgical Reviews
Transactions of the American Society for Mechanical Engineers

To these and to all who have contributed our gratitude is due.

C. E. P.
R. N. P.

Preface to First Edition

THE process of extrusion has undergone such vigorous development in the course of the last thirty years that it is now entitled to rank among the foremost of the technical methods by which metals are wrought into shape. Among industrial alloys there are few indeed to whose working it is not applied to some extent; and for many it possesses unique importance. Add to this that it would be difficult to overstate the contribution which extruded products of all kinds have made during the war towards meeting the insistent demands of the supply services, and it is clear that, whatever may be the shortcomings of the present book, no apology need be offered for writing it.

It is quite evident from the existence of an extensive literature that a lively interest is taken in extrusion problems. Unfortunately, the data relating to it are widely dispersed, and since, in addition, practice in extrusion has tended to diverge in meeting the special requirements of different materials, it has become a matter of difficulty to obtain a comprehensive view of its various branches. The author has endeavoured in this volume to collate the scattered information existing on the subject and to present from it a concise account of extrusion practice relating to different classes of work and materials. The historical development of the process has been shortly indicated, since it appears not to have been dealt with previously. An attempt has been made to avoid offering a mere description of plant and procedure by introducing theoretical aspects where possible. With this object, chapters have been included to deal with flow phenomena in the process; and with factors, such as temperature, the speed and extent of deformation, etc., in their influence on the extrusion of metals. In regard to this, the author has drawn, besides his own experiments, upon the important investigations carried out in Germany. The subject of impact extrusion tends to fall into a class by itself, and has received separate treatment. Some space has also been given to those specialized methods of extrusion which form a connecting-link between it and forging.

In the compilation of data for the book the author owes much to individuals and firms, too numerous for separate mention, who have been generous in providing advice and facilities for observation, and to them he extends his grateful thanks. He is indebted also to the Leverhulme Research Fellowship Committee, with whose support he was enabled to travel in Germany and the U.S.A. for purposes of studying extrusion technique. Specific acknowledgment has been made in the text so far as possible to the many companies which have kindly supplied drawings and photographs, and to the professional and technical journals which have sanctioned the use of their illustrations. The opportunity is taken here to refer to the courtesy of the Controller of H.M. Stationery Office in permitting the inclusion of Figs. 22, 55, 57, 58, 59, 71, 140, 142, taken, respectively, from British Patents Nos. 457,445; 335,124; 308,569; 408,187; 533,468; 533,082; 469,550; 459,742; also to that of the Editor of *Engineering* in sanctioning the use and lending blocks for the diagrams in Chapter I, which derive from a paper by the author to the Newcomen Society. Figs. 84–87, 96, 99–102, 104, 111, 120, 122, 128 are reproduced from the *Journal of the Institute of Metals* with the kind agreement of the Secretary, Mr. G. Shaw-Scott, M.Sc.

The author is especially indebted to Mr. Kenneth Gray and Mr. O. Kennedy for criticizing sections of the work; also to Mr. R. Hiscock, Lecturer in Engineering, and Mr. H. Walker, Photographer to the Library, both of King's College, Newcastle-upon-Tyne, for valuable assistance in connection with the illustrations. Finally, he wishes to record his sincere appreciation of the painstaking work of his friend, Mr. J. E. Newson, M.Met., in criticizing the subject matter and in the revision of the proofs.

C. E. P

Contents

CHAPTER I

Historical Survey

EXTRUSION is a comparative new-comer among the industrial methods by which metals are wrought into useful forms, but it has succeeded in establishing itself firmly as one of the foremost of these. Essentially the process is one by which a block of solid metal is converted into a continuous length of uniform cross-section by forcing it to flow, under high pressure, through a die orifice which is so shaped as to impart the required form to the product.* In the main it is a hot working operation, the metal being heated to give it a suitable degree of softness and plasticity; but it can also, in some instances, be carried out in

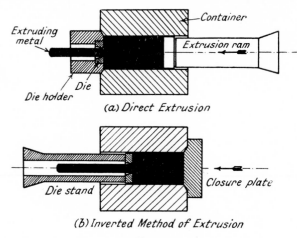

(a) Direct Extrusion

(b) Inverted Method of Extrusion

FIG. 1.

the cold. In the method chiefly adopted, cast billets of cylindrical shape, placed within a strong walled enclosure, are caused

* ' To extrude ' means literally to thrust or force out (L. *ex* + *trudere*). The New English Dictionary gives as one definition of ' extrusion '—the act of expulsion by mechanical force.

I

to extrude through the die under the powerful pressure exerted by a ram, actuated hydraulically or mechanically.

The sketches in Fig. 1 serve to illustrate the essential principle of the process, and, at the same time, enable the distinction between two methods of working, known as direct and inverted extrusion, to be made clear. These depend on the arrangement of the tools. The characteristic of the first is that the die is located at one end of the container and the metal to be extruded is driven towards it, thus moving relatively to the container, by the ram entering from the opposite end. In the case of inverted extrusion, the die is placed on the end of the ram, which is bored out to allow the passage of the extruded bar, and moves through the container from one end, the opposite end being closed. In neither of these methods is it essential for the ram to be the moving member: it can have a fixed position and the container be made to move over it. It is, in fact, generally more convenient, in using the inverted process for the container to be made to travel under the power stroke, and for the die to be attached to a stationary ram, or as it now becomes, a die stand which is attached to the head of the press frame.

The Origin of Extrusion

It is probable that the earliest perception of the principles of extrusion was due to Joseph Bramah, the famous hydraulic engineer, who, in a patent granted in 1797, described a press, shown in Fig. 2, ' For making pipes of lead or other soft metals of all dimensions and of any given length without joints '. Lead, maintained molten in an iron pot (a), by a fire beneath, was forced by a pump (b) into a long projecting tube (c), which served as a die. A tapered mandrel (d) was supported concentrically with the tube by means of a bridge in its enlarged end. The lead passing through the annular space between the tube and mandrel was kept molten by the fuel gases inside the outer casing until it approached the outlet, where it was chilled to cause it to solidify so that it emerged in the form of a pipe. Though it is doubtful whether this apparatus, which, it may be remarked, was devised to make pipes for the distribution of beer and similar liquors, ever operated satisfactorily, it claims attention in providing the first record of a machine which embodies a conception of the idea of extrusion, while it contains, too, the germ, of the idea of die-casting.

There was no immediate development of Bramah's idea, and the earlier methods of making lead pipes by casting a hollow cylindrical billet, and either drawing this through holes in an iron plate, or rolling it on a mandrel between grooved rolls, continued to be used, and it was not until 1820, when Thomas Burr, a Shrewsbury plumber, constructed a press operated by hydraulic power, that the manufacture of lead pipes by extrusion or, as it was then called, squirting, came into actual operation. Burr's

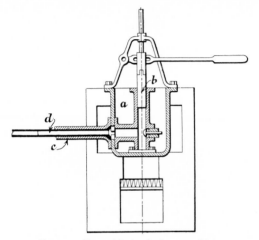

FIG. 2.—Bramah's lead-pipe machine.

machine, of which Fig. 3 is a sketch, consisted of a strong cylindrical container (*a*) secured to the top frame of a hydraulic press, and having in its upper end a steel die (*b*). The bottom end was sealed by a close-fitting plunger (*c*), into which there was screwed a mandrel rod (*d*), and which was attached to the hydraulic ram. After withdrawing the plunger to the full extent, lead was poured into the container through the die orifice, and, following an interval for solidification of the metal, the hydraulic ram was operated to force the lead up through the die, to form the pipe. At the end of the stroke the pipe was cut off above the projecting mandrel and hot lead was poured on to the remaining piece to melt it and clear the die. A difficulty was encountered, by no means unknown even to-day, in securing pipe of uniform thickness in its wall. This was due to the long mandrel bar becoming displaced so that it lay out of centre in the die, and recourse was had to wedging the tip of the mandrel in the die before filling the container.

By substituting a rectangular container provided with a slit aperture, Burr also made sheet lead. For this one side of the slit die aperture was formed by a plate, adjustable by means of screws, so as to allow sheets of different thickness to be formed.

A modified press was made by J. and C. Hanson in 1837 in

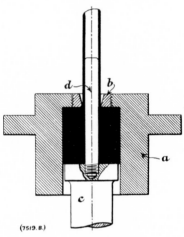

(7519. B.)

FIG. 3.—Arrangement of first press for hydraulic extrusion of lead pipes.

which the lead container was made the movable part by mounting it on top of the main ram of a hydraulic press, and a stationary plunger, attached to the head of the press frame, was used. The die was now fixed in the bottom of the container so that the awkwardness of the previous charging method was avoided; this being now done through a hole in the upper part of the container wall which was sealed by the plunger at the beginning of the working stroke. Two features introduced to secure improved concentricity in the pipe are retained in principle in certain types of lead press to-day. The first consisted in a means of centring the die by four adjusting screws; and the second in the use of a primitive form of bridge die, by which the long mandrel could

4

be replaced by a short one (*a*), held in a support of cruciform shape (*b*) over which the stream of lead divided, to re-unite before actually entering the die. These arrangements are shown in Fig. 4.

The process of extrusion had become firmly established for the working of lead by the middle of the century, and the next note-worthy developments arose from the interest which was then being taken in the production of tin-lined pipes to overcome the

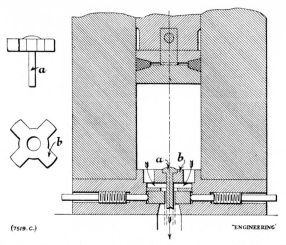

(7519.C.)

'ENGINEERING'

FIG. 4.—Early pipe press (1837), showing use of bridge die.

danger of corrosion which occurs when lead pipes are used to convey certain waters and other liquors. In the first place this had been accomplished by running molten tin inside lengths of extruded pipe, but in 1863, Shaw used a press in which precast hollow billets of lead, with an internally cast sleeve of tin, as shown in Fig. 5, were charged cold into the container. Several billet presses of this kind were designed, but records show that very considerable difficulty was met in arriving at the correct shape of sleeve to give a uniform lining of tin in the pipe. This is not to be wondered at in view of the complexity of the flow which is now known to occur, especially in the direct method of extrusion, which was solely used at that time.

A remarkable press for this work, invented in France by Hamon in 1867, which embodies many advanced features, is shown in

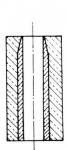

FIG. 5.—Form of tubular billet, with cast-in sleeve of tin, used in making tin-lined pipe.

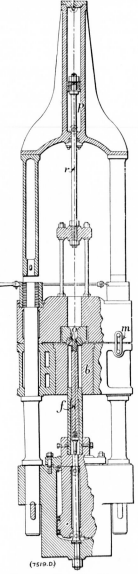

(7519.D)

FIG. 6.—Press by Hamon, with many novel features.

Fig. 6. The principal points of interest are (1) the use of a fixed mandrel bar, *f*, into which could be screwed points of different sizes, over which the extrusion ram travelled. (2) The container, *b*, was made with ducts in its outer jacket through which steam or hot gases could be circulated to raise its temperature to 210° C. This provides the first example of the use of a heated container. Pointing out the necessity for careful adjustment of the temperature to avoid melting the tin sleeve, Hamon suggested the use of a pyrometer. (3) An auxiliary hydraulic ram, *r*, was used to bring the die, *o*, and die-holder into position against the container, where it was locked, *m*. (4) An accumulator was introduced into the hydraulic system. Although the hydraulic accumulator had been invented by Sir William Armstrong in 1840, it does not appear to have been used hitherto in connection with extrusion.

The next stage in the evolution of the pipe press came with the introduction by Haines, and by J. and W. Weems, both in 1870, of the indirect or inverted method of extrusion. On the application of this method to copper alloys at a much later date, it was shown to have the effect of so altering the course of deformation occurring in the billet as to obviate a characteristic defect in extruded material. This will be discussed more fully elsewhere, but it is of interest here to note that the Weems', even at that time, claimed for the method that, since relative displacement of the billet and walls of the container was avoided, the metal remained undisturbed except in the neighbourhood of the die, and so made it possible to produce a more even coating of tin in the pipe.

A sketch of the Weems press is given in Fig. 7, and in more detail in Fig. 7 (*a*). The die is fixed on the end of a stationary extrusion ram which is bored out to allow the passage of the extruded pipe, formed when the container is raised by the main ram to force the extrusion ram against the end of the billet. The lead may be cast into the container instead of using precast billets, and when used in this way, the press has the advantage over the older ones that the open-topped container allows dross to be skimmed off the surface of the metal.

The indirect extrusion press is the one used for the manufacture of lead pipes at the present time, and improvements have been of

B

detail only, so that the arrangement shown above is substantially that now in use. Although the development of extrusion has hitherto been traced in connection with the lead pipe industry, since that was by far its most important application, some use

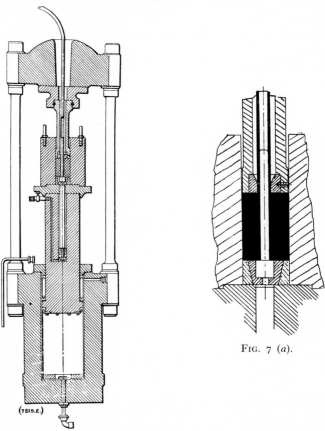

FIG. 7 (a).

FIG. 7.—The first application of the inverted method of extrusion in 1870.

of the process had also been made in the production of sheet and of special shapes, such as cames for leaded windows, by the use of dies of suitable form. For solid sections of simple shape multiple-hole dies were commonly used, the use of which for pipe-making, though attempted, was not successful. Moreover,

8

although lead was the metal chiefly used, there were extruded to a limited extent, in addition to the composite billets already referred to, other soft metals such as tin and solder alloys and even zinc. A noteworthy offshoot of the main line of development is provided by a series of ingenious devices for making, directly by an extrusion process, curved lead pipes for use as syphons, bends, or traps, which followed Cunningham's original patent in 1873. Two representative examples of these may be discussed. In Fig. 8 a casing (b), containing a mandrel (c) and a sliding diaphragm (a), was fitted to the end of an extrusion

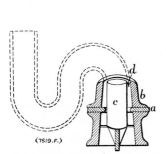

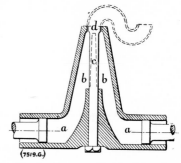

FIG. 8.—Early bend press. FIG. 9.—Device for extruding lead bends.

press. When the aperture of the diaphragm was centrally placed in the casing, lead delivered by the press could be extruded through the orifice at (d), forming the die, as a straight pipe; but by displacing the diaphragm laterally, the supply of lead could be regulated so that a greater quantity passed to one side than the other, causing the issuing pipe to bend over to a desired curvature.

In an alternative machine, shown in Fig. 9, lead was poured into the cylinders (a) (a) of a steel casting, which were closed by two rams each connected with a hydraulic cylinder. The rams were advanced to force the lead, after it had solidified, through the semicircular passages (b) (b) in which partition fins (c), on the mandrel (d), kept the two streams of lead separated until just below the die orifice, where they united to form a pipe in the annulus between the die and the mandrel. By controlling the speed at which the hydraulic rams moved forward, the operator could vary the rate of flow of lead on either side of the partition so that the greater volume passing through one side of the annulus produced a curved pipe, as in the case above. Bend presses of the latter type continue to be in common use.

Extrusion Presses for Sheathing Electric Cables

The rapid development of the electrical industry in the second half of last century brought with it a need for a protective envelope for cables which would shield them against mechanical damage and be impervious to water. Lead suggested itself as almost the ideal material for this purpose, on account both of its pliability in facilitating the laying operations and its relative immunity from corrosion. It had been used as early as 1845 by Wheatstone and Cooke in the form of a strip which was wound spirally round the insulated conductor and finally soldered along the overlapped edges. Subsequently, cable was threaded through 50-foot lengths of ordinary lead pipe, which were then joined end to end by soldering. The cables were only loosely encased in this way, and required to be tightened up by drawing or rolling. In a further method, a length of cable was laid out over rollers, with one end attached to the tip of the mandrel projecting through the die of a lead pipe press, and lead pipe was then extruded over the cable.

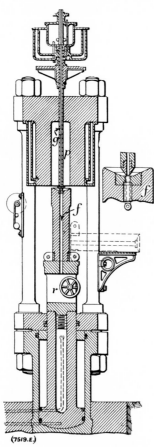

(75l9.e.)

Fig. 10.—The first cable sheathing press made by Borel in 1879.

In 1879 there were devised by Borel in France and Wesslau in Germany the first methods by which a lead sheath could be directly extruded on to cables. In both cases vertical extrusion

10

presses were used in which hollow-cast billets of lead were extruded as a tubular sheath over an insulated conductor which was passed into the press through a hollow mandrel and issued through the tubular ram. Fig. 10 shows the general arrangement of the Borel press. With the ram, *f*, swung aside, a billet heated to 120° C. was placed in the container, *p*, and extruded as a tube through the annulus between a die carried on the nose of the extrusion ram and the conical end of a mandrel tube, *g*.

FIG. 11.—Drawing of the Borel press.

The latter moved with the extrusion ram, being connected to it by means of a cross-head (not shown in the diagram). The conductor entered the press via a bath of molten insulating wax, through the mandrel tube, and passing thence inside the lead pipe as it formed, emerged through the hollow extrusion ram, running finally over a pulley, *r*, to the coiling drum. An illustration of this historically interesting press is given in Fig. 11. Although it worked successfully, it had the disadvantage that a continuous length of cable could not be sheathed owing to the necessity of cutting it to allow a fresh billet to be inserted, and while this could have been avoided by casting the charge of metal in the container, it was apparently considered impracticable because of the damage which the high temperature would have caused to the insulation where the cable passed through the mandrel during filling.

Two years after this, there was brought out by Huber in Germany the press illustrated in Fig. 12. This operated on the same principle as a lead bend press already described above, to which its origin has been attributed, in having two hydraulic rams $(a)(a_1)$, Fig. 13, acting in cylinders opposite to each other, to force lead into the die-block placed between them. Holders (c) (d) carrying the hollow mandrel or point-holder through which the cable entered at right angles to the axis of the containers, and the die (f) and base ring (h) were screwed into the back and front of the die-block, respectively; both the point of the mandrel and the die being replaceable to suit the size of cable which was required. In addition to the longitudinal adjustment by means of the screwed holder, the die could also be moved laterally by four wedge bolts (g), to afford a means of controlling the concentricity of the sheath. The two cylinders, heated by an oil-fired furnace beneath, were filled with lead through openings in their wall at a point farthest from the die-block, from a melting-pot set in a furnace on top of the press, after which the press rams were moved forward sufficiently to expel air and some of the dross carried in with the lead, and then seal the filling holes. When the lead had solidified, the rams, set to provide equal pressure by an equalizing valve, were operated to drive it round the point-holder where the two streams met at the top and bottom of the latter, flowing forward subsequently through the die aperture as a sheath over the cable, which was thereby drawn through the press. These machines met with considerable success and found wide application at one time. By their means long lengths of cable could be sheathed without necessity for soldered joints since consecutive charges of lead could be made into the containers at the end of each extrusion stroke. Large units up to 5000 tons total pressure capacity were in operation by the beginning of this century and their use has only recently been abandoned. The chief difficulty which arose with them appears to have been in maintaining an even flow of lead from each container, due to small differences in temperature between the

FIG. 12.—The Huber cable press.

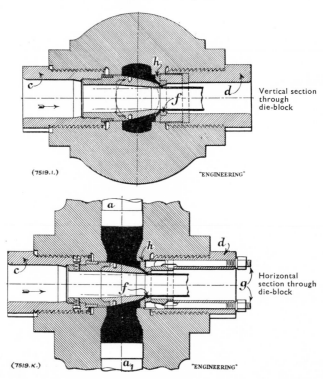

Vertical section through die-block

(7519.I.)   "ENGINEERING"

Horizontal section through die-block

(7519.K.)   "ENGINEERING"

FIG. 13.—Showing the arrangement of the die and mandrel in the die-block.

13

latter and thus of plasticity in the metal, so as to insure that two equal streams came together in the die-block to form a closed sheath which was free from the danger of splitting along the weld seams.

Concurrently with the development of the horizontal press just described, there was evolved a vertical cable press, which had its origin in America with the design in 1880 by Eaton, shown in Fig. 14, and which was adapted from the ordinary pipe press.

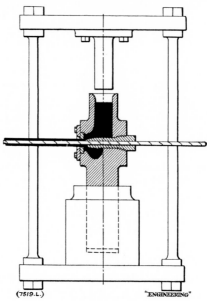

(75I9.L.)   "ENGINEERING"

Fig. 14.—Eaton's vertical press for sheathing continuous lengths of cable (1880).

A charge of lead cast and solidified in the container was made to flow circumferentially round a mandrel set transversely across the bottom of the container and was extruded, at right angles to the axis of the latter, over a cable threaded through the mandrel. This press lent itself to the sheathing of long cables in the same way as the previous one. It was much improved in 1885 by Robertson, who made a special block to hold the die and mandrel, upon which the now separate container rested. In its modern form, which is described in Chapter III, the vertical press has almost entirely superseded other types.

Application of Extrusion to Copper Alloys

The advanced state to which extrusion had been brought in the service of the lead industry and the manifold advantages which it offered naturally directed attention to the possibility of its utilization for other metals possessing better mechanical properties, such as the brass alloys, which, while much harder than lead at the ordinary temperature, were capable of being wrought when at a red heat. Records exist of several efforts to do this during the last century, but the difficulties, at first, proved too great, and the lead presses which were, in many cases, used for experiment were unsuitable. A report of one trial states surprisingly that ' it was anxiously and unexpectedly found that when the brass block came to be subjected to pressure, the zinc left the copper, thereby producing a zinc pipe and leaving the copper behind . . . proving that the atoms of brass composition, united by fusion, were only mechanically arranged, not chemically combined '. The main difficulty as compared with previous practice was that even the brasses most susceptible to hot work do not become sufficiently plastic to undergo the heavy deformations involved in extrusion until they are heated to a temperature of at least 600° C., so that the problem was by no means only that of providing a powerful press. Not only had the temperature of the metal to be maintained within the working range where it could be dealt with under the pressures available during the extrusion stroke, but the question also arose of providing dies, containers, and other parts of composition and design to withstand the unusually severe thermal and stress conditions, and that at a time when little development of such special steels as are now available for such service had taken place. It is therefore hardly possible to overestimate the achievement of Alexander Dick (see footnote, p. 18) in successfully overcoming the obstacles involved. On his inventive genius has been laid the foundation of the modern hot extrusion process, which has now been extended far beyond its original limitations to a stage where it covers most of the technical non-ferrous alloys, and where it has become one of the major metal-working processes in the field. Dick's first patent for an extrusion press was obtained in 1894 and was followed in the next few years by several others as experience was gained. Instances which he gives of alloys to which the method was applicable are shown below

				Cu	Zn	Fe	Al
1	.	.	.	58	40	2	—
2	.	.	.	85	10	—	5
3	.	.	.	90	—	—	10
4	.	.	.	60	40	—	—

One of his early designs is shown in Fig. 15. The horizontal press frame was braced together by four tie-rods (*a*). A heavy

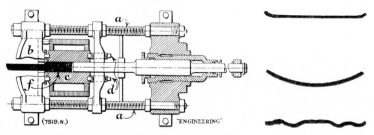

FIG. 15.—Horizontal extrusion press designed by Alexander Dick in 1894.

FIG. 15 (*a*).

cross-head (*b*) formed one end of the press and supported the die, which was held in position against the container by a pair of jaws, pivoted at the base of the cross-head in the manner

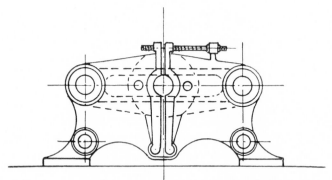

FIG. 16.—End view of above, to show the method of securing the die.

illustrated in Fig. 16. The container (*c*) held and centred by the set-screws (*d*) was surrounded by a furnace jacket heated by coke or gas. The billet (*f*) heated to a plastic state was fed into the container from the front. With the object of preventing the ram from becoming wedged by the escape of metal past its sides, a dished or corrugated disc (Fig. 15a) was placed between it and the billet. At the end of the extrusion, the jaws were opened to allow the die and unextruded remnant to be pushed out. A persistent source of trouble was encountered in that the heat given up by the billet caused unequal heating of the thick-walled container so that it frequently cracked. To meet this, compound containers were introduced. One of the first of these, shown in Fig. 17, has a thin tapered inner liner (a) surrounded by casings

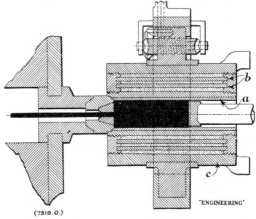

(7519.0.)

Fig. 17.—Dick's insulated container, mounted on trunnions, for the direct casting of billets.

(b) (b), with the annular space between them packed with some such material as crushed granite or asbestos to afford heat insulation; the whole being encased in the strong outer shell (c). The idea of this was that although the inner liner became hot it would suffer less damage from heat stresses than a thicker one, and would moreover be easily replaced, while the outer shell being at a much lower temperature would retain its strength and therefore be capable of resisting the pressure. In addition, the heat of the billet being better maintained, it could be extruded much more readily. This construction did away with the need for external heating of the container, though it had to be warmed up to begin with by a gas-burner or by inserting a hot block of iron. For a time, as an alternative to the use of preheated billets, the practice was also followed of casting the metal directly in the container, which was mounted for this purpose on trunnions so that it could be turned into an upright position for casting. A plate closed the bottom of the container during this operation. An improved method of supporting the die in a holder placed in a diehead, as seen in Fig. 17, was soon adopted, and this assembly was locked during operation by a transverse slide buttressed against the cross-head of the press.

The diagram also shows the use of a loose follower block behind the billet which could be preheated so as to avoid cooling the latter; the ram, being then made with a clearance in the container, could be readily withdrawn.

The production of round rod and other solid sections was soon augmented by the manufacture of tubes from hollow-cast billets, though considerable difficulty had to be met, owing to the inadequate material available for the mandrel, in keeping it cool enough to prevent breaking; and in securing tubes of concentric bore. Many of these troubles yielded only slowly as steps were taken to improve machinery and materials, and as technique and experience were gathered, but Dick must be credited with many of the first steps which opened the way to progress, as, for instance, in his experiments with various types of fixed and floating mandrels. Such possibilities, too, as the application to copper alloys of inverted extrusion through a hollow ram, and the use of an electrically heated container, were also envisaged by him. In concluding this historical survey it may be said that although radical changes in design and accessory equipment have taken place during the last sixty years, extrusion presses at the present time continue to embody the principles discovered by Dick.

FOOTNOTE TO CHAPTER I

George Alexander Dick was born in 1838 at Offenbach-am-Main in Germany, his father being of Scottish descent and his mother English. After studying under Fresenius, Bunsen and Kirchoff, he became an analytical chemist in a German ironworks, and was subsequently appointed blast-furnace manager to a works in Spain. Later, with his brother C. A. J. Dick, he opened up a general engineering business in Paris, which was successful until the outbreak of the Franco-German

War in 1870, when he settled in England, where, with others, he founded the Phosphor Bronze Company of London, which he managed until 1881. For the next few years he devoted himself to investigating the possibilities of other copper alloys and to improving the brasses. The benefit of adding iron to brass had already been found by Baron Rosthorn in Austria, but difficulty had been met in introducing it into the alloys. Dick discovered that this could be done with more certainty by the use of an iron zinc alloy. He finally began the manufacture of some of these alloys under the name of Delta, converting his business in 1888 into the Delta Metal Company Limited. After making a study of the behaviour and flow of copper alloys in connection with the production of stampings and pressings, he became interested in the idea of making rods, tubes, and sections by a cheaper process than those of rolling and drawing, and, after preliminary experiments in a small vertical hydraulic press, he was eventually successful in 1894 in extruding certain brasses and other copper alloys, and started to manufacture by the process in London, Birmingham, and Dusseldorf. Upon his inventions, which he continued to improve up to the time of his death in 1903, the modern process of extrusion has been founded.

The above biographical details have been derived from notes prepared by Mr. Henry Rogers, to whom the authors are indebted.

CHAPTER II

The Extrusion of Lead and Other Soft Metals

IN spite of the fact that tubes of metals other than lead are now used to a considerable extent for the distribution of gas, water, etc., the latter has by no means been superseded, especially in England, for these purposes, and large quantities of pipe are extruded. Lead pipe has also special applications in the chemical industry by reason of its resistance to many corrosive media. This metal in the extruded form, besides its very important use for sheathing electric cables, which is separately considered in the next chapter, is employed also in a variety of special shapes and sections for such purposes as the sheathing of T-section steel bars for patent glazing, mouldings, bullet rod, etc. Vertical hydraulic presses operating by the inverted process are those mainly used for pipes and other products. Their general arrangement follows that shown in Fig. 7. Changes in design during the last fifty years have been slight and consist mainly in improved materials for their construction and in the ancillary gear, such as pumps, etc. A unit of recent type is shown in Fig. 18. The container is moved during the stroke of the main ram, on top of which it is mounted, over the fixed extrusion ram, being guided in its travel by slides on the press columns; and the return stroke takes place by means of the two small hydraulic rams arranged at either side of the frame. A cooling channel, through which steam is passed, is provided between the jacket and liner of the container to hasten setting of the charge of lead. The die is carried on the nose of the extrusion ram, and as the pipe is formed it passes up through the latter and is bent over the pulley above on its way to the coiler. Pipes above about 2 in. in diameter are not coiled but are seized by special crane hooks and drawn up to a higher floor to avoid flattening. The presses are worked directly off the pumps without the use of an accumulator. A common capacity is 500 tons, with containers holding a charge of 250 to 500 lb. of lead, though much larger units have been built for special purposes, as, for example, that installed by the American Smelting and Refining Company having a total pressure of 1500 tons, in which a charge of 4000 lb. is cast, and which is capable of extruding pipe from $\frac{1}{2}$ in. to 12 in. inside diameter. The particular advantage secured is that very large pipes, e.g. 12-in. diameter, $\frac{3}{4}$ in. wall thickness, and 22 ft. in length, for use in chemical plant, can be made from a single charge of lead, and thus the presence of a weld where consecutive charges meet, which is liable to unsoundness, as described below, is avoided.

In the operation of a pipe press, molten lead at a temperature of about 400° C. is supplied through a chute to the container from a melting kettle holding 2–3 tons of metal. After skimming off the dross which collects on the surface of the charge, the container is raised so as to bring the ram

FIG. 18.—Robertson press for lead pipes. (*Courtesy of John Robertson Company.*)

against the surface of the lead under a small pressure in order to lessen oxidation and avoid a contraction pipe in the casting. A thin coating of tallow is applied to the mandrel and ram between each operation. The lead having set, pressure is increased to start the extrusion of the pipe. The temperature at which the latter issues varies between 200° C. and 250° C., tending to rise during the operation. When a slug or ' sud ' of an inch or so in thickness is all that remains in the container, the press is stopped and the container is recharged.

The mandrel, which is secured to the base of the container, passes for the greater part of its length through the die during the working stroke, and in order to diminish friction between the emergent portion and the pipe, which is moving much faster, a slight taper of 1–2 thousandths of an inch is given to it. In making pipe of a very small bore, the mandrel, being thin, is easily bent out of centre, leading to eccentric pipe, and to meet this the practice is sometimes adopted of using a bridge die in which a short mandrel bar is connected to the die below the constricted aperture by spider arms, as shown in Fig. 19. This

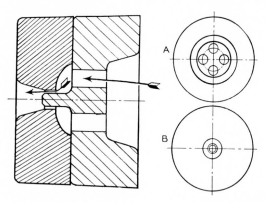

FIG. 19.—Four-aperture bridge die. A—Back view. B—Front view.
(*Smith*, '*J. Inst. Metals*'.)

device is, however, not regarded with favour and its use is being abandoned due to the fact that the radial welds formed where the streams of lead re-unite after dividing over the supporting arms are frequently imperfect. The reason for this is that inclusions of dross and oxide contained in the metal become strung out longitudinally in the wake of any obstruction placed in the lead stream, and prevent metallic union between the separate parts. Transverse sections of pipe made in this way show, when etched, a discontinuous crystalline structure at the welds, which may lead to splitting of the pipe in service.

Defects occurring in Lead Pipes

Lead pipe made in the foregoing manner is liable to certain defects which are directly associated with the extrusion process. Apart from eccentric pipe which has its origin in wear, faulty adjustment, or unsatisfactory press design, the chief troubles are those arising from oxide and other inclusions, and from excessive and irregular grain-size in the metal. First of all, unless special precautions are taken during melting, such as are discussed in Chapter III, the molten lead carries with it into the container considerable amounts of dross which, though it tends to rise to the surface where it can be skimmed off, can never be completely eliminated in this way, so that the top layer in particular is relatively impure. As a result the first few feet of pipe produced are of poor quality and are cut off and rejected; unless, of course, the pipe being made forms part of a continuous length requiring more than one charge, when this is obviously impossible. In the usual form of press, in which the slug remaining from one operation is left in the container, the surface of the slug becomes oxidized during its exposure to the atmosphere, and it is also the seat of dross and of charred oil from the lubricant on the ram. Although the wash of incoming hot lead of the next charge tends to melt the surface and flush away the impurities, it is by no means completely effective in doing so, and there remains therefore after solidification a stratum of dirty metal at the junction between the two charges. The course of deformation in the lead during its extrusion, which is discussed with reference to the inverted method in Chapter V, is such that this stratum, lying as it does towards the bottom of the container, does not become involved in the flow and pass into the forming pipe until a late stage in the extrusion of a charge, and is then carried into the die to form a long, tapering scarf joint which appears in a transverse section of pipe as a ring of oxidized material between annuli of sound metal. This gives rise to the defect known as lamination. As a rule only a portion of the dirty stratum passes into the die in this way before the press is stopped for refilling, and the remainder of it is left in the slug. Fig. 20 shows a section of part of one of these slugs, extracted from the container after several successive charges, in which the separate layers due

C

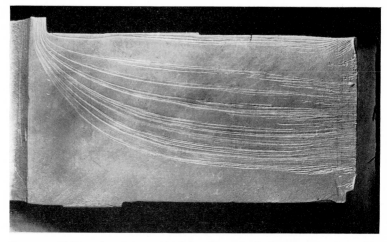

FIG. 20.—Half-section of the residual slug from a lead pipe press showing oxide layers at the interface between successive charges.
(*Natural Size.*)

FIG. 21.—Transverse section of lead pipe with concentric rings of oxide.
($\times$ 4.)

to each are easily identifiable. It will be appreciated therefore that the slugs become the source of multiple laminations such as are seen in the section from the back end of a length of pipe in

Fig. 21. Here again the rejection of potentially faulty material from the back end of the extruded pipe may be practicable.

A means of circumventing lamination is obtained by removing the slug at the end of each operation, and this is arranged for

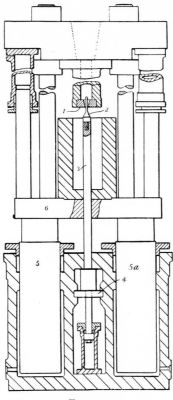

FIG. 22.

in a patented press,[1] shown in Fig. 22, which is possibly inspired by the old Hamon press already described. It operates, as is usual in lead presses, by the indirect method; the die (1) being fixed on the stationary ram, but the mandrel (2), instead of being rigidly attached to the base of the container, is screwed into a robust mandrel bar (3) passing through the bottom of the container and held securely during extrusion by a hydraulic block (4). The container is raised vertically for the extrusion on the two hydraulic rams (5, 5a) connected by a cross-head (6). By this arrangement the relative position of die and mandrel remain unaltered during the working stroke, and thus comparatively short mandrels, which are readily interchanged, can be used, while for pipes of a very small bore the difficulty ordinarily met of adequately supporting a long thin mandrel is obviated. A solution of this particular difficulty had, in fact, already been found in Germany along similar lines.[2]   At the end of the operation, the slug in the bottom of the container is resting on the tapered shoulder of the mandrel, and when the container is lowered, it stays behind on the mandrel.   A slotted plate is then placed on top of the container beneath the slug to hold it while the mandrel is lowered by means of the small hydraulic ram at the base of the press, when it can be severed from the pipe and removed, thus leaving the container empty for the next charge of lead.

The continuous extrusion press developed primarily in connection with the sheathing of cable, described in Chapter III, has also been adapted in England to the production of lead pipes which are free from the defects brought about by the intermittent nature of extrusion in hydraulic presses.

The relatively slight deformation which is imparted to extruded pipe when it is bent over from the vertical to the horizontal position on leaving the press, and that occurring during coiling, while it is still at a high temperature, may bring about those critical conditions which cause the development of huge crystal grains, frequently occupying the whole cross-section of the wall of the pipe at opposite sides of the diameter corresponding to the inside and outside of the bend in the pipe.   An example of such a 'zoned' structure is shown in Fig. 23.   Jones[3] has associated such structures with cracking in service and Butler[4] has studied their influence upon creep and fatigue in some detail. Creep tests indicate that 'zoned' pipes have properties intermediate between those of pipes having uniform grain sizes similar to those of the fine- and coarse-grained regions observed in the heterogeneous product, but in practice the 'zoned' pipe would probably be no better than the fine-grained one if failure was due to creep.   In the case of fatigue tests, however, the zoned material proved less resistant than either the uniformly fine- or uniformly coarse-grained lead, which behaviour is ascribed to

stress-concentration arising at the boundary between the fine-
and coarse-grained regions of the zoned pipe as the result of
the greater instantaneous strain developed in the coarse-grained
zone upon loading.

Steps are taken in many instances to avoid this heterogeneous
grain size by cooling the pipe as it leaves the press and before
it is coiled by passing it through a water-trough or by spraying

Fig. 23.—Etched cross-section of lead pipe showing zoned structure.
(*Back, 'J. Inst. Metals '.*)

it. Alternatively the use of alloying additions, referred to below,
so as to increase the resistance of the lead to critical grain-growth,
has the advantage that it will still be effective if strain is imparted
during service. Butler has further suggested working the pipe
uniformly and fairly heavily so that, if recrystallization does occur,
it will result in a desirable grain structure. This working may
be achieved by passing the hot pipe over two suitably disposed
pulleys, instead of the more usual one, so as to bend it in two
directions at right angles.

In a further paper[5] Butler has given details of the conditions under which recrystallization may occur in manufacture or service to yield heterogeneous structures. By determining the critical strains which must be exceeded to produce recrystallization and grain growth, he is able to indicate how the chances of zoned structures being formed may be minimized by suitable control of manufacturing conditions, e.g. by delaying quenching until just before any bending is applied. The development of zoning during service is probably best prevented by the use of alloying additions, as already stated, and Butler has shown that lead containing 0·04 per cent Te + 0·06 per cent Cu, or 0·005 per cent Ag + 0·005 per cent Cu, has most favourable characteristics in this respect.

Lead and Lead Alloys* used in Extruded Products

Among the chief characteristics of lead upon which its applications as pipe and other extruded forms depend, are its pliability in manipulation, the comparative ease of its extrusion, and the high degree of immunity which it possesses to corrosion in the atmosphere and in a variety of media. Its resistance to sulphuric acid, for instance, makes it especially valuable in the manufacture of the latter. On the other hand, it suffers the drawback of extreme mechanical weakness, and is liable to undergo continuous deformation, or creep, under very small stresses, and indeed, in some cases, under its own weight; and it is readily susceptible to cracking or brittle fracture under vibration or other fluctuating stresses, due to its low fatigue range.

Whilst the majority of lead pipes are made from soft and common varieties of lead, the actual grade used depends on the particular applications for which they are intended (B.S.S. 602 : 1956). Ordinary commercial lead pipes frequently contain a small quantity of tin, which is added to increase the stiffness, an average figure for the addition being 0·5 per cent. Moderate amounts of alloyed lead are now utilized, especially with the aim of reducing failure due to fatigue and creep. An example of one of these which enables a saving of weight of one-third to be made, owing to its enhanced mechanical properties, is that developed by the British Non-Ferrous Metals Research Associa-

* See also Chapter III.

28

tion, containing 1·5 per cent tin, 0·25 per cent cadmium, the application of which for water pipes is the subject of a British Standard Specification (603 : 1941). For chemical purposes especially pure lead containing only traces of other elements are required, though selected additions of other metals have been found of value in raising creep and fatigue resistance. Interesting progress has been made with an alloy containing the eutectic amount, 0·06 per cent, of copper in bringing about better control of grain-size, together with improved creep behaviour under load. The benefit of this amount of copper in lead for acid chambers is well recognized. The following analysis, given by Peters,[6] is for an acid-resisting lead produced by the American Smelting and Refining Company

	Percentage			Percentage
Copper	0·06	Iron		0·0001
Bismuth	0·019	Nickel⎫		
Antimony⎫		Cobalt⎭		0·0001
Arsenic ⎬ . . .	0·0001	Cadmium		0·0002
Tin ⎭		Silver		0·0004
Zinc	0·0002			

The reason for the bismuth addition is the enhanced resistance to chemical attack which its presence is reputed to confer.

The effect of these alloying additions upon the grain structure and mechanical properties of lead is influenced by the extrusion variables, temperature, speed and ratio, employed in fabricating extrusions in such compositions.[7] Butler[8] has made a detailed study of the effect of these variables on the grain size of commercially pure lead and of lead to which additions of antimony, copper and tin had been made. The temperature of extrusion has the greatest effect upon grain size, which is about doubled for a 50° C. increase in extrusion temperature in the case of air-cooled material. When the extrusion ratio is varied by keeping the container size constant and varying the die size, the grain size of air-cooled material decreases with increasing ratio, possibly because the products, having varying surface/volume ratios, cool at different rates. Similarly the effect of extrusion speed, which, as it is increased causes a reduction in grain size, can be explained in terms of its effect upon cooling rate. The effect is only observed when water quenching is employed, which indicates that variations in the rate of extrusion alter the severity of quenching by producing differences in the time of delay before quenching and thereby promoting variations in the time for which grain growth can occur. Copper additions are more effective than either antimony or tin in producing grain refinement, which behaviour Butler ascribes to the fact that copper is less soluble in lead than antimony or tin and so exists as insoluble particles which inhibit grain growth and may also have some effect upon the recrystallization characteristics of the material.

Solders of varied composition are extruded as thin rod or wires from small vertical or horizontal presses, using multiple-hole dies having up to 15 apertures. Solder in the form of a thin tube with a flux core is also made in presses resembling those used in sheathing cable. Small precast billets, heated to approximately 100° C., are generally used for this. Extrusion is used in the manufacture of certain ornamental sections in alloys of the pewter class. The proneness to cracking or ' feathering ' of the edges of sections in the extrusion of these alloys can only be avoided by extruding them very slowly.

REFERENCES

[1] British Patent No. 457,445.
[2] *Metallbörse*, 1926, **16,** 2830–1.
[3] B. Jones. *Engineering*, 1938, **145,** 285.
[4] J. M. Butler. *J. Inst. Metals*, 1957–8, **86,** 161.
[5] J. M. Butler. *Ibid.*, 1957–8, **86,** 155.
[6] F. P. Peters. *Met. Ind. (London)*, 1940, **56,** 436.
[7] L. H. Back. *J. Inst. Metals*, 1949–50, **76,** 541.
[8] J. M. Butler. *Ibid.*, 1957–8, **86,** 145.

CHAPTER III

The Extrusion of Cable-Sheathing

BY far the most important branch of the extrusion process, as it relates to lead and its alloys, is that devoted to the production of protective sheathing on electrical conductors for power and telegraphic transmission.   Indeed, the use of lead for this purpose constitutes one of the major industrial outlets for the metal. In both the U.K. and U.S.A. over 100,000 tons of lead is currently being used each year for cable manufacture, corresponding to about 30 per cent and 10 per cent respectively of the total lead production in these countries.[1]

The vertical hydraulic cable-sheathing press to which reference

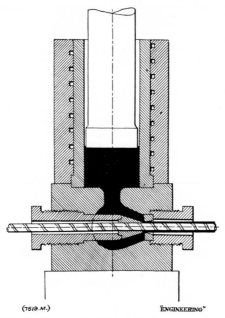

(7519.M.)   "ENGINEERING"

FIG. 24.—Diagrammatic section through the container and die-block
of a vertical cable press.

31

has already been made in Chapter I, is the one most widely adopted at the present time. Its operation may be explained with the aid of the sketch, Fig. 24, which shows a section through a die-block and container. To begin the cycle of operations, the container is filled through a chute from a lead-melting kettle, and the foam and dross which collect on the surface of the metal are removed as far as possible, after which the container is brought under slight pressure against the extrusion ram to avoid oxidation and to prevent a contraction pipe forming in the lead as it solidifies. A period of 7 or 8 minutes is allowed for the metal to freeze and cool to a suitable temperature for extrusion. This is generally

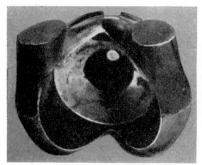 

FIG. 25.—The shape of the mass of lead in the forming chamber of a die-block, with two entries from the container.
(*Göler and Schmid.*)

about 250° C. The cooling may be hastened by passing steam or a trickle of water through a helical channel formed between the container jacket and the liner; though if the latter method is used, care is necessary to avoid the setting up of thermal stresses causing cracked liners, by passing the water first through a preheater coil. The solid lead is then forced by the ram through the channel in the top of the die-block into a forming chamber which surrounds the hollow point-holder or mandrel, in the nose of which a detachable point is mounted. The lead divides into two streams in passing round the point-holder, which meet and weld together on its under side, finally flowing as a reducing annulus to the die, from which it emerges as a sheath which grips the cable sufficiently to draw it forward through the point-holder off a drum placed behind the press. In some forms of die-block the lead enters from the container through two channels with a bridge between, the separate streams in this case passing round the point-holder to form seam welds on top of, as well as below, the latter. Fig. 25 shows the shape of the mass of lead occupying a die-block of this kind. As it leaves the press the cable is usually cooled by passing through a water-trough, or by means of a spray, and is then coiled directly on to a drum. When the greater part of the charge has been ex-truded the press is stopped, the ram is withdrawn and a new charge of lead is run in on top of the residual slug. The cycle is then repeated. During the stop for recharging, the cable in process of being sheathed remains in the die-block. In this intermittent manner several charges of lead may be applied as a continuous cover to one length of cable.

In general construction the press takes the form of a closed cast-steel frame—or more usually, one built up with tension columns—in either the head or base of which the hydraulic operating cylinder may be placed. An example of the second type is shown in Fig. 26. The container and die-block are carried on the main ram and ascend with it against the extrusion ram, which is fixed to the head of the press frame. A cross-head sliding on the press columns guides the container during the extrusion stroke, and to it there are also attached the rams of the two drawback cylinders for the return stroke of the main ram. This arrangement of the press has the advantage of re-quiring less headroom in the factory than the first type, since the main cylinder can be sunk in a pit below floor level; and in addition, there is no fear that water leaking past defective packing may enter the container or fall on to the cable entering the press. One minor drawback is that the position at which the cable enters and leaves the press varies with the height of the die-block during the stroke. A press using the alternative method, in which the container position remains fixed and the extrusion ram is attached to the main ram of an overhead hydraulic system, is illustrated in Fig. 27. The latter method, with moving ram and fixed container, is sometimes erroneously referred to as the inverted process. Actually, unlike the usual type of lead pipe press, both types of cable press employ the direct method

FIG. 26.—Vertical cable press by Hydraulik, with underlying hydraulic cylinder.

of extrusion. In practice there seems to be little to choose between the two arrangements and both are in current use.

In size, which depends primarily on the diameters of cable to

FIG. 27.—Modern 3800-ton press for sheathing cable with lead or aluminium and employing a 'fixed' container, at Süddeutsche Kebelwerke.

be made, presses range from 600 to 3000 tons total pressure capacity, with containers taking from 300 lb. to as much as one ton of lead in a charge, of such diameters as will allow a maximum extrusion pressure of 25 to 28 tons per square inch to be exerted. For making lead alloy sheathing, containers of somewhat reduced diameter may be required so as to increase the available pressure. The operating power is derived, almost universally, directly from pumps, which are usually of the three-throw variety on account of the steady delivery of water which they provide, and which are driven by variable speed motors of 25–150 H.P.

The die-block is a vital part of the cable press and great importance attaches to its design. A range of blocks suitable for each size of cable may be provided, or as in some modern machines, a universal block into which the appropriate points and dies may be fitted is used. In some instances the blocks may be split so that the inner surfaces against which the lead flows may be carefully shaped and finished by hand. The wall thickness of the sheath is regulated by adjustment of the relative position of the die and point, affected by the screwholders in the block. The concentricity of the product depends chiefly on the accurate positioning of the point in the die ring and on the uniform temperature of the metal entering the annulus from all sides. In most presses, provision is made for radial adjustment of the die by means of wedge bolts, whereby, when changing over to a new size of cable, correction can be made for eccentricity by extruding short trial lengths of sheathing and gauging the wall thickness. Some press manufacturers, however, prefer to fix the radial position of the die in relation to the point after test runs under working conditions in the assembly shop; taking the view that press operators tend to use any adjusting device to correct for eccentricity caused by bad temperature distribution round the die, instead of rectifying the latter, with the result that as the temperature conditions may alter during working, trouble is experienced. The question of temperature control in the die-block is one which calls for close attention in the production of sheathing to exacting specifications. To secure as uniform a temperature as possible, gas jets or electrical heaters are arranged along either side of the die-block and around the die. Thermocouples inserted in holes bored in the block at suitable positions provide the necessary indication for control. The die-block temperature aimed at varies in different works, but is generally between 160° and 200° C., 180° C. being most commonly used. Due to the replacement of the lead already in the die-block by hotter material from the new charge in the container, there is a liability for the temperature of the metal entering the die to rise during the extrusion so that a slight longitudinal variation in the wall thickness of the sheath is caused. The tendency for the heavier cables to sag as they leave the die, causes a variation in the wall thickness of the sheath between the top and bottom, and this may be corrected by adjustment of the die position or by providing a guide pulley in front of the press, to support the weight of the cable.

Defects in Cable Sheathing

In regard to the quality of the product, attention was for long directed principally to uniformity of dimensions of the sheath and to securing inconspicuous press stop marks; and little consideration was given to the possibility of internal flaws and weaknesses in the lead itself. But increasingly stringent demands on cable materials such as have come about, for example, with the introduction of high-voltage, oil-filled cables, as well as the costliness of breakdowns, have endowed the question of metallurgical defects with special importance, the more so since the other main cause of cable failure, insulation breakdown, had already been largely removed, thus throwing the former into greater prominence. In the last twenty years a great deal of careful study given to the production methods has provided a clearer understanding of many of the faults which are liable to arise and of their originating causes, and this has brought in its train many improvements in technique. In consequence, a marked reduction in the incidence of failures attributable to extrusion faults has resulted, and the proportion of these in comparison with those arising from other causes such as fatigue, creep, etc., is now relatively small. The work of Dunsheath and Tunstall,[3] Bassett and Schneider,[4] Atkinson,[5] and others has shown beyond any doubt that the chief defects arise from the entraining, principally at the surface between two successive charges in the container, of lead oxide and dross, and to the occlusion of gas and air bubbles, already referred to in Chapter II in connection with the making of lead pipe. The subsequent distribution of these impurities in the product varies, however, from the latter case, not only because we are concerned here with the direct method of extrusion, itself causing

37

a different type of flow, but also, of course, as a result of the peculiar flow of metal round the horizontally disposed mandrel. The diagram, Fig. 28, gives some impression of how the initially plane surface between two charges after filling becomes displaced as extrusion proceeds. As a result both of friction along the

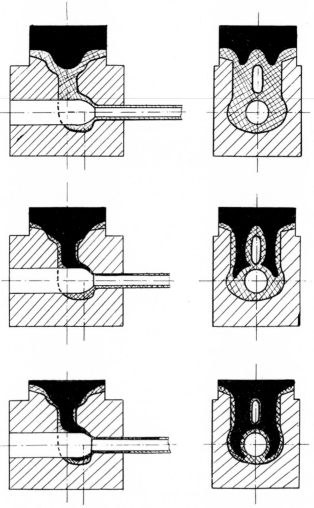

FIG. 28.—Showing the inter-penetration in the die-block of the metal of the old charge by that of the subsequent one.

walls of the container and the internal surfaces of the die-block, and of the higher temperature in the centre of the charge, movement towards the die-block is fastest in the middle, where tongues of hot lead of the new charge intrude into the forming chamber inside the old lead. These pass gradually round the point-holder, the separate branches ultimately meeting to form weld seams above and below it. It will be recognized that, on starting up after refilling, the sheath will continue to consist for a considerable length entirely of the metal of the previous charge, and the new metal when it appears will do so as two tongues near the top side of the sheath. Over the next few feet of sheath, these tongues increase in size at the expense of the old lead, until

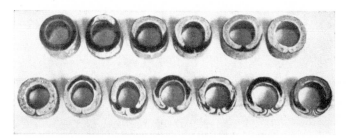

FIG. 29.—Sections of a tube resulting from the extrusion of alternate light and dark coloured charges through a single-entry die-block of the form used in the vertical cable-sheathing press.

(*Courtesy of the Institute of Electrical Engineers.*)

they meet round the point-holder. As a rule the intrusion of the new into the old lead in this way can be traced in etched sections from successive positions along the sheath, being revealed by flow lines. Meanwhile the residue of the old charge becomes almost stagnant in the bottom corners of the container and contributes less and less to the stream of metal entering the die-block. By an illuminating series of experiments in which alternate cylinders of light and dark coloured wax were extruded through a model press, Dunsheath and Tunstall were able to follow the distribution of each charge in the final sheath. Fig. 29 shows, in the top row, sections cut from a length of tube in which a charge of dark wax was followed by a light one. The effect of several superimposed charges is shown in the row below.

D

In view of the fact that the intersurface is a principal seat of inclusions, it is not difficult to understand that that length of the sheath in which the replacement of one charge by the next occurs is potentially a place where discontinuities may arise and trouble be experienced during service. This region, located a certain distance, according to the size of cable, behind the stop mark, is well recognized as one specially liable to show faults. The longitudinal weld seams at the top (when a twin entry die-block is used) and bottom of the sheath, which extend, of course, over the full length of the sheath, are also liable to be the sites of inclusions. The soundness of these seams depends on clean streams of lead being brought into contact under suitable conditions of pressure and temperature so that intergrowth of the crystals takes place across the junction. Perfect unification can only occur in the absence of oxide membranes and other deleterious impurities, and unless these are suitably reduced by precautions during melting and casting of the lead, the danger arises that, under stresses incidental to coiling or laying the cable, or those set up in service, a particularly objectionable defect in the form of longitudinal splits is met with. Microscopic examination of transverse rings of sheath reveals that without these precautions the granular structure of the metal in the neighbourhood of charge joints and weld seams is frequently very irregular, with fine grained areas which, even after annealing, are not brought up to the general grain size of the sheath as a whole. This feature is attributable to the presence of minute particles of oxide, drawn-out gas cavities, etc., which obstruct the normal process of grain-growth during hot working. Ordinary mechanical tests or short period bursting tests do not indicate that special weakness is associated with these areas; they may, in fact, show increased strength, but, as Atkinson has shown, during tests in which internal pressure is maintained for several weeks, which approximate much more closely to service conditions, rupture occurs there preferentially. Photomicrographs of badly contaminated top and bottom seams, from examples given by Göler and Schmid,[6] are reproduced in Fig. 30. It would be unfortunate if the foregoing remarks gave the impression that sheathing from the ordinary vertical cable press is inevitably defective in the sense discussed; on the contrary, it should be emphasized that under conditions of good practice perfectly satisfactory cable can be produced with regularity.

Among other defects which may be formed in extrusion are transverse cracking and blisters on the surface of the sheath.

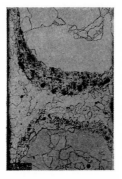

FIG. 30.—Example of the segregation of impurities in the top and bottom seams of cable sheathing in a particularly bad case.

(*Göler and Schmid.*)

The former, which is met with in all forms of extrusion, is due to intergranular weakness in the crystal structure at temperatures approaching the melting-point. Its occurrence in practice results, as a rule, from too high an extrusion speed, or temperature, especially with some of the lead alloys, such as that containing 0·85 per cent of antimony, in which small amounts of a low melting liquid phase may be formed at the die surface where

41

friction is high. The occasional presence of blisters arises from air entrapped during pouring or to gas dissolved in the metal during melting.

Prominent stop marks, in the form of a circumferential ridge on the sheath, are often regarded with some dubiety. They are produced at that place on the sheath which is just emerging from the die when the press is stopped for refilling, due to the diminution of pressure at the die and its sudden increase on restarting. By careful operation of the hydraulic control valve, the marks can be rendered less conspicuous. Identical marks are formed when any extrusion press is stopped and restarted. Experience under service conditions and the results of bursting and other tests reveal no special liability on the part of cable sheaths to failure at such places. The possibility that a deterioration in properties might result from grain-growth in the metal adjacent to the stop mark during the waiting period has been examined by Radley[7] for lead and several alloys; he concludes that this is unlikely to occur unless the temperature is above 200° C. at this point.

The recognition of the causes underlying faults in cable sheathing has led inevitably to the development of a variety of preventive measures and devices. It is impossible to deal in detail with all of these, but the importance of the question as a whole calls for a description in outline of the chief methods. The main sources of contamination of lead in the sheathing process can be classified as (1) impurities contained in and on the surface of the original pigs. (2) Dross and oxide formed during melting and carried over to some extent with the liquid metal into the container. (3) Oxidation of the lead stream and the entraining of air during pouring. (4) The layer of oxide and other dirt on the exposed surface of the residual slug from the preceding charge in the container. The last two of these have received a good deal of attention, and much effort has been devoted to means of liquefying the top of the old charge so as to set free the dirt and promote a clean metallic junction between it and the newly poured metal, to the protection of the molten lead during casting, and to the elimination of the dross and froth which gathers on the surface by skimming or other means. Methods for this purpose include the use of an electric arc, or oxy-acetylene burner, which is lowered into the container to fuse the top of the slug. With the same object, bottom pouring in which the lead is led in down a conduit so that it impinges directly on the old lead, is frequently employed. Various methods have been devised to procure more complete removal of the impurities which accumulate towards the top of the charge. One of these consists of a spill-head attached to the top of the container as described later, while in another, illustrated in Fig. 31, a rectangular false head placed on the container has as one wall a sliding plate (*a*), which is moved across during solidification of the lead by a small hydraulic ram, pushing aside the metal in the false head, and exposing a clean surface, level with the container top, which is immediately brought into contact with the extrusion ram. To

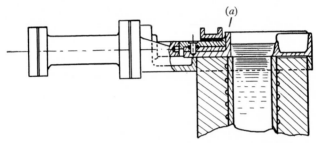

(*a*)

FIG. 31.—Drossing head fitted to the container of a cable press.

avoid oxidation during pouring, a number of operators have made use of CO_2 or other gases to flush out the container and produce an inert atmosphere, while success is also claimed in producing a good weld between the two charges, and reducing the amount of oxide inclusions, by a method in which the metal enters the container through burning hydrogen.[8] No one system or combination is universally preferred, and individual manufacturers adopt different practice in this respect.

An interesting solution of the problem of oxidation of the old slug and in the pouring stage, which at the same time prevents gas unsoundness due to frothing, is by working *in vacuo*, the achievement of which has been described by Atkinson.[9] Fig. 32 shows a diagrammatic drawing of a press of the fixed container type, in which a metal hood secured to the container has a vacuum-tight stuffing box round the ram. Lead enters through a closed spout from the melting kettle. A high vacuum is continuously maintained, being released only when it is required to remove the shell of lead which squeezes up past the ram. This is kept small by having little clearance between the ram and the container. Alternatively, electrically heated plates placed as shown in the diagram, which melt and return the squeezed-out lead, can be fitted. In applying the vacuum method to a press in which the container moves during extrusion, the lead is fed

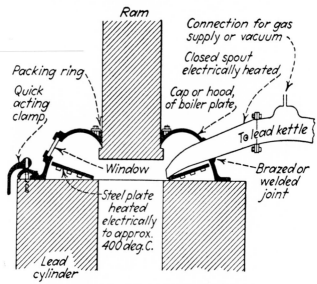

FIG. 32.—Vacuum-sealed container on a cable press.
(*Courtesy of Wire and Wire Products.*)

in via an electrically heated pipe passing longitudinally through the ram. In this case, filling is carried out as the container is moved down, so that the lead enters without splashing.

All the above measures relate to the protection of the metal in the press itself, but it is now recognized that it is also necessary to assure that the lead is delivered from the melting unit in a clean condition and at a suitable temperature. The ordinary type of lead kettle in use prior to the introduction, in the last few years, of special units, is shown in the diagram (Fig. 33). Furnaces of this kind are heated by gas, oil, coal or electricity, gas being the commonest fuel. It will be seen that the products of combustion are passed over the metal bath, contained in a steel or cast-iron pot, to create a semi-inert atmosphere. The pot must hold at least enough metal to fill the container, and has usually a capacity of two to three tons. Larger ones capable of holding up to nine tons are now built, and have the advantage

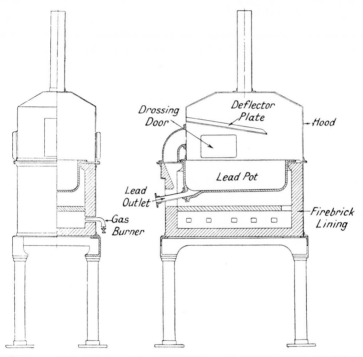

FIG. 33.—Sketch of an ordinary type of gas-fired lead-melting furnace (*Dunsheath*).

of ironing out fluctuations in temperature which occur when metal is withdrawn and replaced with cold pig lead. A casting temperature of about 400° C. is aimed at, and provision to control this automatically is favoured in newer furnaces. This aids in maintaining uniform conditions at the die-block, while excessive oxidation in the furnace is avoided; the point here being that, when lead is melted under oxidizing conditions, its surface becomes coated with litharge, the amount increasing with the

45

temperature and becoming excessive above 500° C. In a kettle of the kind shown, surface dross carried down during charging, and that set free from melting pigs, remains disseminated to some extent in the bath whence it passes to the press. In addition, the dross removed from the furnace represents a loss of about 1 to $1\frac{1}{2}$ per cent of metal.

It is natural to consider whether, if this mechanical transfer is prevented, oxide might not also be carried over in solution. In the absence of evidence for such solubility of oxygen in lead, this has been regarded as unlikely by most authorities, but the point has not been definitely settled. Work by Baker[10] has thrown some light on the question. He has determined the oxygen content of lead held molten for 15 minutes, while exposed to air at various temperatures and then chill cast. Samples heated at 400° C., 650° C., and 900° C. contained 0·006, 0·035, and 0·7 per cent of PbO respectively. While, therefore, a very considerable solubility is shown to exist at high temperatures, it would appear that the danger of contamination arising in this way is not serious at those used in good practice.

Reinitz and Wiseman[11] state that an improved product, resulting in a decrease in the number of cable faults, is obtained by pretreating the lead during melting with a sodium-lead alloy, so as to introduce 0·005–0·05 per cent of sodium. It is said that the products of the deoxidation reaction rise readily to the surface. They claim that a trace of sodium remaining in the solid sheath has no effect on the mechanical properties or on the corrosion resistance.

A representative example of one of the newer melting furnaces may well be considered in conjunction with some of the measures already briefly mentioned, so as to obtain a picture of a complete lay-out. A comprehensive system, described by Piercey,[12] and adopted at the works of the General Electric Company of America, in which the lead is kept from contact with air from the time it is melted until it emerges from the press, will serve to show the care which is now given to extrusion in cable plants. The general arrangement is shown in Fig. 34. The melting furnace is divided into two chambers, both of which are heated by electric immersion heaters. In the first (1), which is open to the atmosphere, the pigs of lead are melted on a perforated grill and the

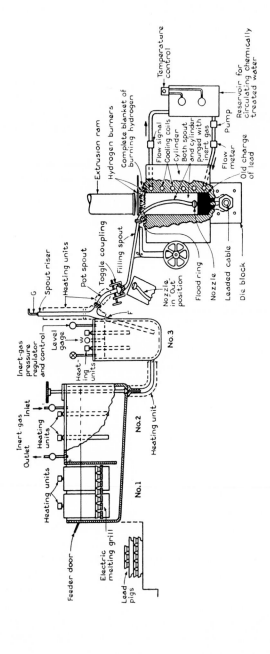

FIG. 34.—Complete sequence of melting and casting for the 'nozzle-swirl' process.
(*Courtesy of 'General Electric Review'.*)

dross and oxide rise to the surface while the liquid metal flows under a partition into the larger chamber (2), serving as a reservoir, where it is maintained under a neutral atmosphere. In this compartment a further opportunity occurs for entangled dross to separate so that clean lead flows into chamber (3). By raising the gas pressure in this unit, lead can be forced out, when required, through the filling spout into the container of the press. The total amount of metal held in the furnace system during operation is 22,000 lb. An atmosphere of nitrogen maintained

FIG. 35.—The nozzle used in the nozzle-swirl process.
(*Courtesy of ' General Electric Review '.*)

in the pot spout prevents oxide being formed at the surface of the metal in the spout, and as a further precaution when the filling spout has been connected at the toggle joint, the whole supply line is swept out by gas, which purges it and the press container of air before the lead is pumped through. The filling spout, terminating in a nozzle (Fig. 35), provided with vanes to impart a swirling motion to the metal as it rises in the container, is lowered until it is just above the surface of the slug of the old charge so that the incoming hot metal washes across the latter, melting the surface and so removing the oxide layer. The swirling action, automatically controlled by the gas pressure in (3), Fig. 34, drives the relatively light impurities to the centre of the

surface of the new charge, where they are removed by skimming
or by overflowing 150 lb. of metal into a flood ring on top of
the container.   The diagrams, Figs. 36, 37, illustrate these points.

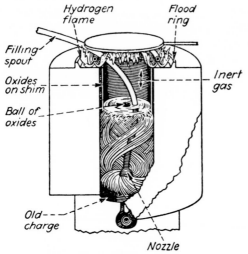

FIG. 36.—A vertical section of lead-press cylinder, showing swirl imparted to
molten lead to free it of oxides and impurities.

(*Courtesy of ' General Electric Review '.*)

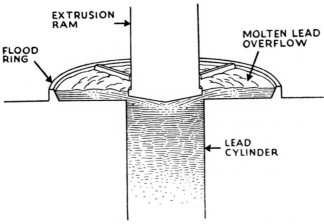

FIG. 37.—Diagram showing the flushing action of the tapered face of the ram
in the cylinder of lead press.

(*Courtesy of ' General Electric Review '.*)

The motion of the lead also causes the oxidized sleeve of lead, adhering to the walls of the container from the previous extrusion, to be melted off. During filling, a pan burner brought down over the top of the container maintains a blanket of burning hydrogen over the lead until it can be sealed from air by the extrusion ram. It is claimed that this combination of precautionary devices leads to a high degree of freedom from extrusion defects in the cable-sheathing made under the system.

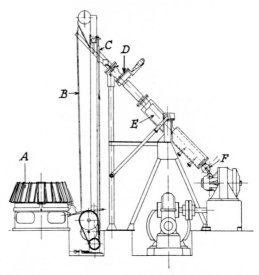

FIG. 38.—Lead-melting furnace for use with the Henley extrusion machine.
(*Courtesy of the Institution of Electrical Engineers.*)

For the continuous extrusion machines referred to later in this chapter, no large reservoir of lead is required, and economy can be effected by melting it down at a rate corresponding to that at which it is being drawn off. Dunsheath's[13] design of a furnace for this purpose, for use with the Henley continuous extrusion machine, is shown in Fig. 38. It consists of a pig magazine (*a*), discharging into an elevator (*b*), which feeds the furnace. The latter in the form of a **D**-section tube set at 45°, is divided into three zones—an entrance lock between gas-tight doors (*c*) and (*d*); a melting zone (*e*); and a lower chamber controlled by a valve (*f*), containing molten lead at a thermostatically controlled temperature. The melting zone and lower chamber have independent gas or electric heating systems. An atmosphere of nitrogen is maintained in the furnace. In the sequence of operation, the withdrawal of lead from the furnace, by altering the level of the metal, operates a float which increases the heat supply at the melting zone, and speeds up the melting of pigs lying in the furnace tube. As each of these slides down it operates a trigger, causing the bottom door of the gas lock to open and allow the pig therein to slide down. As it does so, this in turn trips a switch which starts up the elevator motor, brings a fresh pig to the gas lock, and finally lowers the elevator cradle to pick up another pig from the magazine.

The Judge Press

There now remains to give a short account of some machines which have been designed to avoid some of the faults inherent in sheathing made in vertical hydraulic presses. One of these,

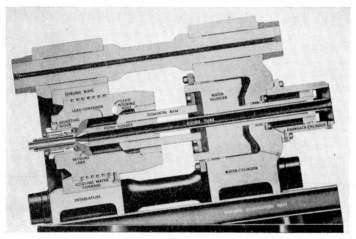

FIG. 39.—Section through the Judge cable press.
(*Courtesy of ' The Engineer '.*)

in which the pressure is applied parallel to the direction of the cable, is the Judge press,[14] seen in section in Fig. 39, which appeared in 1924. The design recalls the earliest Borel press, but differs in using the ' cast-in ' method of charging. Its special

feature is that, during extrusion, the lead, after flowing longitudinally, travels radially inwards over the point towards the die,
and thus avoids the formation of a longitudinal weld seam such
as is produced in the ordinary press. The container, set in the
head of the press, is connected by tension bolts to the hydraulic
cylinder. The die with its assembly is located in a screw block
in the front end. The point-holder is screwed into the back of
the container and has slots cut in its base through which a seg-
mental extrusion ram passes, as shown in Fig. 40. Cable enters
from the back via a guide tube passing through the main ram.

FIG. 40.—Showing
the assembly of
slotted point-
holder and seg-
mental ram.

The drawback cylinder for the ram is shown
at the rear of the press. The latter is set on
its foundation so that the front end is inclined down about 10° from the horizontal so
as to permit the escape of air from the container while it is being filled. This is done by
passing metal from a chute through an orifice
in the back of the container which is un-
covered when the ram is fully withdrawn.
The level of the incoming lead rises against
the face of the plug remaining from the last
charge and finally overflows through the filling
hole. Setting occurs under slight pressure
from the ram. It is claimed that solidification
in a closed container will reduce oxidation,
but it is clear that care will be required to
prevent entry of dross since it is more likely to
become entrapped than in the open, upright type of container.

Although the press makes seamless sheathing there still remains
to be considered the effect of the oxidized surface between charges
in the container. Actually it has been shown that, due to the
differential flow in the die, the joint formed is not a sharp one,
likely to cause radial weakness, but has the form of a vee-shaped
weld, extending along the sheath for several feet, which is satisfactory from the point of strength. (See Fig. 41.)

It is interesting that lower extrusion pressures with a maximum
of 12 tons per square inch, or of 15 tons per square inch for
dilute alloys, are required with this press, on account of the
simpler course of deformation and reduced friction losses in the

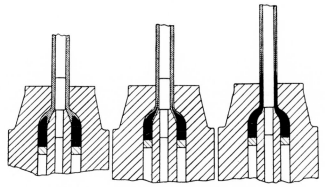

FIG. 41.—The junction between consecutive charges in the Judge press.
(*Courtesy of ' The Engineer '.*)

metal. The production capacity of a 2800-ton unit, taking a charge of 1000 lb. of lead, is about 2 tons an hour.

Continuous Extrusion Machines

The idea of making pipes, and of covering cables with lead by a continuous process has long been attractive. Its appeal is increased by the possibility that it offers of obviating defects inherent in the ordinary hydraulic method, arising from the intermittent nature of its operation. A number of patents have been filed in which a container is fed continuously with liquid lead under pressure by a set of reciprocating pumps, but these, and a number of ingenious variants of the method, do not appear to have progressed beyond the experimental stage. A design[15] put forward in 1906, however, in which a rotating screw was employed to carry lead forward through a cylinder to a die, though unsuccessful at the time, can be regarded as the fore-runner of the continuous methods of extrusion now in com-mercial operation. The first continuous machine to extrude lead pipe successfully was the Henley Telegraph Works Company machine, developed by Dunsheath[16] as the outcome of small-scale experiments started in 1929. The machine developed by the Pirelli-General Cable Co. operates in a generally similar manner and is now in extensive use; this machine is shown in diagram-matic section in Fig. 42. The extrusion screw (4) is driven through a ' Michell ' thrust race (2) and rotates in a barrel-shaped

53

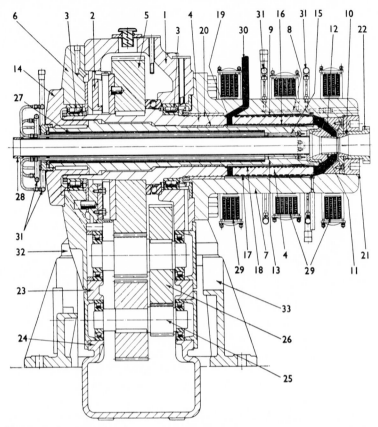

FIG. 42.—Sectional drawing of continuous lead extrusion machine. The lead
flow from inlet pipe to the dies is shown in solid black.

1. Main steel casing
2. 'Michell' thrust bearing.
3. Double row roller journal bearings.
4. Extrusion screw.
5. Final drive gear.
6. Back flange.
7. Extrusion barrel.
8. Extrusion barrel cooling channels.
9. Longitudinal slots.
10. Ring die.
11. Core die.
12. Spider (four port, ring and core die support).
13. Stationary tube.
14. Steel flange, locating stationary tube.
15. Stationary tube cooling channels.
16. Stationary tube outer longitudinal grooves.
17. Outer extrusion passage.
18. Inner extrusion passage.

19. Port holes for lead access to inner extrusion.
20. Lead retainers on stationary tube and extrusion screw.
21. Spider front screw.
22. Ring die adjusting screw.
23. } Two piece subsidiary casing.
24. }
25. First reduction gear.
26. Second reduction gear.
27. Outer protecting tube—stationary tube.
28. Inner protecting tube—stationary tube.
29. Induction heating coils.
30. Point of lead entry into machine.
31. Circular pipe manifolds—cooling channels.
32. Bottom flange.
33. Cast iron stool.

54

casing (7), while having a stationary tube (13) located within its bore. This tube, which lies concentrically inside the impeller, terminates in the die assembly and, like the casing, has longitudinal grooves which serve to key the lead against the rotating action of the impeller screws. Molten lead admitted at (30) has access to both inner and outer sides of the impeller, so that a double extrusion stream is delivered into the first compression chamber. This mass of lead is then forced through the ports of the spider or die support (12) and again compressed before emerging as a tube. Maintenance of the correct temperatures at different points is achieved by induction heating coils (29) and cooling channels. When in production only the back induction coil is used, to maintain the lead molten and allow it to enter the extrusion barrel where the cooling medium, passing through the channels, causes it to freeze and be forced forward under the action of the screw. A layout for three of these units is shown in Fig. 43.

The chief claims made for continuous machines may be summarized as follows

(a) Since they have not to be opened up for recharging, the metal is not exposed to oxidation.

(b) No longitudinal weld seam, and no stop marks are produced on the sheath.

(c) Exactness of temperature control giving close dimensions and uniform properties.

(d) The economic merit of continuous operation.

The principal defects observed in cable from presses are, therefore, rarely met in machine produced sheaths, although the maintenance of a constant wall thickness is only achieved by careful control of the working conditions even on continuous machines. A feature which is peculiar to the continuous product, but which does not appear to have any deleterious effect upon properties, is shown in Fig. 44 and has been termed ' whirl-lines ' by Back.[17] He has ascribed this to a high degree of segregation as the result of solidification under extreme mechanical disturbance, and has noted that it is particularly prevalent when antimony is present. The subsequent heavy shearing of one section of

E

FIG. 43.—Layout of Pirelli continuous extrusion shop.

A. Extrusion machine.   B. Heated stores.   C. Lead-melting furnace.
D. Lead ingots.   E. Drying ovens.   F. Take-off stands.
G. Control panels.   H. Sheathed cables.   J. Unsheathed cables ready for drying.

(Courtesy of Pirelli General Cable Co.)

flow over the other causes thin transverse layers of segregated material to pass through the ports of the spider, after which the layers are drawn out longitudinally and appear as a series of concentric rings between the positions of the spider arms. The segregate is dispersed by prolonged ageing at elevated temperature.

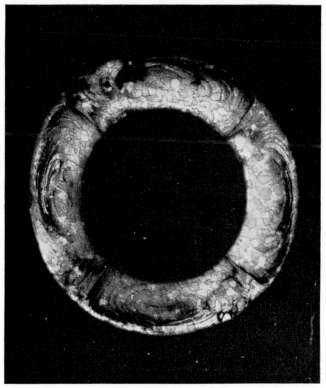

FIG. 44.—Etched cross-section of lead pipe from continuous machine showing whirl-lines.

(*Back*, '*J. Inst. Metals*')

Lead Slug Extrusion

When one considers the methods of extrusion as applied to different groups of metals and alloys, it is perhaps a little surprising that lead should be exceptional in that the practice of casting and freezing the charge in the container rather than the use of precast billets should be that almost invariably adopted,

FIG. 45.—Slug-fed press for covering rubber hose.
(*Courtesy of John Robertson Company.*)

though it is obvious that a special reason exists where cables
have to be sheathed in long lengths. In spite of the large increase in production which could be achieved by the use of billets,
owing to the elimination of the setting period, it is only employed
in a few instances where the quality of the product is of little

importance. The reason put forward in the lead industry for this is that defects occur with greater frequency and are more difficult to avoid when billets are used. Experience in connection with the harder metals, for which the use of liquid charging was soon abandoned, has, of course, been the contrary of this. Fig. 45 shows a press of the kind used in the cable-making industry applied to the covering of rubber hose with a sheathing of lead in which it is then vulcanized and the lead is afterwards stripped off to be used again. The billets or slugs, weighing approximately half a ton, are preheated to about 100° C., and are extruded with the container and die-block heated to 180° C.

Alloys for Cable Sheathing

The earliest cables were sheathed exclusively with lead, and while this continues to be widely used, an increased measure of protection has been obtained in some directions from the substitution of lead alloys. Apart from the essential requirements that a sheathing material should be easy to extrude at economically high speeds, and should have a high degree of immunity from corrosion, a combination of other properties is required in varying degree, such as pliability for purposes of coiling and uncoiling, and handling during installation; tensile strength and hardness; and resistance to fatigue and creep. The relative importance of these depends on the class of cable, the method by which it is installed, and the special conditions to which it is exposed during working. A particular trouble experienced with overhead cables, and those laid in proximity to railways, pinned to bridge structures, and those used in ship's wiring systems, is that of intergranular cracking of the sheath. One reason for this has been made evident by the work of Haehnel,[18] Beckinsale and Waterhouse,[19] and others, who have shown that lead is susceptible to failure under very low fatigue stresses such as may easily arise in service as the result of vibration, expansion and contraction caused by temperature changes, and by wind pressure. The liability of lead and its alloys to deform continuously, or ' creep ', under prolonged loading is another matter which is receiving much consideration and is now influencing the selection of sheathing material. Very pure lead, as Greenwood[20] and his collaborators have shown, has an extremely poor resistance to creep, but impurities, even in the small amounts present in commercial grades of lead, have a marked effect in diminishing the rate of creep. Thus, a specially prepared lead with a total of 0·0005 per cent of impurities broke under a load of 500 lb. per square inch after 25 days; while a commercially pure lead withstood the same load for 500 days before failure. The addition of as little as 0·01 per cent of silver, or 0·06 per cent of copper, confer much improved properties in this respect. By suitable alloying both the fatigue limit and the creep resistance can be raised considerably, and a wide range of compositions has been proposed, and in some cases adopted, for cable purposes as the result of the close investigation which this subject has received.[21, 22, 23]

The principal alloying additions to lead for the purpose of improving creep and fatigue strengths are silver, copper, antimony, tin, calcium, cadmium, and tellurium, either singly or in various combinations. The quantitative effects of these additions are in some doubt because of the lack of reproducibility of creep and fatigue data obtained on alloys extruded in commercial presses where many variables, such as grain size, are not under sufficient control. However, inasmuch as commercial products are produced under such conditions the degree of reproducibility to be expected, which has been the subject of a study by McKeown and Hopkin,[24] is, *per se*, of some importance. A second criticism of the work in this field is that, as is frequently the case in the compilation of creep data, tests have usually been carried out at stresses which are above those most likely to be encountered in service and it is assumed that the comparative behaviour of the materials at these high stresses will be the same as at service stresses. The danger attached to such assumptions in the cases of alloys undergoing phase transformations and grain size changes during creep are well known.

Notwithstanding these difficulties some valuable work has been conducted in this field in recent years, of which that by Hopkin and Thwaites[25] is noteworthy. By a systematic study of the creep and fatigue properties of single-phase (Pb–Sn), two-phase (Pb–Cu) and age-hardening alloys (Pb–Sb), with appropriate control of grain size, these authors suggest the constitution of an alloy likely to have good creep and fatigue resistance. The improvements in mechanical properties which result from these alloying additions must be greater than the reduction in creep strength which accompanies the grain refinement, for a constant extrusion temperature, brought about by alloying. It is suggested that this requirement is likely to be met in lead alloys containing additions causing as much solid-solution hardening, or age-hardening, as possible and forming a relatively large amount of a hard second phase. The effects of copper and silver additions have been studied by a number of workers,[26, 27, 28, 29] who have confirmed the beneficial effects of copper but have indicated the ineffectiveness of small silver additions at stresses below about 400 lb. per square inch. On the other hand, McKeown and Hopkin[24] have obtained very good creep properties from a lead containing 1 per cent silver and with a very small grain size at stresses down to 400 lb. per square inch. Greenwood and Cole[29] have shown that the eutectic amount of copper, 0·06 per cent, which decreases the creep rate by a factor of about ten, is only effective when in a state of fine dispersion.

Antimony forms an age-hardening system with lead, arising from the change with temperature in the solid solubility, which falls from a maximum of 3·45 weight per cent at 252° C. to about 0·2 weight per cent at the ordinary temperature. Full hardness is not developed on standing after manufacture for several months, after which it slowly falls off, due to the agglomeration of the precipitated antimony particles. Where the hardening is regarded as undesirable, the cable is frequently blanketed as it leaves the press so as to diminish the rate of cooling instead of being passed through a water trough, as is normally done with cables to protect the core and to avoid flattening and adherence of the turns when it is coiled on the drum. Cooling by the use of steam is sometimes considered a satisfactory alternative in order to reduce age-hardening, but tests made by Chaston[30] indicate that this is not very effective. He gives figures to show that even on cooling in air from 250° C. the Brinell hardness of an alloy containing 1 per cent antimony, 0·06 per cent copper, increases on ageing from 6 to 10, as compared with a final value of 12 obtained as the result of quenching in water. If the lead is strained while antimony remains in solution, a likely occurrence during handling of the extruded product, then the course of the precipitation may be altered, with discontinuous precipitation and recrystallization being observed in certain cases.[31]

Calcium also forms an age-hardening system with lead, due to the precipitation of Pb_3Ca, but has the advantage that while it develops its maximum hardness in about one day it does not subsequently exhibit overageing. Even the addition of 0·005 per cent of calcium changes the order of magnitude of the creep rate and 0·05 per cent calcium will allow the imposition of twice the stress that can be applied to copper-lead for a rate of creep of 1 per cent per year.[32] The calcium, as Pb_3Ca, does not impair the corrosion resistance, although care is needed in casting and extruding the alloys.

The quantitative effects of these various alloying elements upon the creep and fatigue properties of lead are structure dependent, i.e. they are influenced not only by the type and amount of alloying but by the state of heat treatment and grain size. This is particularly so in the case of creep but neither are these effects negligible in the case of fatigue.[25] Notwithstanding these difficulties some idea of the effects of alloying upon the fatigue and creep properties of lead is apparent from Table 1.

The choice of the lead to be used in sheathing a cable is, of course, dependent upon the conditions to which the cable is to be subject while in service.[33] Aerial cables are especially subject to heavy stresses, and it was in connection with these that lead hardened by alloy additions was first introduced, particularly for overhead telephone cables. To begin with, the alloys adopted contained 1 to 3 per cent of tin; these continue to be used extensively for small cables for house wiring, but on account of the high cost of tin, and the quantity which would be involved, this metal has been replaced by antimony in amounts between 0·75 and 1 per cent. The latter alloy, adopted in 1912 by the Bell Telephone System, and now often made with the further addition of 0·06 per cent of copper, has become the standard for telephone cables in the U.S.A. In England, the alloy with 0·85 per cent antimony is also favoured to some extent. Antimony contents above 1 per cent are more or less excluded on the score of cost and difficulty in extrusion.

Cables which are laid underground in ducts or trenches, such as the majority of power cables, have to fulfil rather different

TABLE I

Material	Nominal Composition per cent	Fatigue Strength (tons/in.^{2}) 10^7 Cycles	Min. Creep Rate (in./in./hr.) at 500 lb./in.^{2} Grain size in brackets
Lead, high purity . .	Pb 99·99	0·18	1·4 × 10^{-4} (0·84 mm.^{2})
Pb–Sn . . .	Sn 0·5	0·25	10 × 10^{-6} (0·045)
	Sn 1·0	0·31	11 × 10^{-6} (0·023)
	Sn 2·0	0·44	—
Pb–Sb–Cd (B.N.F. Ternary No. 1)	Cd 0·25 Sb 0·5	0·74	18 × 10^{-4} (0·0014)
,, No. 2	Cd 0·25 Sb 1·5	0·57	4 × 10^{-4} (0·0054)
,, No. 3	Cd 0·15 Sn 0·4	0·35	17 × 10^{-4} (0·0028)
Pb–Te . . .	Te 0·05	0·50	20 × 10^{-4} (0·0018)
	Te 0·15	—	1·2 × 10^{-6} (0·20)
Pb–Ca . . .	Ca 0·03	0·73 (preheated and extruded at 250° C.)	—
Pb–Ag–Cu .	Ag 0·005 Cu 0·005	—	4 × 10^{-6} (0·17)
Pb–Sb . . .	Sb 0·25	0·37	
	Sb 0·5	0·43	5 × 10^{-6} (0·0032)
	Sb 0·8	0·60	6 × 10^{-4}
Pb–Sb–Sn	Sb 0·4 Sn 0·25	0·43	5 × 10^{-6} (0·06)
Pb–Cu . .	Cu 0·06	0·22	5 × 10^{-5} (0·005–0·01)

From C. J. Smithells. *Metals Reference Book* (2nd Edition), Butterworth. Based on data provided by British Non-Ferrous Metals Research Association, London.

requirements which are in most cases satisfactorily met by the use of unalloyed lead. The A.S.T.M. specification for metal for this purpose fixes a lead content of not less than 99·85 per cent. However, the advantages of some degree of alloying in reducing the number of breakdowns is now generally recognized, especially since the advent of oil-filled high-tension cables working under internal pressure.

Where only a moderate improvement in the properties will

suffice, the amount of the alloying addition can be limited. For example, 0·25 per cent of antimony is sometimes present in power cables. The ternary alloys developed by the B.N.F.M.R.A., two of which are given in Table 1, and another with the composition 0·4 per cent tin, 0·15 per cent cadmium, have found some applications as sheathing alloys, having been used in England by the Admiralty for ship's cables, and by the G.P.O. for telephone cables.

Pressure and Speed for Extrusion

Higher pressures are necessary to extrude most of the lead alloys than are used for lead, and this frequently makes it essential to reduce the diameter of the container, consequently decreasing the length of cable covered at each operation. The following figures obtained by Pearson and Smythe[34] exemplify this point :

Alloy	Increase in Extrusion Pressure at 240° C. as a Percentage of that for Lead
0·8 per cent Sb	56
0·15 per cent Cd, 0·4 per cent Sn . .	59
0·25 per cent Cd, 0·5 per cent Sb . .	75

For the copper-bearing alloy, the increase in pressure is of the order of 10 per cent only.

When metals are worked at temperatures approaching their melting-points, failure readily occurs by reason of the low inter-granular cohesion which then obtains. At high speeds of extrusion, temperatures considerably in excess of the nominal are built up, due to friction within the metal and at the surface of the die, which may reach the danger-point locally, giving rise to the appearance of circumferential or spiral cracks on the surface of the sheathing. This ' checking ' is infrequent in lead sheaths in which it occurs only if the temperature comes within 2° C. of the melting-point, and a considerable latitude is thus possible in respect of the extrusion speed, the maximum to which is generally only limited by the delivery rate of the hydraulic pump. Much greater care is required with some of the alloys, in which liquefaction begins at lower temperatures. In the case of the 1 per cent antimony alloy, for example, the top of the safe range is about 290° C., and it is necessary to regulate the speed of extrusion to suit the material and the size of section which is being produced.

The Sheathing of Cables with Aluminium

The likelihood that any other metallic material would be found to replace lead for the protection of cables had hardly been envisaged until recently, but the economic policy adopted in Germany, in the years preceding the war, of substituting metals derived from domestic raw materials for those of external origin, has led to an examination being made of this problem. The qualities which lead possesses, which may be broadly summarized under the headings of ease of extrusion at temperatures which do not harm the cable insulation, pliability in handling, and ability to resist corrosion, are difficult to find in combination in any substitute. On the other hand, the relative weakness of lead and even of the best of its alloys so far developed is such that in providing sheaths of thickness to withstand the stresses imposed in oil-filled and in marine cables, the weight of lead used may, in extreme cases, be as high as 80 per cent of the cable as a whole, and runs in ordinary cases between 30 and 50 per cent.

The metal regarded as most likely is aluminium, which in the early trials was used in high purity grade (99·99 per cent), but is now also being used in normal commercial grade (99·5 per cent). A comparison of some of the properties of these grades with those of lead and the 1 per cent antimony alloy is given in Table 2.

TABLE 2

	Lead	Lead with 1 per cent Sb	99·99 per cent Al	99·5 per cent Al
Brinell Hardness . . .	3·5	6·5	14·0	22
Yield Point, tons/sq. in. .	—	—	0·9	—
Max. Stress, tons/sq. in. .	0·9	1·6	2·3–3·0	5
Elongation, per cent . .	55	36	40–50	40
Fatigue Limit, tons/sq. in.	±0·28	±0·56	±1·5	±2·5
Resistance to creep, tons/sq. in. (0·1 per cent extension per year) . .	0·04–0·06	0·06–0·13	0·5	1·0

65

The specific weight of aluminium (2·7) is only a quarter of that of lead (11·3), and even if the wall thickness of the sheath is unchanged, an economy results which would offset the higher price of the former. Aluminium also shows up favourably in respect of its behaviour towards fatigue and creep, and in the fact that it is not prone to grain growth, like lead, at the temperatures and under the stresses engendered in service.

In some early experiments Czempiel and Haase[35] claimed some success in using an ordinary vertical cable press, suitably modified, and a ' cast in ' method of charging. The weld between successive charges was satisfactory but some charring of the paper insulation was noted in the cable where it lay in the die-block during the stop for refilling. Hauff, Hosse and Deisinger[36] at the Siemens works also experimented with a vertical cable press but they experienced some difficulty due to the attack of the molten metal on the container. They used, in addition, a horizontal press of the type used for copper alloys in which precast billets were charged into the press in succession when the preceding one had been extruded to half length; a bridge die being used, in order to see whether a continuous length of tube could be produced. The probability of obtaining a good weld between the billets in this way may not have been regarded with enthusiasm, but they state that fault-free tube, in which the longitudinal seams due to the bridge die could only be revealed by deep etching, were made at 400° C.

Although considerable progress has been made since these early experiments extruded aluminium sheathed cable is not yet in extensive use, only a few organizations having developed their technique to the point where they can supply cable of appropriate quality. The difficulties associated with sheathing in aluminium, as compared with lead, arise from the greater resistance which it offers to deformation, as the result of which it has not proved possible simply to apply the technique used in lead sheathing. The extrusion temperature is generally higher than that for lead, leading to a greater risk of damaging the cable insulation and hence the necessity for die boxes of more complicated design. The problems arising from this and other sources have been tackled in a number of ways, sometimes with the use of cable presses of conventional design, such as that shown in Fig. 27, and in other cases with presses designed with regard to the particular problems associated with sheathing in aluminium.

The General Cable Corporation in the U.S.A. have installed a Schloemann Press of 1760 tons capacity which is a horizontal double ram–double billet unit designed for the use of commercially pure aluminium (99·5 per cent). The design permits the use of solid billets and also is instrumental in keeping the cavity in the die block very small Because equal pressure is

Fig. 46.—1600-ton Schloemann press for aluminium sheathing at General Cable Corporation.

applied on opposite sides of the die block, equal radial pressures are built up against the die and core die so that a radial displacement of the tools in the die block is prevented; additionally, the flow of aluminium is greatly facilitated. A general view of the press and its auxiliaries is shown in Fig. 46, while Fig. 47 shows the basic features of its design in diagrammatic form. The press frame is a single rectangular steel casting at the centre of which is mounted the die block with billet containers on each side. The dieholder is adjustable for opening or closing the spacing between the die and core die to regulate the wall thickness of the aluminium sheath while the press is in operation or stopped. This adjustment is controlled by a large ' ratchet spanner ', A, which is operated by a double-acting hydraulic cylinder mounted on the lower part of the press frame. Two automatically controlled billet loading devices, each consisting of two hydraulically operated swinging arms, are mounted on the upper part of the press frame. Low-pressure air accumulators are located at each end of the press frame and provide for the rapid forward motion of the rams and the inserting of billets into the containers. A high-pressure accumulator furnishes the energy for upsetting the billets and for rapid withdrawal of the rams after the billets have been extruded. The actual extrusion of the sheath is done by

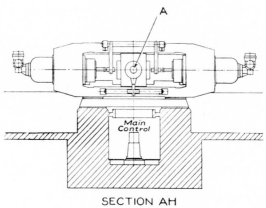

SECTION AH

Fig. 47.—Essential design features of the press shown in Fig. 46.

a combination of fourteen constant-volume pumps. Two low-frequency induction furnaces are used for heating the billets to 500° C., which are sprayed with water on the end facing the extrusion ram to reduce the temperature there to 400° C. prior to placing in the container. The whole sequence of events, transferring the billets to the furnaces, then to the containers and the extrusion itself, is carried out automatically, and the advance of the two rams is synchronized so that the metal flows evenly on both sides of the die.

The high extrusion temperature used on this press has necessitated more than usual ingenuity in the design of the die block to prevent those defects arising in the cable which would normally result from a high temperature. The cable core, which passes through the die block horizontally and perpendicular to

68

the direction of motion of the extrusion rams, is protected from the high temperature of the die block by means of a specially designed water-cooled tube assembly. The end of this assembly is in positive pressure-contact with the core die. On the cable exit side of the press, the cable sheath is uniformly sprayed with water around its circumference very near to the point of exit from the die. The removal of heat by the two cooling devices on the core and sheath side of the cable is so effective that, even though the aluminium is extruded at 500° C., it is in contact with the cable core at this temperature for only a small fraction of a second, so that the core is no more severely treated than in a conventional lead press.

As the extrusion cycle nears completion the extrusion speed is gradually reduced to zero over about a half-minute, during which period the cooling water on the extrusion side reduces the die temperature. While the press is stopped the cool die absorbs the heat from the annulus of aluminium between die and core die so that damage to the cable core is prevented. The stopping of the press for the purpose of charging billets normally lasts about one minute, but paper-insulated cables have remained in the press for periods of about five minutes without damage to the insulation.

The stop marks formed on the product when any extrusion press is stopped, and which are due to the elastic deformation created by pressure variations (page 42), are also observed on aluminium sheathed cable (Fig. 48). These are further aggravated in the case of aluminium sheaths by the greater thermal transfer during the stop period than in the case of lead sheathing. In the Schloemann press, these dimensional changes have been compensated for by the hydraulically operated 'ratchet spanner', which facilitates the opening and closing of the spacing between die and core die. The operation is done by moving a threaded section which supports the die and so allows adjustment of wall thickness while the press is in operation.

The formation of blisters on the surface of the sheath, sometimes observed with lead, appears with aluminium also if steps are not taken to avoid entrapping air during upsetting of the billet after charging. The practice at General Cable Corporation of spraying one end of the billet with water so as to produce a 'thermal taper' prevents this by producing a variation in resistance to deformation which increases along the length of the billet as the colder end, adjacent to the ram, is approached. Upsetting therefore starts at the hot end and produces a billet of conical shape, which becomes cylindrical again as the deformation advances towards the ram and displaces the air from the container.

The approach to the extrusion of aluminium-sheathed cable adopted by the Hackbridge Cable Co., Ltd., in the U.K., differs in a number of ways from that used by General Cable Corporation, but has also succeeded in producing cable of appropriate

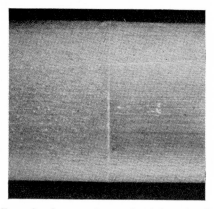

FIG. 48.—Stop marks on aluminium sheath.
(*Courtesy of ' Metallurgia '.*)

quality. The press is of the horizontal type and employs the inverted process, i.e. with a moving die, to reduce the power requirement from that necessary when the billet is moved through the container. By making use of the relative ease with which super-purity aluminium extrudes, as compared with commercial grade, extrusion can be carried out at a pressure of about 25 tons per square inch on a hollow billet of 13 in. outside diameter and 9 in. bore and an extrusion temperature of about 400° C.

The risk of charring the electrical insulation, reduced by the lower extrusion temperature, is further minimized by the ingenious device of applying over the insulation a wrapping of paper which is backed with a metal foil suitably embossed to give point contact with the insulation at suitable intervals (British Patent

No. 632,534). The die box is also designed so that the tube of aluminium, representing the sheath, is applied loosely over the cable with a radial gap of 0·005 in. to 0·010 in. The combination of the reflecting surface of the metal foil and the insulating air-gaps retards the rise of temperature of the dielectric, thus permitting cooling to be carried out before the electrical insulation has reached the charring temperature.

The arrangement of the working tools in this installation is shown in Fig. 49. The metal is formed in a port hole die box

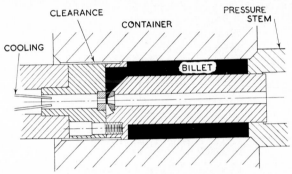

FIG. 49.—Arrangement of working tools for sheathing cable with aluminium at the Hackbridge Cable Co., Ltd.

made in two parts, one of which is attached to the die stem and the other to the hollow mandrel or cable guard. It is obvious that it is on the details of the design of this particular feature of the whole assembly that the success of the process depends, since a compromise must be effected between those features of design which ensure adequate strength of the die box, easy withdrawal from the container and low extrusion pressures. The fact that aluminium-sheathed cable is being produced on this press is a clear indication of the fact that a die of appropriate design can be made and that the more extensive use of extruded aluminium cable, to replace or augment the supplies of drawn aluminium cable which have already proved the value of such sheathing, is very near.

REFERENCES

[1] 'Statistical Tables on Al, Pb, etc.' 44th edition. Metallgesellschaft Aktiengesellschaft, Frankfurt-am-Main. 1957.

[2] P. Dunsheath. The Continuous Extrusion of Lead Cable Sheathing. *J. Inst. Elec. Eng.*, 1937, **80,** 353–67.

[3] H. A. Tunstall and P. Dunsheath. The Physical Properties of Lead Cable Sheaths. *Ibid.*, 1928, **66,** 280–9.

[4] W. H. Bassett and C. J. Schneider. The Occurrence of Irregularities in Lead Cable Sheathing and their Relation to Failures. *Trans. Amer. Inst. Min. & Met. Eng.*, 1933, **104,** 254–71.

[5] R. W. Atkinson. *Wire and Wire Products*, Dec. 1936, 695–704.

[6] F. v. Göler and E. Schmid. Flow Phenomena in the Extrusion of Cable Sheaths. *Z. für Metallkunde*, 1939, **31** (3), 61–8.

[7] *J. Inst. Elec. Eng.*, 1937, **80,** 371.

[8] L. Zickerick. *Elec. World*, Jan. 19, 1935, 30–1.

[9] R. W. Atkinson. *Ibid.*

[10] W. A. Baker. Estimation of Oxygen in Metals. *J. Inst. Metals*, 1939, **65,** 345–53.

[11] B. B. Reinitz and R. J. Wiseman. *Elec. Eng.*, 1940, **59,** 165–70.

[12] C. A. Piercey. The Nozzle Swirl Process. *Gen. Elec. Rev.*, 1940, **43,** 489–91.

[13] P. Dunsheath. *Ibid.*

[14] The Straight-Through Press for Lead-Sheathing Cables. *Engineering*, 1931, **131,** 568–70.

[15] Brit. Pat. No. 12265 (1904).

[16] P. Dunsheath. *Ibid.*

[17] L. H. Back. The Hot Working of Lead and Lead-Rich Alloys. *J. Inst. Metals*, 1949–50, **76,** 541–56.

[18] O. Haehnel. On the Origin of Splits in Cable Sheathing and Other Sheathing Defects. *Telegr- und Fernsprech-Technik*, 1935, **24,** 179–82.

[19] S. Beckinsale and H. Waterhouse. The Deterioration of Lead Cable Sheathing by Cracking, and its Prevention. *J. Inst. Metals*, 1928, **39,** 375–406.

[20] J. N. Greenwood and H. K. Worner. Types of Creep Curves Obtained with Lead and its Dilute Alloys. *Ibid.*, 1939, **64,** 135–58.

[21] H. F. Moore and N. J. Alleman. The Creep of Lead and Lead Alloys used for Cable Making. *Univ. of Illinois Eng. Exptl. Sta. Bull.*, No. 243, 1932.

[22] H. F. Moore, B. B. Betty and C. W. Dollins. Creep and Fracture of Lead and Lead Alloys. *Ibid.*, No. 272, 1935.

[23] J. McKeown. The Creep of Lead and Lead Alloys. *J. Inst. Metals*, 1937, **60,** 201–22.

[24] J. McKeown and L. M. T. Hopkin. Creep and Fatigue Tests on Commercially Extruded Lead and Lead Alloy Pipes. *Metallurgia*, 1950, **40,** 135–43 and 219–23.

[25] L. M. T. Hopkin and C. J. Thwaites. The Effects of Some Constitutional Factors on the Creep and Fatigue Properties of Lead and Lead Alloys. *J. Inst. Metals*, 1953–4, **82,** 181–95.

[26] G. R. Gahn and W. C. Ellis. The Effect of Small Percentages of Silver and Copper on the Creep Characteristics of Extruded Lead. *Amer. Soc. Test. Mat.*, 1948, **48**, 801–14.

[27] H. S. Phelps, F. Kahn and W. P. Magee. Influence of Small Percentage of Silver on the Tensile Strength of Extruded Lead Sheathing. *Ibid.*, 1948, **48**, 815–24.

[28] C. W. Dollins. *Univ. of Illinois Eng. Exptl. Sta. Bull.*, No. 378, July 1948.

[29] J. W. Greenwood and J. H. Cole. The Influence of Various Factors on the Creep of Lead Alloys. *Metallurgia*, 1949, **39**, 121–6.

[30] J. C. Chaston. The Properties of Lead and Lead Alloys for Cable Sheathing. *Elec. Communications*, 1934, **13** (1), 31–50.

[31] E. J. Hooker. An Investigation into Some Ageing Characteristics of Lead-Antimony Alloys, with Particular Reference to the Effect of Strain. *J. Inst. Metals*, 1957–8, **86**, 98–107.

[32] J. N. Greenwood and J. H. Cole. The Influence of Calcium on the Creep Characteristics of Lead. *Metallurgia*, 1949, **39**, 241–5.

[33] British Standard 801 : 1953. Lead and Lead Alloy Sheaths of Electric Cable.

[34] C. E. Pearson and J. A. Smythe. *Brit. Non-Ferr. Met. Res. Assocn. Report*, No. 18, 1931.

[35] A. Czempiel and C. Haase. On the Question of Using Aluminium as a Cable Sheathing Material. *Aluminium*, 1937, **7**, 521–8.

[36] F. Hauff, G. Hosse and W. Deisinger. Aluminium as a Material for Cable Sheathing. *Siemens-Zeitschrift*, 1939, **19**, 357–68.

CHAPTER IV

Equipment for the Hot Extrusion
of Hard Metals

IN tracing the historical development of extrusion in Chapter I, it was not taken beyond the point at which, at the beginning of the present century, its employment for copper alloys had been successfully accomplished. This can be regarded as the turning-point in the wider application of the process. It would serve no useful purpose to follow chronologically the subsequent stages in progress which have been made, and it need only be said that these have not involved any radical departure in the principles employed, but have come about almost entirely as a consequence of continuous progress in the design of hydraulic presses and the elaboration of suitable adjunctive gear. There is given below a summary of the principal features which contribute to the improved performance of present-day presses : (a) an increase in size and total power; (b) the incorporation of hydraulic and mechanical auxiliaries for such purposes as conveying billets, manipulating and locking the die assembly, cutting off the extrusion and separating the discard, etc., which have increased the speed of operation; (c) the introduction of better hydraulic systems, embodying either direct drive or accumulators of the pneumatic type, which with improved valves, pumps, and regulators available, ensure the smooth delivery and control of large volumes of high-pressure oil or water; (d) the satisfactory solution of the problem of successively piercing and extruding solid billets for the production of tubes and hollow sections by the inclusion of hydraulic piercing equipment operating independently of the main cylinder; (e) methods of construction designed to preserve the co-axial alignment of the working parts, and simple adjustment for taking up wear, contributing greatly in ameliorating eccentricity in tube manufacture; (f) the evolution of steels suitable for the onerous conditions of heat and stress combined

74

with abrasion under which such members as mandrels and dies operate.

Horizontal and Vertical Presses

For general purposes the horizontal press is the one principally used, with the die assembly and container pressed against the end platen, to which are fastened the two, three or four columns which sustain the full working load. As press capacities have increased the two-column construction has given way to the three-column and, with the advent of the larger presses of recent years, this in turn is being replaced by the four-column construction. The move towards heavier presses, of 15,000 to 20,000 tons capacity, has been accelerated by the necessity for the production of larger extrusions requiring less subsequent fabrication, such as integrally stiffened aircraft sections, although other benefits are also to be had from such a trend. Thus, it becomes possible to extrude the stiffer alloys, such as steel, titanium and high strength aluminium alloys, in more useful sizes or to increase the extrusion ratio and so improve mechanical properties. Similarly, some alloys which were previously extruded at temperatures approaching the solidus, so as to reduce their strength and hence the power requirement, may be extruded at lower temperatures where better mechanical properties may result.

Presses giving ram pressures between 1000 and 2000 tons are still in extensive use, particularly for work on copper-base alloys. In the brass industry it has been usual in some quarters to differentiate between presses for making rod and those intended especially for forming tubes; those for the former being of simpler construction and lower precision. This distinction has lasted longest in the U.S.A., where the practice has also been conditioned by the fact that it was until recently rare for rod presses there to be operated off an accumulator, and hence the somewhat low rate of extrusion set by the delivery of the pumps makes them, in any case, unsuitable for tube-making. In England, due to the more general use of accumulators, adaptation for extruding hollow products has usually been possible, and the separation of function is more infrequent. At the present time, the universal type of horizontal press, fully equipped for piercing, with safeguards in its design to secure and retain good accuracy,

FIG. 50.—Fielding and Platt semi-automatic press of 2000 tons for general purposes.

has been generally accepted as the best solution where a programme which includes a multiplicity of fabricated forms has to be covered. For the general run of copper alloys, a press similar to that shown in Fig. 50 of 2000 tons, capable of working at ram speeds up to 8 in. per second, and with means where necessary of heating the container, has been found satisfactory. For dealing with billets up to 8 in. in diameter in the more refractory alloys, a number of units of 2500 tons, and occasional more powerful

FIG. 51.—12,000-ton Hydraulik Press.

ones, are installed, but it does not appear likely that the heavy presses necessary for high strength aluminium alloys will be required for copper-base alloys.

For the light alloys, particularly those based on aluminium and having high strength, the tendency in recent years has been to put in powerful presses with up to 12,000 tons ram pressure and capable of handling billets in the region of 30–35 in. diameter and 70–80 in. long. A typical example of the type of press installed under the Heavy-Press Programme of the United States[1] is shown in Fig. 51. The need for such presses has largely arisen

77

from the requirements of the aircraft industry[2, 3, 4] of one-part extrusions, which would prove stronger and lighter than composite pieces. Integrally stiffened skin panels, and hollow, stepped or tapered sections of complicated profile are the types of component produced and which had previously to be machined out of solid stock, an operation sometimes involving the removal of as much as 80 per cent of the weight of the original material. The production of such shapes has resulted in the necessity for press designs showing considerable departure from previous ones, not the least of which are those features associated with the use of rectangular containers. The demand for sections whose height is relatively small compared to their width has led to this particular development because of the more favourable metal flow and the more effective press utilization when such sections are produced from rectangular billets.

For certain purposes, such as the production of small diameter tubes with thin walls, like those used for condensers, etc., many manufacturers prefer presses of the vertical type to those which work in the horizontal position. The advantages claimed for them are: (a) it is somewhat easier to secure alignment of the press tools, and to assure an even flow of the metal into the die, so that tolerances in dimensions are more readily adhered to; (b) a high speed of operation; throughputs of 70 small billets an hour can be attained; (c) the presses occupy less floor space in the factory. On the other hand, they must be erected on a platform, or over a pit into which the tube or other section passes down a curved chute on to the cooling bench, and a further limitation is set by their weight and the amount of headroom which they require, with the result that the majority of those in operation are from 600 to 1000 tons in capacity, and only exceptionally are units of greater power than 1500 tons installed.

Although hydraulically operated presses are generally to be preferred for the majority of extrusion work, there are some purposes for which mechanically driven presses find application in connection with hot extrusion. They are sometimes used, for instance, in the manufacture of small tubes, and are in common use for operations of a semi-forging nature such as are involved in the fabrication of articles like poppet valves in steel. The units for these purposes are usually of small size, from 400 to 600 tons pressure capacity, though in a recent development use has been made of very heavy presses in making steel tubes. Further reference to this is made in Chapter X. While they permit a high rate of production to be achieved, mechanical presses lack the precision in control which is so important a feature of hydraulic working.

Presses for Inverted Extrusion

The inverted process has been in use since 1870 in almost all lead-pipe presses. A premature proposal to use it for the extrusion of steel billets was made in 1893,* and a design embodying it was also put forward by Dick, who patented the idea of extruding simultaneously through dies placed at both ends of the container. The practical development of inverted extrusion of brass and other metals did not come about until after 1926, when it had been shown by Genders that, owing to the manner in which flow of the metal occurred in this process, the well-known extrusion defect met with in material made by direct extrusion, could be avoided, and that, moreover, lower extrusion pressures were required. These points are referred to later, and it will suffice at present to say that although the inverted method has aroused much interest, it has not made the headway which was at one time anticipated. There are, it is true, instances of its successful employment, but in the main, where dual-purpose presses have been installed, the direct method of working is the one preferred. Among the main drawbacks are that the size of section which can be made is necessarily limited by the need to avoid undue weakening of the hollow die stand, and the difficulty, when multiple-hole dies are used, of preventing the extruded rods becoming twisted and entangled inside the die-stand.

Horizontal Presses for Direct Extrusion

A typical arrangement for the production of rods or solid sections is shown in the diagrams in Fig. 52. It comprises the container (1), consisting of a heavy steel shell, fitted with alloy steel liners; the extrusion ram (2), in front of which is placed a pressure disc, or follower pad (3), fitting the container more

* U.S. Patent No. 498,304.

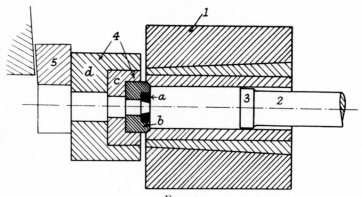

FIG. 52.

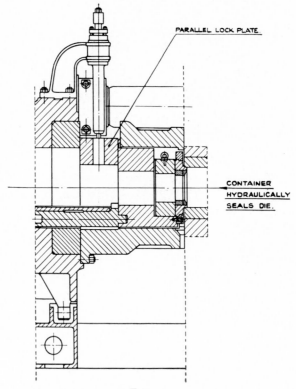

PARALLEL LOCK PLATE

CONTAINER
HYDRAULICALLY
SEALS DIE.

FIG. 53.
(*Haffner and Elkan, ' Metallurgical Reviews '.*)

closely than the ram; the die assembly (4), locked against the container during working by the wedge (5). The die assembly is made up of several parts. For most sections the actual die is in

FIG. 54.—Lateral die-slide and horseshoe-shaped head.
(*Haffner and Elkan, 'Metallurgical Reviews'.*)

the form of a plate insert (*a*), fitting in a recess in the face of a die-holder (*b*), which is in turn supported by a bolster (*c*), held in the die-head (*d*). A conical seating between the die-holder and the container centres the die and prevents escape of metal.

In recent years attempts to increase the productivity of presses by reducing the time during which the press is not actually extruding have resulted in modifications to this arrangement,

more particularly with regard to the die assembly.[5] The disadvantages of the type of arrangement shown in Fig. 52 are the
time taken in changing or cleaning the die between extrusions,
uneven wear upon the wedge and the unequal support imparted
to the die assembly by the single wedge, a factor which has
become increasingly important as the extrusion process has been
extended to include harder alloys. In modern installations the
use of a moving container, as opposed to a moving die assembly,
has made it possible to replace the wedge by parallel locking
plates, with the closing power of the container resulting in an
effective seal between the die-holder and container. Such an
arrangement is shown in Fig. 53.

The idle time due to the necessity for changing or cleaning a
die has been reduced by the use of a modified die head and the
introduction of multiple die stations. By replacing the circular
die-head of Fig. 52 with a horseshoe-shaped head, such as is
illustrated in Fig. 54, the die holder and bolster may be readily
withdrawn upon removal of the container-sealing action. Tool
inspection, cleaning or changing may be carried out during extrusion if a unit incorporating multiple die stations is available,
so that when one die is on the press centre line and in use, a
second die is at an outer station where it can be worked upon.
The unit may be of the rotating type, as indicated in Fig. 55, or
it may be designed as a lateral slide, as shown in Fig. 56.

A normal sequence of operations may now be followed by
reference to Fig. 57. With the ram in the retracted position as
shown in (A), a hot billet is brought to the cradle in front of
the container and, (B) is pushed in by the ram, working for this
and for other idle strokes on a low-pressure storage cylinder.
(C) The pressure disc having been inserted, the ram is advanced
to upset and then extrude the billet, the latter being effected under
pressure from the accumulator. The billet is never completely
extruded (but see page 241). Even were it desirable to do this,
it is impossible to exert sufficient pressure to eliminate the thin
final disc. As will be seen later, the press is stopped in practice
for other reasons when a short stub of the billet, referred to as
the discard, remains in the container. (D) The wedge having
been raised, the ram is advanced further to push out the discard
and is then retracted. By means of the hydraulic reciprocating

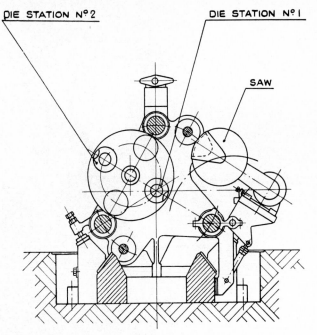

FIG. 55.
(Haffner and Elkan, 'Metallurgical Reviews'.)

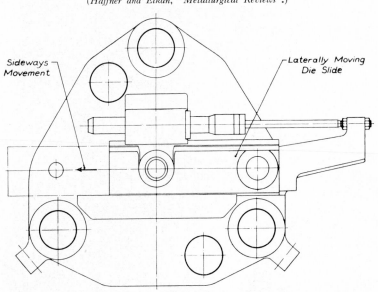

FIG. 56.
(Haffner and Elkan, 'Metallurgical Reviews'.)

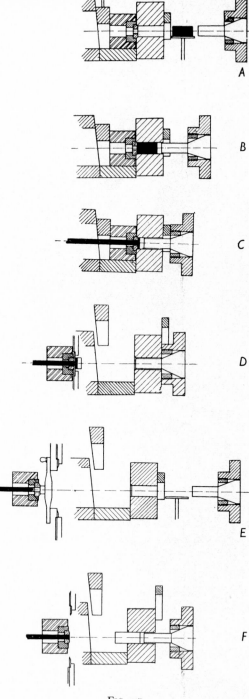

FIG. 57.

gear attached to the die-head, it is moved clear of the press-head to a position where a pair of shears, or a motor-driven circular saw swinging in on an arm, severs the extruded length from the discard close behind the die (see Fig. 58). (*E*) The die-head is

FIG. 58.—Die-head withdrawn from press. Saw swinging in to sever discard from extruded tube.
(*Courtesy of Reynolds Tube Co.*)

now moved back against a small ejection mandrel swung in to dislodge the end of the extruded bar from the die, allowing it to be passed down the runway to the cooling bench to be roughly straightened by hand while it is still hot. (*F*) The final step is to dislodge the thin sleeve or shell of metal which is, in most forms of practice, left on the wall of the container as the result of the clearance purposely provided between the pressure disc and the container. The sleeve may come away with the discard, or it may, as shown, have to be ejected, using a close-fitting clearing disc, by a further stroke of the ram.

The Extrusion of Tubes

Before the advent of hot extrusion, tubes in brass and such

85

other metals as it was possible to hot work were chiefly made by Mannesmann rolling, the thick shells so produced being later drawn down to the sizes required. Alloys such as cupro-nickel, to which this was inapplicable, were made into tubes by the tedious and expensive method of cold drawing from hollow-cast or bored billets. When the extrusion of brass was achieved, its use for tube making was at first mainly confined to the forming of thick-walled blanks, on which a good deal of cold drawing was still needed, on account of their poor concentricity. With the presses and tool steels now available, the direct production of fine tubes down to $\frac{1}{16}$ in. wall thickness, needing little cold finishing, has been rendered possible even in alloys which are stiff to extrude.

The production of tubes now constitutes an important branch of extrusion. As has been seen already, the essential arrangement requires that a mandrel, passed axially through the billet, should be located with its tip lying in the aperture of the die so as to form an annular space through which, when pressure is brought to bear on the hot billet by the extrusion ram, the metal is forced out in the form of a tube, the wall thickness of which depends on the difference in the diameters of the die aperture and the mandrel.

There are several ways in which the press tools may be arranged for this purpose. (1) A slightly tapered mandrel is attached either rigidly as at Fig. 59 (a), or in a way that gives it some freedom of movement, to the end of the extrusion ram. As the latter is moved forward, the mandrel passes through a hollow-cast billet, or one in which a central hole has been preformed, and enters the die before the ram puts pressure on the metal. (2) Alternatively, the mandrel may be made a floating member which is left free to centre itself in the die. To prevent it from being pulled through the die by the faster flowing metal it is enlarged at the base which may be made conical in shape, engaging behind the pressure disc, as shown in Fig. 59 (b). In both the above cases the mandrel moves forward with the extrusion ram and projects increasingly through the die inside the tube.

Of the two, the floating type can be regarded as the better in point of accuracy in wall thickness, concentricity within 1 per cent being obtainable when accurately bored billets are used, since if flow in the billet is evenly distributed, as it should be if the metal is in a uniformly plastic condition, the mandrel will undoubtedly tend to centre itself, whereas an attempt to fix the position of the mandrel will, if flow should for any reason be uneven, not only fail to give concentric tube, but is likely to cause the mandrel to bend or break. A means occasionally used to

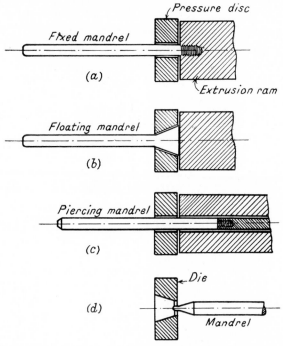

FIG. 59.—Types of mandrel for the extrusion of tubes.

centre the loose mandrel to begin with, while the billet is being upset, is to insert a close-fitting bush into the die-holder, having its end recessed to take the tip of the mandrel. The bush stays in position until it is pushed out by the metal starting to extrude (Fig. 60). On the whole it is doubtful whether this device serves a very useful purpose, for it can only centre the mandrel at the outset, and it can become deflected almost immediately if other circumstances are unfavourable.

(3) *Piercing.* The preparation of hollow tube billets, whether

by casting, boring, or piercing in a special press, is expensive, and there is the additional disadvantage that such billets become oxidized on their inner surface during preheating, increasing mandrel wear and leading possibly to defects in the tubes. Rapid and economical production of tubes in many materials is nowadays greatly facilitated by piercing and extruding solid billets in the press as part of a single operation. It is certainly possible to do this with a mandrel fixed to the end of the ram, and which, with its nose specially shaped for piercing, penetrates the billet first and then, as the extrusion ram makes contact with the billet, serves as an ordinary mandrel during the extrusion stroke, but it is impossible to make tubes of uniform thickness in the horizontal press in this way, because the hole pierced in the loose-fitting billet as it lies in the bottom of the container is not concentric. Better results are obtained in the vertical press, especially if a small hole is drilled in the back end of the billet to locate the piercer.

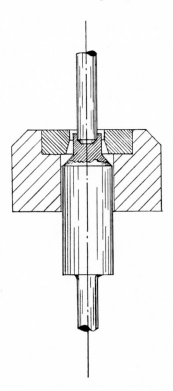

FIG. 60.—Use of bush to centre mandrel.

In the practice adopted in many modern presses, the piercing mandrel is actuated by a separate hydraulic system, and moves coaxially with, but independently of, the extrusion ram, within which it is withdrawn initially to allow the billet to be fed into the container. This permits the billet to be upset first of all by the extrusion ram, before the piercer is driven through it. The advantage gained in thus combining piercing and extrusion in a single operation, as compared with piercing beforehand in a special machine, is the saving in reheating the billets. Piercing is not without certain disadvantages in that the operation may sometimes

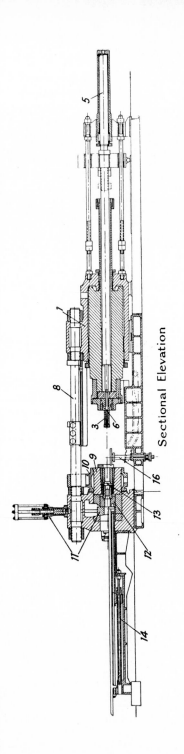

Sectional Elevation

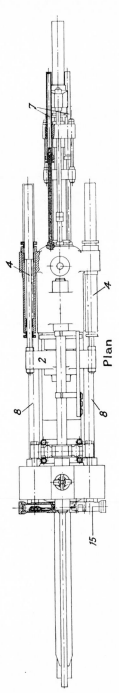

Plan

FIG. 61.

1. Main press cylinder and ram.
2. Main ram crosshead.
3. Extrusion ram.
4. Drawback cylinder for main ram.
5. Operating ram for piercing mandrel.
6. Piercing mandrel.
7. Mandrel retractor cylinder.
8. Press tension columns.
9. Container body.
10. Container holder.
11. Wedge for locking die-head, and hydraulic operating mechanism.
12. Diehead.
13. Die.
14. Hydraulic reciprocating table for die-head.
15. Hydraulic cut-off shears.
16. Billet cradle.

give rise to cracks and tears in the bore of the billet, leading to defects on the inside of the tubes. Moreover, the lubricant applied to the mandrel to begin with is mostly rubbed off during piercing so that lubrication is deficient during the actual extrusion, to the possible detriment of the inner surface finish of the tubes.

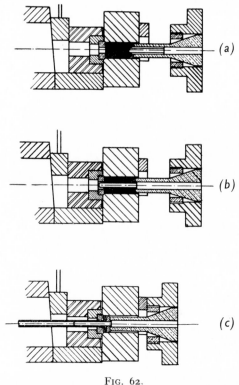

FIG. 62.

Finally, piercing requires rigorous accuracy in the construction of the presses designed to perform it.

The Schloemann press shown in section in Fig. 61 illustrates the construction of a unit of 1500 tons, equipped in this way, in which are seen many features of modern design. As it is shown, it is fitted with a special inner liner in the container for extruding tubes from short billets. The operation of the press when making tubes can be followed with the aid of Fig. 62. (a) With the piercer withdrawn flush with the end of the ram, the billet is pushed into the container and the pressure disc, which is bored out to pass the piercer, is placed in position. (*b*) The billet is upset by the ram, which is then withdrawn slightly to allow the billet to elongate during piercing. (*c*) The piercer is driven through, ejecting a small wad of metal through the die. The ram and piercer, the latter acting now as a mandrel, next advance together to extrude the tube. The piercer is then withdrawn, and the final operations are the same as those described above in connection with the extrusion of bar. When this method is used for piercing billets with a large mandrel to produce large-diameter tubes, the plug of metal ejected by the piercer prior to the start of extrusion proper may amount to as much as 50 per cent of the billet weight. Lorant[6] has described a method for application in such cases where the scrap may be reduced to about 4 per cent. During piercing the die is closed and the displaced metal is allowed to backfill the container instead of being pushed through the open die, as in Fig. 63. When a thick-walled cup has been so formed and only a thin disc of metal is left between the piercer head and the closure plate the latter is replaced by the die and extrusion proceeds after this relatively thin wad of metal has been ejected.

Severe tensional stress is set up in the mandrel during extrusion by the frictional drag of the metal flowing over it and tending to pull it through the die. This led at one time to a good deal of trouble, frequently causing mandrels to elongate and, sometimes, to rupture. By allowing the mandrel to move forward through the die at a rate which need not be the same as that of the ram, this stress is considerably reduced. With the newer mandrel materials, it is not essential with most metals to do this, and when it is desirable, the mandrel can be held stationary. It can be arranged to do this in any position by providing the mandrel with very powerful hydraulic actuation, or by the adjustment of special stops to limit its travel. With a mandrel having a considerable taper over the first inch or two, tubes of different bore can be made in this way, while a mandrel tapered suitably over its length, which is advanced at a controlled rate during the extrusion, can be used to give tubes which vary progressively in bore and wall thickness. Other applications of the independent regulation of mandrels are referred to later in this chapter.

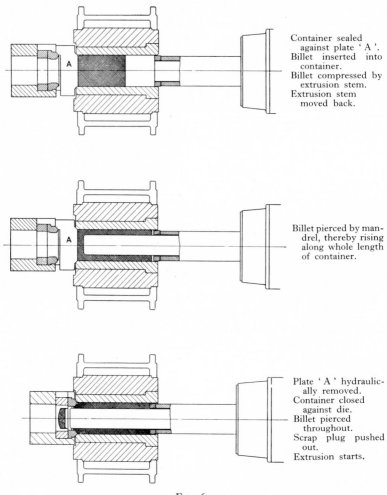

Container sealed
  against plate ' A '.
Billet inserted into
  container.
Billet compressed by
  extrusion stem.
Extrusion stem
  moved back.

Billet pierced by man-
  drel, thereby rising
  along whole length
  of container.

Plate ' A ' hydraulic-
  ally removed.
Container closed
  against die.
Billet pierced
  throughout.
Scrap plug pushed
  out.
Extrusion starts.

Fig. 63.
(*Haffner and Elkan, ' Metallurgical Reviews '.*)

Factors Affecting the Production of Tubes

It is opportune to consider these at the present stage, since
the manufacture to meet specified dimensions, important for all
extruded products, and beset with greater difficulty in the case
of tubes, is closely bound up with questions of press design and
methods of working. The chief requisites in the production of

concentric tube appear to be: (*a*) that the extrusion ram and mandrel travel in axial alignment with the container and die; (*b*) the provision of tubular billets, either previously prepared, or by piercing *in situ*, in which the hole is concentric; (*c*) that the billet should offer equal resistance to deformation over its cross-section. It is one of the principal merits of the vertical press that these requirements, in general, are more easily attained in it than in the horizontal type. Under heading (*c*), for example, a billet is loosely inserted in the latter and resting at the bottom tends to become chilled at that point before squeezing up occurs, and in consequence the piercer tends to be deflected up into the hotter metal. The unequal temperature distribution also affects the plasticity of the metal, increasing the flow in the hotter zone during extrusion and displacing the mandrel towards it, so causing the tube formed to be thicker at its under side. A further point is that any lubricant applied to the container may run down to the bottom and, by affecting the friction between it and the billet, induce variations in the flow of the metal. These are all ways in which the concentricity of the tubes may be affected.

With regard to (*b*), hollow tube billets can be made by casting them directly in moulds round tapered steel cores, or oil-sand cores, or by boring out from solid ingots. The use of sand cores, once common in brass practice, is now less frequent, and where it is still employed, the billets are generally bored out subsequently to get rid of sand inclusions in the casting skin which cause defects in the bore of the tubes and damage to the mandrels. Hollow-cast billets in aluminium alloys are usually bored in any case to remove the hard oxide skin. Though, on grounds of cost, it is not possible invariably to true up billets by machining them externally and internally, this certainly forms the best starting-point in the manufacture of accurate tubes, besides eliminating surface defects. For those metals for which it is suitable, piercing, either in a special piercing press, or more usually in the extrusion press itself, has been almost universally adopted on account of its economy. In its present form the horizontal press gives very satisfactory tube by this method. An example of its reliability in this respect is afforded in the manufacture of condenser tubes. Until recently these were almost invariably made in vertical presses, in which fine tubes only $\frac{1}{16}$ in. in wall thickness requiring only light final drawing, could be produced with the necessary precision; but for alloys like 70/30 cupro-nickel, which are comparatively difficult to work, and require a high extrusion temperature, the obvious advantages in being able to extrude so near to finished size are offset by the need to use bored billets on account of the inability of thin mandrels of small diameter to stand up to the work of piercing. It is noteworthy that several manufacturers have now found it advantageous to pierce and extrude, from horizontal presses, tube blanks of about 2 in. outside diameter and 0·25 in. thick in such alloys, and then to draw these down to condenser size, using for this purpose the new tube reducing machines; the increased amount of drawing being compensated by the elimination of the cost of boring and the loss of metal which this entails.

The explanation of the improved performance of the horizontal press in this sense turns a good deal on the measures now adopted to secure the conditions set out in (a) above, and these may next be examined in relation to some general features of press design. The arrangement seen in Fig. 61, in which the container is mounted in a holder carried on the press-head, which is connected to the main cylinder by heavy tension columns, is that commonly adopted, though an alternative method in which the container holder is mounted, independently of the press-head, directly on the baseplate of the press, and with freedom to be moved axially by means of small auxiliary rams, is also frequently used on large presses. While on grounds of general accessibility, especially for charging billets, the three-column type of construction, and still more the yoke frame press shown in Fig. 71, are to be preferred to that in which four tie-bars are used, the operation of changing the container is not so easy in the two former, and where this weighs several tons, the latter arrangement has the advantage of allowing it to be lifted out directly through the top pair of columns. The trend for very large presses is to revert to the four-column design used in the earlier presses.

For the purpose of considering how alignment of the working parts of the press is achieved and maintained, we may consider it to consist of two groups—the first comprising the main cylinder and ram, the extrusion ram, and the piercing gear; and the second composed of the press-head, the container and the die assembly.

In the press shown in Fig. 61 the ram for the piercer is guided over the whole length of the main ram in a central bore so that the axes of the two coincide. The main ram is itself supported

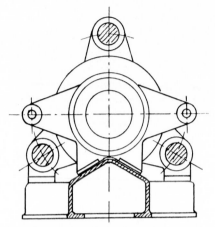

FIG. 64 (*a*).—Section through main crosshead, showing method of supporting it through shoes on prismatic slide.

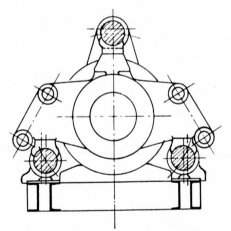

FIG. 64 (*b*).—Former arrangement with main ram cross-head supported on press columns.

in long bronze bushes within the main cylinder and, in addition, the main ram cross-head, to which the extrusion ram is attached, travels on a prismatic slide on the baseplate, provision being made at this point for adjustment and for taking up wear on the shoes (Fig. 64, *a*). It is no longer usual, as was formerly done, to guide this cross-head on the press columns (Fig, 64, *b*), on account of the possibility of these distorting under pressure. Particular care is needed to ensure that the initial position of

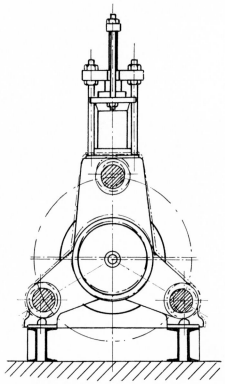

Fig. 65.—Vertical section through container cross-head, showing offcentring due to thermal expansion.

the container in exact axial relation with the ram and mandrel does not become disturbed during working. This is very liable to occur because the container, heated by the billets, and often heated also externally, transmits heat to the neighbouring parts of the press, such as the holder and press-head, causing them to expand. The effect of this, unless precautions are taken to arrange that this expansion can take place freely about the horizontal axis of the press, is to cause offcentring of the container, so that, with the base of the press-head resting on the base plate as shown in Fig. 65, vertical displacement of the container results. This is important enough to merit a brief survey of the measures taken to overcome it. So far as heat changes in the container itself are concerned, Fig. 66 shows a method to ensure radial expansion while keeping the container (1) immobile as a whole, by surrounding it by a loose-fitting holder (2) with which it engages by means of radial ribs (3). Fig. 67 refers to a construction by which the press-head is carried on stools forming part of the baseplate, the tops of which are in the

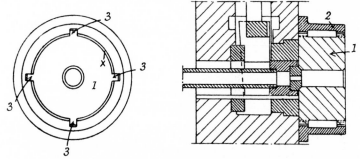

Fig. 66.—Method of mounting container in holder to permit radial expansion.

same horizontal plane as the press axis, so that thermal expansion is equally distributed about this. Another design is that illustrated in Fig. 68, in which the press-head and container are carried on bevelled supporting surfaces, (x, x), on the baseplate. The planes containing these surfaces intersect at the longitudinal axis of the container, and thus the position of the latter is unchanged by expansion of the adjacent parts. In the Eumuco press semicircular projections (1) on the bottom of the main cylinder casing rest in two troughs (2) (Fig. 69), side by side on the base-plate, so that this end of the press can pivot about a horizontal axis perpendicular to the direction of working. The press-head (3), carrying the container (4), is supported on rollers (5), mounted on slippers (6) on the base-plate. The main cylinder and press-head are rigidly connected by the tension columns so that when the press-head expands, displacing the container

97

upwards, the entire press makes a pivotal movement about the troughs under the main cylinder, while any lengthwise movement is permitted by displacement of the slippers. In a further recent device illustrated in Fig. 70, two links (1) are used to support the press-head (2). The links are attached to a carrier

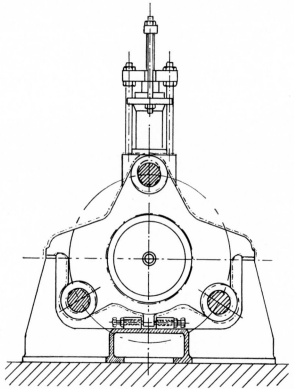

Fig. 67.—Press-head carried on stools lying coplanar with press axis to distribute thermal expansion equally.

block (3) and to lugs (4) on the press-head, and are so located in relation to the container that they are substantially perpendicular to the direction of expansion of the press-head at the points of support. Any expansion of the press-head will cause a slight rotation of the links on their pivots, but will result in no bodily movement of the press-head or container. Screws (5)

98

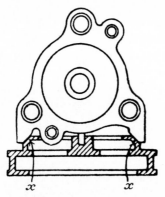

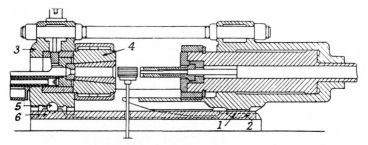

FIG. 68.—Press-head carried on bevelled surfaces which intersect at axis of container.

FIG. 69.—Pivoted mounting to avoid the effects of thermal expansion.

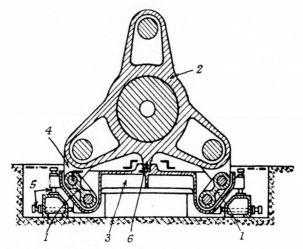

FIG. 70.—The press-head is supported on links to accommodate thermal expansion.

between the carrier block and baseplate provide the means of setting in the first place. A lug (6) on the head projecting into a groove in the carrier block prevents lateral displacement in relation to the vertical central plane. A feature of this scheme is that the thermal effects are taken care of without need for sliding movement between the heated and the supporting parts.

A Horizontal Press for Direct and Inverted Extrusion

A press which differs considerably both in design and operation from the more general type hitherto dealt with is illustrated in Fig. 71. Although it is not unique in this respect, it offers a good

Fig. 71.—Krupp press of unorthodox design, with cast steel yoke frame and movable container, capable of being adapted to work by the inverted process.

example of a press in which the container is movable over a long distance, and one which provides the alternative use of either the direct or the inverted method of extrusion. The press frame, formed by a heavy steel casting in one end of which is set the main cylinder, is carried on two transversely set baseplates in a way which permits longitudinal expansion but prevents lateral displacement. The main ram cross-head and the container in its holder are carried, freely of the frame, on slideways on the baseplates, where adjusting screws are fitted. The main ram is guided also by means of a thick-walled extension tube on its back end passing through a radially adjustable stuffing box at the rear of the main cylinder. The piercer ram is also guided in this tube. The container is set in the holder by radially adjustable segments in the latter engaging in a ring nut on the container. The container is not carried in attachment with the head of the frame, but is given a long travel by an independent ram. The die-holder is set in a sliding locking bar which is buttressed against a plate in the head of the press. At the end of an extrusion, the product is cut off and the discard removed between the die-holder and the container by moving the latter back clear, and since, when this is done, the die is accessible for inspection and attention, it can, if required, be left in place for the next extrusion. In order to change the die, the locking bar is moved transversely to bring the die-holder in front of a small ejection ram on the side of the frame. The yoke frame and the arrangement of all auxiliary mechanism on the back of the press afford particularly ready access to the tools. This press can be used to illustrate some possible modifications in extrusion procedure to that already described.

The series of sketches in Fig. 72 show the process of extrusion for solid sections. It will be seen that, for charging, the container (c) is drawn back over the ram (b), and that the billet is brought up in front of it (1). The container is then moved forward over the billet until it engages with the conical rim of the die-holder (2). The pressure disc (f) being inserted (3), the extrusion ram is advanced to extrude the billet (4). Both container and ram are now drawn back about 8 or 9 in., and a pendulum saw (h) is swung in to cut off the bar close behind the die. Next, the container is drawn back further, so that, the ram remaining stationary, the billet residue and pressure disc are pushed out (5). Finally, the ram is fully withdrawn and the container advanced to allow a clearing disc (g) to be inserted (6), whereupon the container is drawn back over the ram pushing out the sleeve in front of the disc (7). In the case of a sticker, where there may be insufficient power to eject the billet by moving the

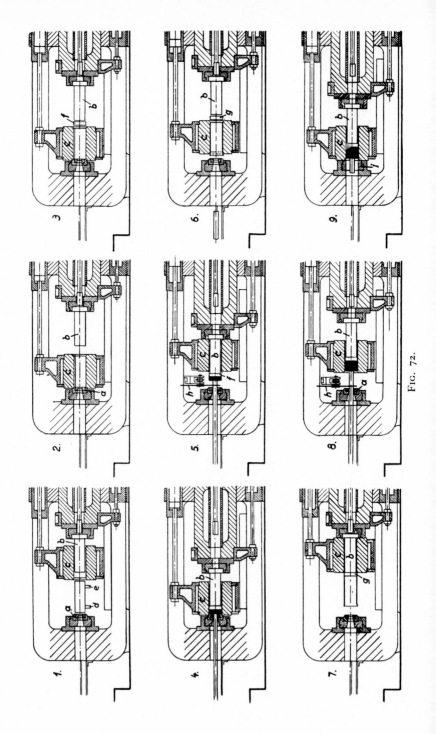

Fig. 72.

H

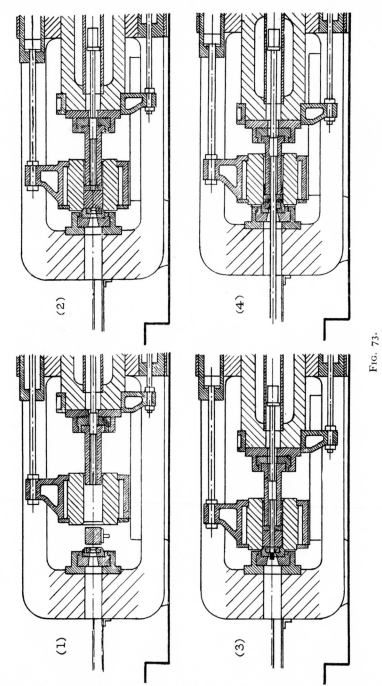

(1)   (3)   (2)   (4)

Fig. 73.

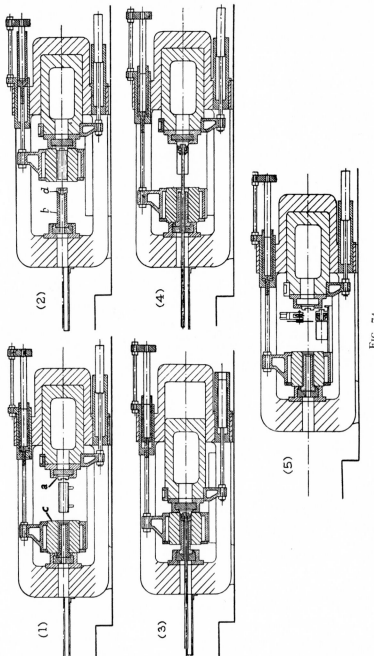

Fig. 74.

container as above, then, the length of bar already extruded having been cut off (8), the locking bar (*j*) is slid across until a hole in it coincides with the container bore, when the billet may be pushed out through the press-head by the ram (9). The insertion, compression, piercing and extrusion of solid billets into tube requires no further explanation than is provided by Fig. 73. The final stages of the cycle in this case are the same as those just described.

For extrusion by the inverted method, the die-holder is replaced by a die-stand (*b*) in Fig. 74, equal in length to the container (*c*), and the extrusion ram is replaced by the closure plate (*a*), attached to the main ram cross-head. The sketches show the method of working. In (2) the container is moved over the billet, and the die (*d*) is set in position. The extrusion stroke now begins, and it will be observed that the container is advanced under power from the main cylinder, so that the die is pressed into the end of the billet; the extruded rod passing out through the die-stand as seen at (3). (4) and (5) show the ejection and sawing off of the sleeve and discard.

Vertical Presses

In the introduction to this chapter reference was made to the pros and cons of vertical presses. As compared with the extent and variety of production from the horizontal, they are of far more specialized application, being confined very largely to the manufacture of high-quality tubes of small thickness and diameter in brass and other copper alloys, using small billets, and extruding as a rule at high speed. What has already been said concerning the factors of importance in the extrusion of tubes will probably have suggested that the most favourable combination for the production of concentric tubes is to be found in this form of press, using a floating mandrel and with hollow cylindrical billets accurately machined inside and out. All the same, extremely satisfactory results for most purposes are obtained at lower cost by starting with solid billets and piercing them in the press. As compared with horizontal machines, accurate piercing is rather easier to secure owing to the absence of unidirectional thermal expansion in the press itself and in most designs equipment for piercing is provided. Fig. 75 shows a vertical press.

Fig. 75.—Schloemann vertical tube and rod press with piercing equipment and electric sequence control.

fitted with a water-cooled piercing mandrel and employing the direct process. Actually all the methods of operation used in horizontal working, including direct extrusion with and without piercing, with fixed and movable container, and extrusion by the inverted process, are also to be found in vertical plant and, in view of the descriptions already given, the only example described will be a press in which a very successful use has been made of the inverted principle. The movable container is guided on vertical columns, which serve also as the

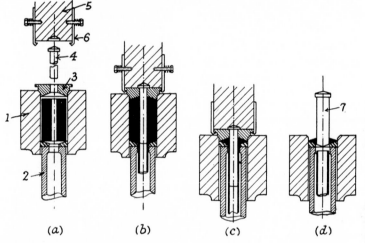

FIG. 76.—Diagram showing extrusion of tubes by inverted method.

return cylinders for the main operating ram. The arrangement of tools and conduct of an extrusion may be followed in Fig. 76. The sketch at (a) shows the container (1) in its top position just covering the end of the die-stand (2). When a hot billet has been charged, a closure plate (3), which also serves as a guide bush to the mandrel (4), is placed over the open end of the container and the mandrel, of floating type but fitting into a recess in the end of the operating ram (5), is put in place and entered into the hole in the closure plate. In the next stage (b), the operating ram pushes the mandrel through the billet, and then, as the ram comes against the closure plate, the container is forced down over the die-stand to extrude the billet. When the ram is

drawn back after the extrusion the closure plate and mandrel
are also withdrawn, being held by the extractors (6). Meanwhile the container which is mounted on pneumatic rams is held
down in the bottom position by a catch. The last operation,
which is shown at (d), is to replace the mandrel by a punch (7)
which, in a further stroke, trims off the tube at the die and lifts
out the residual disc of the billet. A vertical press employing
the indirect process, but without a floating mandrel, is shown
in Fig. 77.

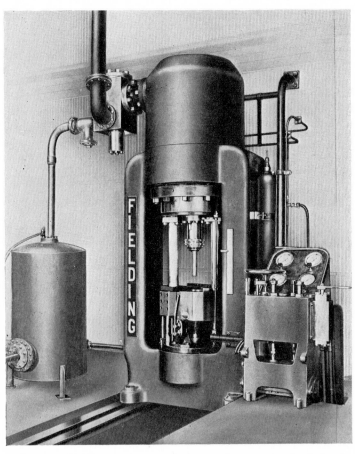

FIG. 77.—Fielding 1450-ton vertical press for extrusion by indirect
process

Extrusion tools

Certain of the press components, such as dies, mandrels, pressure discs and containers, constitute the really essential tools in connection with the process. These work under very arduous conditions, being, in varying degree, exposed to the hot metal, and having to sustain the combined effect of thermal and mechanical stresses. The high temperatures and pressures employed in certain phases of extrusion at the present time impose conditions which are extremely severe, testing to the limit the special steels used in making the various units. On the other hand, tools for use in connection with the more readily extrudable metals, like most of the brasses, and for less onerous duties for such parts as die-holders, present problems of a lower order which are fairly easily met. The steels employed for various functions naturally vary a good deal according to the metals being worked and the preferences of users; data regarding them exist only in a scattered form, although Plankensteiner[7] and Rodgers[22] have given surveys of the main requirements.

Dies

The die takes some of the heaviest duty and is the tool which is subject to the greatest alteration in use. It must possess heat resistance and temper-retaining characteristics of a high order for its work in bringing about the deformation of the metal and withstanding the abrasive wear which this causes. The properties required are a high degree of hot strength in association with sufficient toughness to allow the die to adjust itself without risk of cracking. This involves a compromise in which most users incline towards toughness rather than extreme hardness, especially with dies of complex shape. Even so the Brinell hardness can rarely be allowed to fall below 300 and is generally in the range 320–75, only occasionally going as high as 450.

Typical steels of the kind now chiefly employed are as follows

C	Si	Mn	Cr	Ni	Mo	W	V	Use
0·6	0·3	0·3	2·0	2·0	0·45	–	–	Light alloys.
0·35	0·8	0·5	5·0	–	1·3	–	0·9	Light alloys and Cu base alloys.
0·35	0·3	0·4	3·5	–	0·5	9·5	(0·4)	More difficult alloys.

Treatment consists in oil hardening from temperatures up to 1200° C. and tempering, according to requirements, at temperatures up to 650° C. These are steels which are capable of retaining in use the properties imparted by the heat treatment. Steels of composition such as C 0·4 per cent; Si 1·3 per cent; Cr 12 per cent; Ni 12 per cent; W 2 per cent, which are entirely austenitic in structure and possess superior properties at elevated temperatures, have been put into use for very high temperature work. A steel of this kind cannot be hardened in the ordinary way, but its strength can be increased by cold forging the die blank in the first place.

Loewy[8] has referred to the use of a 5 per cent Cr hot work steel having no tungsten for dies in steel extrusion. The inherent tendency of tungsten bearing steel dies to crack is thereby avoided while the die life is prolonged and 'washing-out' minimized by the deposition of a cobalt-chromium-tungsten alloy hard facing.

In recent years, with the development of grades having increased toughness, sintered carbide dies have become available and are being used in the production of some extrusions.[9] With appropriate design and care in use phenomenal lives may be obtained with such dies in comparison with those made in steel and this frequently with an increased extrusion speed.

Mandrels

Being of relatively small mass, and surrounded entirely by hot metal, so that they heat up quickly, mandrels required in extruding tubes are exceptionally exposed to heat in use, the more so when they are of small diameter. Those used to pierce solid billets have to sustain powerful compressive and bending forces. During subsequent extrusion, severe friction occurs and a strong tension is set up by the drag of the metal flowing round the mandrel, this sometimes restricting the length of billet extruded. Owing to the nature of the flow, this stress is highest a short distance in front of the pressure disc. Mandrel steels suitable for medium and high temperatures respectively are

C per cent	Si per cent	Mn per cent	Cr per cent	W per cent	Mo per cent
0·35	1·0	0·5	1·3	4·25	0·35
0·35	0·25	0·25	2·5	9·0	—

These are treated to an ultimate tensile strength of 95–100 tons per square inch. In order to retain their temper, mandrels require to be cooled after each operation, either by using a fine spray cooler on them *in situ*, or in an oil-bath. This, however, does not apply to tools for light alloy presses, which are actually preheated to the extrusion temperature of the metal. The repeated heating and cooling to which mandrels are subjected cause alternating stresses which may result in dimensional changes or even cracking or crazing of the surface, more particularly with larger mandrels where the thermal gradients are likely to be greater. For this reason cooling after extrusion should not be complete, i.e. the thermal cycle should be reduced by cooling only to 200–300° C. Internal cooling of the mandrel affords a method of reducing thermal cycling even further and is a matter which is receiving attention. As with other extrusion tools, mandrel design can frequently influence the working life.[10]

Containers

The press container undergoes severe thermal stress as the result of heat gradients set up by the hot billets, besides taking the heavy internal pressure exerted by the ram during the extrusion stroke. Much of the early trouble from cracking and scoring of the cylinder bore has been obviated by the invariable use now of replaceable liners made of special steel, which are shrunk inside the container body. The residual internal stress induced by this method of assembly serves to counteract appreciably the dangerous tensile stresses in the tangential direction during working.[11, 12]

In recent years the subject of extrusion press containers has received some theoretical treatment which, although involving some simplifying assumptions, has resulted in certain design criteria. Thus, Horne[13] has developed an elastic-plastic theory which may be of value in the design of containers for operation in the lower temperature ranges. The theory is based upon plastic behaviour because containers are invariably observed to increase in diameter during use, so that from a calculation of the values of internal pressure sufficient to produce complete plasticity a design method can be established. As Horne points out, however, the ultimate internal pressure may not be the only factor which has to be considered in design since failure may occur due to alternating plastic deformation, fatigue or driving of the liner along the taper. The latter is likely to occur when the container has a lower yield stress, and therefore smaller range of elastic strain, than the liner so that when the internal pressure is removed a gap may develop between container and liner. If the liner is held in position by a step this will not matter but if tapered the liner will move along the taper to an extent depending upon the degree to which the container becomes plastic.

For extruding such metals as copper, high nickel-silvers, nickel, etc., for which the temperatures are high, a steel of the following analysis, treated to 95–100 tons per square inch U.T.S. is suitable. C 0·25 per cent; Si 0·2 per cent; Mn 0·2 per cent; Cr 2·5 per cent; Ni 1·5 per cent; W 10·0 per cent; Mo 0·2 per cent; V 0·2 per cent. Where extrusion is carried out at under 800° C., this liner can be more cheaply made from a steel of the nickel-chrome-molybdenum type, or from one having C 0·4 per cent; Cr 1·5 per cent; W 2·5 per cent; Mo 0·5 per cent; brought by heat treatment to 90–95 tons per square inch U.T.S.

Outer liners, being less subject to heat, are usually made of lower alloy nickel-chrome steel, with a tensile strength of 75–80 tons per square inch. The container body is forged from 0·7/0·8 C steel of acid quality, or from a low alloy steel as, for example, C 0·35 per cent; Cr 1·5 per cent. This does not hold good for extrusion presses for strong light alloys, when the whole of the container is heated to a temperature in the region of 450° C., at which carbon steels are insufficiently strong. In these cases, the whole assembly must be made in the special heat-resisting grades of steel.

Pressure discs are made, for medium heat, from steel containing C 0·25 per cent; Cr 1·3 per cent; W 4·0 per cent, or, for heavier duty, C 0·35 per cent; Cr 3·0 per cent; W 9·0 per cent. Extrusion rams, which are protected from the worst temperature effects by the pressure disc, are mainly subject to compressive and bending stress. Steels, for this purpose, to which are given tensile strengths of 100–110 tons per square inch, are suitably made to contain C 0·35 per cent; Cr 1·5 per cent; Ni 4·5 per cent, and often have, in addition, Mo 0·25 per cent.

The Form of Extrusion Dies

The preparation of dies for extrusion is a highly technical job calling for skill and experience that varies according to their intricacy.   That such a multitude of sections as is now available to meet the needs of engineers and others can be produced, is attributable in no small degree to the resourcefulness of the die maker.   He has many things to take into account, such as the special characteristics of the metal to be extruded, allowances for stress and distortion, and the thermal contraction of the extruded section after leaving the die; as well as the precautions to assure well-balanced flow of the metal into all parts of the die.

FIG. 78.—Die-plate, holder and bolster.
(Courtesy of Reynolds Tube Co.)

The die itself often takes the form of a comparatively thin disc or plate, smaller in diameter than the press container, which fits accurately into a recess in the face of a die-holder, which is, in turn, supported by a bolster (Fig. 78).   To simplify manufacture in the case of very complex dies, the plate is sometimes made in several parts.   Where the design involves high local stresses, and for heavy service in making standard sections, the plate and holder are combined to make massive dies which fit directly into the bolster.

Some modifications of the comparatively simple dies used in making round, hexagon and other plain sections and tubes are shown in Fig. 79.   It is often a matter of surprise that in contrast with those used in drawing operations, the form of die most frequently adopted for extrusion is made with square shoulders with little or no lead-in, like that in the sketch (*a*). Many different profiles have been tried out, often in an attempt to shape the entry to accord with the known streamline path adopted by the metal, but experience has shown that most of these are unsatisfactory. As a rule, a small radius is given to the front lip of the hole. This almost certainly gives rise to a slight increase in extrusion pressure, but is desirable to prevent the closing-in which a sharp-edged die would suffer, and which tends to occur in any case, especially with metals requiring a high extrusion

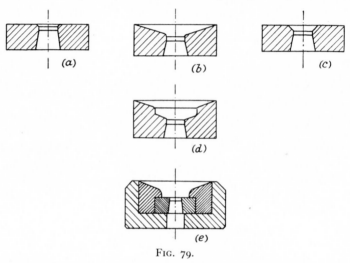

Fig. 79.

pressure. There is some evidence, too, that the slight rounding of the lip helps to prevent surface cracking in extruding metals of low plasticity. For tough materials such as copper, cupro-nickel and monel, Bernhoeft[14] suggests radii, for a 1-in. die aperture, of 2–5 mm., 4–8 mm., and 10–15 mm., respectively. Aluminium, and many of its alloys, on the other hand, works best with practically sharp-edged dies radiused to 1–2 mm., having a short bearing length and well relieved on the back side to do away, as far as possible, with the tendency of the aluminium to adhere to the die surface. A long bearing length, while it serves to strengthen the die and lengthen its life, restricts the easy flow of the metal; it is generally made from $\frac{3}{16}$ in. to $\frac{1}{2}$ in. long, being greatest for large diameter rods and easily extruded materials.

Resort to dies of conical form represented by (b) or less commonly by (c) is frequently made in making tubes, especially in tough metals. The cone angles most used lie between 120° and 160°. They possess some advantages which will be referred to later. The cascade type of die shown at (d) is claimed to give good results with hard alloys. In order to reduce the load on the die plate and prevent it becoming bowed, a novel kind of die (e) in which the die plate is recessed into the back of the die body has been developed in France. The subject of die form, as it affects the force required in extrusion, will be discussed in Chapter VI.

On the highly specialized subject of dies for the more involved sections, no more can be attempted here than to put down some general observations, and to give a few examples of unusual interest. For the extrusion of shaped sections which are of variable thickness in different parts ingenuity is required to obtain a satisfactory distribution of flow through the die. The resistance to flow is lowest in the widest parts and highest where the section is narrow or in the vicinity of sharp corners, and hence the rate of flow tends to be variable. This is partly because less deformation of the metal is entailed in the wider parts, and is partly due to the greater friction at the die surface and the increased cooling effect of the die at the narrow places. Unless it is corrected this leads to buckling and twisting of the extruded section, and to tears and ragged edges in the parts of least thickness. The main means of control is by increasing the friction at the places where flow is easiest, and this is done by increasing the bearing length of the die as illustrated in Fig. 80, or by opening it up at the front to give a slight taper to the bearing at these points, so as to choke the flow. Smooth finish to the working surfaces is needed to avoid transmission of irregularities to the extruded section. Dies for aluminium alloys are generally polished to avoid surface roughness on the section resulting from adhesion. In this connection, chromium-plated dies have shown some promise, but there is difficulty in obtaining satisfactory adherence of the plating.

Dies in which there is a re-entrant tongue, as in such engineering sections as channels, suffer from weakness owing to the difficulty of supporting the tongue, to prevent it from being pushed back or fracturing across its base. This danger is greatest with stiff alloys, and when the flanges are narrow, so that high pressures are required, and this imposes a limit on the depth of channel relative to its width.   Worsdale[15] has referred to a method applied to very deep, narrow channels in strong light alloys; by which they are extruded with the flanges splayed out, these being drawn down parallel afterwards.

The point has been made that in extruding tubes, a homogeneous state of plasticity is wanted so that the metal flows

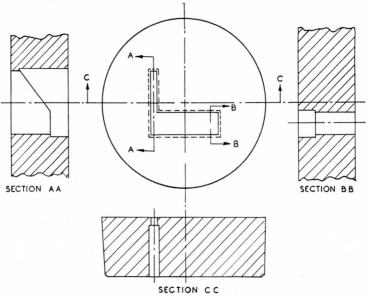

SECTION A A   SECTION B B

SECTION C C

FIG. 80.—Extrusion die for irregular section.
(*Smith, 'J. Inst. Metals'.*)

uniformly into the die annulus and, by exerting an even pressure on the mandrel, maintains it centrally to give a concentric tube. In making hollow sections, the walls of which may be of unequal thickness, it is necessary that their shape should be such as to ensure symmetrical flow round the centrally placed mandrel.   In Fig. 81, the flow round the rectangular mandrel is balanced and this would still obtain if the side walls were given a different thickness from the base and top.   It is possible, exceptionally, when symmetry is unattainable, as in Fig. 82, to overcome the problem by extruding simultaneously through an additional aperture in the die placed as shown.

FIG. 81.—An extruded taper section.
(*Courtesy of Reynolds Tube Co.*)

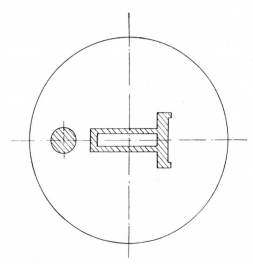

FIG. 82.—Die made with additional aperture to balance flow when extruding
a section of unsymmetrical shape.

Tapered and Stepped Sections

Normally extruded products, whether of solid or hollow section,
have a uniform cross-section over their entire length.   For some
purposes this is a limitation, and considerable importance attaches

117

to the practicability of producing tapered and stepped sections. Thus, the aircraft industry uses many structural components, such as wing spar caps, which have a bulky end portion, where it is to be attached to another component, whilst the remainder of the member may be of very much smaller cross-section. The manufacture of such parts, either by machining from the solid or by joining together appropriate shapes, are either more costly or of lower strength than those produced in the form of an integral extrusion. Some successful developments have been reached in regard to this. In the case of tubes, a taper can be effected by the use of a tapered mandrel moving with the ram, or whose position is independently regulated by hydraulic means. Fig. 81 shows an example, from the works of Reynolds Tube Co., Ltd., of the application of the principle to other hollow forms. The shape of the hole can at the same time be changed over the length, for instance, from round to square.

Tubes can not be extruded with a bore of less than a certain size, depending on the metal being worked, owing to the weakness of mandrels of small diameter, when hot, towards the powerful tensile force exerted by the flowing metal. As an instance of the use of a regulated mandrel position, heavy-walled tubes in 5 per cent manganese-copper alloy are required for locomotive stay-bolts, which are approximately 1 in. in outside diameter, with a bore of only 0·125 in. The mandrel used to produce this, Fig. 59 (d), has a small nipple screwed into its front end, which is maintained stationary just within the die during extrusion.

Several methods of making tapered solid sections have been proposed. A recent design* aimed at avoiding unwanted variations in thickness due to the lateral displacement of the mandrel is illustrated in Fig. 83. The die (1) is traversed during extrusion by the mandrel (2) of changing cross-sectional form. A number of slots (3), tapering lengthwise, which form the apertures through which the metal is extruded, are cut on the surface of the mandrel. Lateral displacement is prevented by the engagement of the mandrel with the die. The mandrel is introduced to begin with into an internal recess in the billet, which is preferably cast in.

The advent of larger extrusion presses has made possible the fabrication of single extrusions containing steps at which are

* Magnesium Elektron Ltd. British Patent No. 533,082.

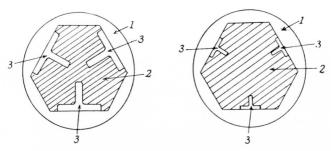

Fig. 83.—Die and mandrel for making tapered solid sections.

joined sections of different cross section, as shown in Fig. 84. The increasing size of aircraft has necessitated such a trend since some of the spar caps now being used are so large that existing equipment would be incapable of producing an extrusion having the uniform full cross section in sufficient length from which the finished component could be machined.[2]

In the manufacture of stepped extrusions the minor section is extruded first and the process interrupted at the appropriate stage for the dies to be changed before proceeding with the extrusion of the major section. The dies are usually in two segments to facilitate changing, since single piece dies would have to be removed or replaced by feeding over the previously extruded minor section. In the simplest system the minor and major dies are completely separate and are merely interchanged, but if a secondary locking device is available on the press then a composite die may be used from which only an insert need be removed to form the major die, as shown diagrammatically in Fig. 85. It will be clear that the major section must completely enclose the minor and that more than one step may be formed if necessary, although it seems doubtful whether more than one step could be justified on cost.[16]

The different extrusion ratios of the major and minor sections would be expected to produce variations in mechanical properties along the length of a stepped extrusion which would be greater than those observed along the length of a uniform section. This is found to be the case, although there seems to be no difficulty in achieving strength specifications if adequate attention is given to the choice of container size and the ratio of the areas of the

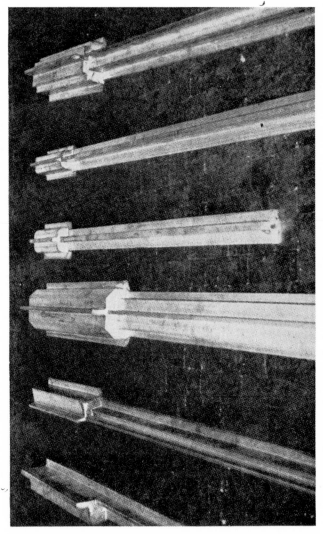

Fig. 84.—Stepped extrusions.
(*Thornton 'Mech. Eng.' 1944.*)

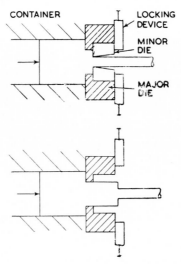

FIG. 85.—Diagrammatic representation of die assembly for stepped extrusions.

major and minor section does not exceed about 5 : 1. Even so the manufacture of stepped extrusions is not without some difficulty, particularly in the formation of what approximates to a dead metal zone in the region of the step and in achieving dimensional accuracy. The coarse grain structure which may occur at the step, but which is sometimes removed by machining, is apparent in Fig. 86. Low ductility is frequently associated with such coarse grained material which, if it is not subsequently to be removed by machining must be avoided by modifying the die design at the region of the step so that there is better blending of the two sections. Dimensional tolerances are, of necessity, somewhat larger than those permitted on uniform extrusions, since, in addition to variations in the dimensions of the major and minor sections, there is the added possibility that misalignment of the dies will cause the two sections to be twisted relative to one another about the plane of the step. It may be reasonably expected that the use of composite dies will reduce such errors, but even now machining allowances of only $\frac{1}{16}$ in. are frequently achieved.

An interesting development from stepped extrusions has been

FIG. 86.—Coarse grains in stepped extrusions.
(*Thornton, ' Mech. Eng.' 1944.*)

referred to by Loewy.[8] This concerns the extrusion of sections which consist partly of a pre-forged or formed part which is integrally connected with an extruded portion of appreciable length. He cites as an example the extrusion, in three steps, of a chromium-nickel-molybdenum steel into propeller blades having an integral shank and a 10 ft. long blade with ' ears ' running from the shank to the tip. The blades are hollow and the wall is tapered from $\frac{3}{8}$ in. at the shank to $\frac{1}{8}$ in. at the top.

Hydraulic Operation of Presses

The high-pressure fluid required in the working of extrusion presses may be supplied straight from pumps or through some form of accumulator. Apart from lead pipe and cable-sheathing presses, it has been customary in this country to operate from high-pressure accumulators, although, as mentioned earlier, direct drives were more common in the U.S.A. In recent years there has been a marked trend towards the more extensive employment of direct oil-drive on presses extruding the harder metals both in the U.S.A. and the U.K., because of the more economical operation of this system under certain conditions. The relative advantages and limitations of the two methods of working have been discussed by Haffner and Elkan,[5] and these are such that direct oil-drive is only favoured on relatively low capacity presses working at slow speeds. This recent trend towards the more extensive use of direct drives has been made possible by the development of high-speed multiple plunger and variable-delivery pumps driven, without intermediate gearing, by high-speed motors. These do not cause the periodic markings on the extruded product, which were a characteristic produced by the older type triple-plunger pump working at slow speeds. Operating pressures of these pumps are usually between 3000 and 5000 lb. per square inch, as also are the pressures delivered by those used in charging accumulators. In addition to the developments in pump design considerable advances have been made in recent years in circuit and valve design, not least in the direction of automatic actuation of valve movements. The use of oil as the fluid transmitting the pressure has not been restricted to direct drives, the water which has almost invariably been used in accumulator systems in the past having been replaced by oil in a few recent installations. The increased cost of oil as the fluid tends to be offset by reduced corrosion and simpler press construction in those features concerned with transmitting the pressure to the ram.

The two main types of accumulator which are in general use are the dead weight and the air-loaded or pneumatic. In the first, a steel cylinder, arranged vertically, contains water which is loaded by a piston carrying on its head-plate a set of large iron discs, or a vessel filled with metal scrap or other heavy material, to a total weight of several hundred tons. The dead weight is

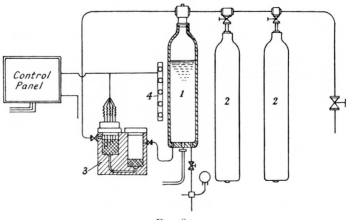

FIG. 87.

arranged in relation to the bore of the cylinder to produce the required pressure. Where discs are used for loading, the accumulator pressure can be varied by removing or adding to these. As pressure water is used, the loaded piston descends and is raised again by delivery of water from the pumps, the latter being automatically switched in or out at fixed points in its fall or rise. There are several drawbacks to this type: heavy foundations are required to carry the load, and severe pressure surges are liable to occur in them, with risk of damage to pipe lines and valve gear, due to the release of kinetic energy of the heavy moving mass when the withdrawal of pressure water is suddenly interrupted. In new installations their use has been almost entirely abandoned in favour of the pneumatic type which has undergone a great deal of improvement in recent years. The majority of those now employed are of the piston-less design, in which there are no moving parts within the pressure vessels and control is done externally. A schematic drawing in Fig. 87 serves to follow the principle of working of one of these. This shows a forged steel water-bottle (1) into which water is delivered by the pumps and from which it can be withdrawn as required by the extrusion press. Load is applied to the water by air compressed in a series of air bottles (2). The automatic external control system consists of a U-shaped vessel (3) containing mercury which has one limb connected to the bottom and the other limb to the top of the water bottle, so that a difference in level in the mercury in the two limbs is established which is due only to the head of water in the bottle. Rise and fall in the level of mercury in the left-hand limb with the supply or delivery of pressure water from the bottle causes the making or breaking of a series of electrical contacts arranged at different levels, and so operates controls on the pressure pumps. A contact is also provided for the functioning of a safety stop-valve in the event of the water level falling to the point where air may be carried into the pipe line. The make and break circuit also gives visual indication of the water level in the bottle by lighting or extinguishing a series of lamps at (4). A large installation by Hydraulik, for driving an 8000-ton aluminium tube and rod press is seen in Fig. 88. The advantages of this and similar methods of control over those based on the internal pressure of the accumulator, which is liable to be affected by temperature variations and provides no trustworthy criterion of the amount of water in the bottle, are obvious. One disadvantage of pneumatic accumulators is that when the water is at its lowest level in the bottle, which, when a single extrusion press is being worked, will be towards the end of the extrusion stroke when a high pressure is often needed, the actual pressure available is slightly reduced due to the expansion of the compressed air; they should therefore be given sufficient capacity to keep this variation within 10 per cent. Quite commonly, however, several presses are supplied from one large accumulator, which reduces pressure fluctuations.

In the cycle of press operations, idle movements occupy a considerable part of the motion of the main ram and it is uneconomical to use pressure water for these; a low-pressure system is incorporated for this purpose. At the end of an extrusion

Fig. 88.—Water power station for 8000-ton press by Hydraulik.

the main ram is retracted by withdrawing pressure from the backs of the drawback rams, which are normally of the constant pressure type working off the high-pressure supply. The water in the main cylinder is pushed out into a vessel partly filled with compressed air. As the water level in this vessel rises, further compressing the air, a release valve opens at a fixed pressure to allow the escape of excess water. The working pressure in the air vessel is generally 40–60 lb. per square inch. To advance the main ram for a new extrusion, pressure is restored on the drawback rams, and the low-pressure water in the air vessel can then move the main ram forward rapidly until resistance is encountered by the extrusion ram coming against the billet, whereupon the control valve is moved to admit water into the main cylinder from the accumulator. There is no danger of air entering from the air vessel, since during the return stroke there enters it not only the filling water supplied for the idle stroke, but also the water supplied by the accumulator during the power stroke, and thus a certain excess of water must pass the overflow valve on the air vessel at each cycle.

The speed at which some sections in copper alloys and the high-strength light alloys in particular are extruded is of great importance, and this calls for special throttling valves, capable of giving determined speeds on the main ram, which may range from as low as 0·04 in. per second, to a maximum of 8 in. per second. The application of corrosion-resisting steels for the internal parts of valves has been a major point in diminishing their erosive wear.

Heating the Container

Hot billets introduced into a container which is at a lower temperature, cool during extrusion to an extent depending on their size, the time required to complete the extrusion, and the difference in temperature existing between the two. Even in presses not specially provided with a means of heating the container, the latter is by no means cold, since it becomes warmed by the passage through it of successive billets. In order to avoid chilling the first billets excessively when starting up from cold, the container is heated by the introduction into the bore of a gas burner or electric resistance heater, or by leaving a hot billet in it for a few minutes. The extent to which additional heating is necessary depends on the extrusion qualities of the metal concerned and on the capacity of the press to carry out the extrusion in as short a time as possible. In those cases where the speed of extrusion must be kept low specially heated containers are essential. The ordinary hot-working brasses which require comparatively low extrusion temperatures, and possess a long working range, do not require any special measures, though there is reason to think that a higher container temperature would not be without benefit in reducing the incidence of the extrusion defect by decreasing the temperature gradient from the centre to the outside of the billet as it lies in the press, and would also be conducive to greater uniformity in mechanical properties over the length of the extruded section. With more difficult alloys, such as some nickel-silvers, cupro-nickel, and monel, additional heating of the container to raise it to 300°–350° C. becomes necessary. This is also particularly the case for most of the strong aluminium and magnesium alloys, which are only extruded satisfactorily at very low rates. The latter remain in the container for considerable periods, and they therefore require that the temperature of the container should be maintained within close limits in the region of 380°–400° C. Vertical presses lend themselves to high rates of production and, on that account, even small billets of stiff copper and nickel alloys can be dealt with without providing container heating.

The heating of containers is done either by gas or electrically, the latter being the chief method for light alloy presses. Gas burners are arranged in rows within the jacket space formed between the container and its holder. Graham[17] refers to the use, in a large press for extruding nickel alloys, of hot waste gases from a near-by billet heating furnace which are led through a duct and made to circulate within the container jacket. Electrical heating, often in conjunction with automatic regulation of the temperature, is generally preferred in light alloy shops, because of the greater precision in control and more uniform distribution of heat. Electric resistance heating of billet containers has been discussed by Brunt;[18] the usual method is to fix resistance panels, backed by thermal insulation, on the inside of the container holder, as shown in Fig. 89. Containers heated by electric induction have been brought into use in recent years; Fig. 90 shows the Schloemann system in which current with the normal frequency of 50 cycles is passed in series through a

FIG. 89.—Container heating by resistance panels inside the container-holder.

FIG. 90.—The Schloemann system of container heating by induction.

set of insulated copper rods in longitudinal holes drilled in the container body. Low voltage current in ranges from 30 to 80 volts, or 50 to 100 volts, is taken from a transformer. The temperature is controlled by thermostat. Heating up a replacement container from cold to 400° C. occupies 6 to 7 hours, but this can be done before fitting. Due to the cost of drilling the containers, the method is expensive and has been used hitherto only on light alloy presses, where the container temperatures are high. It has the advantage that since heat is developed within the container, stresses due to thermal gradients, which play an important part in determining its life, are much reduced. Hemmerich[11] has discussed the effects of resistance and induction heating systems upon the temperature distribution in containers. The French Morane press may be fitted for induction heating by means of a water-cooled induction coil round the outside of the container.

Billet Preheating Furnaces

Smooth working of the extrusion process requires the supply to the press of billets which are heated throughout to a uniformly plastic condition, and frequently involves the control of their temperature within narrow limits.

The preheating furnace which is frequently used for copper alloys is of the ' roll-down ' type. In this, taking advantage of the invariably circular cross-section of the billets, they are placed one behind the other on a hearth which is slightly inclined to the discharge end, so that as they are successively withdrawn, the remainder roll forward and cold ones are fed in at the top end (Fig. 91). The simplicity of construction and absence of moving parts make this furnace cheap to build. By their revolution the billets are evenly exposed to the source of heating which is done rapidly by fuel firing, using gas or oil burners. The high billet temperatures now required for alloys which can be only extruded at temperatures in the neighbourhood of 1100° C., has stimulated the design of other types of furnaces. In one of these, for example, which operates automatically, the billets rest on refractory covered trays which are pushed by pneumatic rams through successive zones of higher temperature into which the furnace is divided.

A recent installation employs a large rotating hearth for heating copper billets, and is illustrated diagrammatically in Fig. 92. The firebrick hearth is in the form of a ring, some 4 ft. 6 in. wide and 21 ft. 0 in. diameter to the centre lines, and is grooved to accommodate two billets in each groove. Billets are fed down a gravity conveyor, are picked up in pairs and loaded on to a charging spoon which deposits them on the hearth at the same time as the discharge mechanism withdraws heated billets from a door adjacent to that used for charging. These operations are fully automatic and are by oil hydraulic equipment. Fig. 93 shows the charging and discharging mechanisms. Firing is by

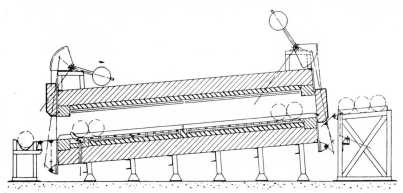

Fig. 91.—Billet preheating furnace of the gravity feed type.
(*Courtesy of ' Metallurgia '.*)

town gas, with independent temperature control and air preheating for each of the three zones into which the furnace is divided. The output amounts to about 8 tons per hour of copper billets heated to 900° C.

The special problems involved in the preheating of aluminium alloys have caused the adoption of new methods. The main object to be secured is uniform soaking of the billets, some of them of very large size, to bring them to a closely controlled temperature. Electrical resistance heating of the furnaces, with thermostatic regulation of temperature, has been most widely employed for the purpose, though firing with town gas has been successfully used in some designs. While electric roll-down furnaces are much used abroad, they have disadvantages for

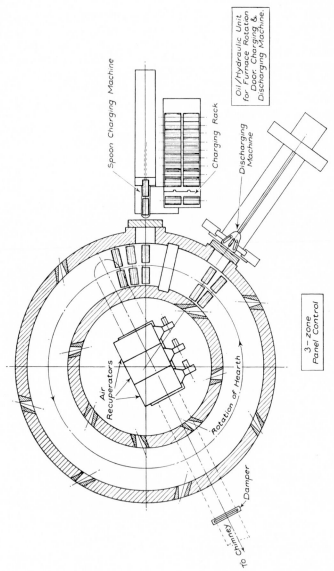

Spoon Charging Machine

Charging Rack

Oil/Hydraulic Unit for Furnace Rotation Door Charging & Discharging Machine.

Discharging Machine

Air Recuperators

Rotation of Hearth

3 - zone Panel Control

To Chimney

Damper

Fig. 92.—Plan of Stein and Atkinson rotating hearth furnace for heating copper billets.

(Courtesy of Yorkshire Imperial Metals Ltd.)

Fig. 93.—Charging and discharging gear of rotating hearth.
(Courtesy of Yorkshire Imperial Metals Ltd.)

heating these alloys which are not easily overcome. For instance, the greater coefficient of friction of aluminium as compared with copper alloys renders the feeding forward of the billets uncertain even when steeper hearths are provided; side doors through which the billets can be urged forward by hand interfere with the arrangement of the resistors, and are dangerous unless the power is cut off whenever they are opened. In England, resort has been general to mechanical means of conveying the billets through the furnace, with the object of making their travel as positive as possible. Only brief reference to these developments can be made here, but the relative merits of modern conveyor systems for light alloy billets has been fully discussed by Lindner.[19]

Early attempts to supersede gravity feed by the introduction of pneumatic or hydraulically driven pusher mechanism operating from the charging end, which acts on billets lying lengthwise in longitudinal grooves in the hearth plates, were not very successful. This was due to high friction against the hearth plates requiring much power to be used, and the consequent danger of damaging the soft billets. In a later modification the billets were carried on shoes sliding on rails in the hearth, while more recently diabolo roller tracks have been used and found to be satisfactory (Fig. 94). This latter furnace has six rows of diabolo-shaped free-running rollers fixed in the hearth, and the billets are pushed through the furnace, butting up against one another, by means of an electrically operated combined pusher gear and hoist which is situated at the charging end. Adjustable stops permit varying lengths of billet to be catered for. Air circulation is provided by means of two double entry type fans situated one at each end of the furnace, which force the air longitudinally down the chamber, and suck it back through heating elements suspended in the upper ductwork of the heating chamber. The equipment may be operated at temperatures up to 450° C. and the maximum output is 1680 lb. per hour at this temperature, with a maximum rating of 165 kW. This rating is divided into two automatically controlled zones, the first having 105 kW, where initial heating of the billets takes place, and the second being rated at 60 kW.

The greatest success has attended the use of conveyor-type furnaces. A system, which can be selected as an example, from which good results have been obtained, is shown diagrammatically in Fig. 95. The conveyor, comprising a number of mild steel strands for temperatures up to 500° C., travels entirely within the furnace and so avoids loss of heat. The shaft of the driven drum at the discharge end of the furnace is taken through the wall and carries outside a pair of ratchet wheels which are operated electrically by means of levers and blocks. Aluminium has a low absorptive capacity for radiant heat and it is therefore

FIG. 94.—G.W.B. Diabolo roller furnace.

necessary to increase the transfer of energy by vigorous agitation of the air in the furnace. The diagram shows the method of obtaining directional air flow over the billets at roughly 30 ft. per second by means of a multi-blade centrifugal fan. The heater elements are mounted in the roof of the furnace, and a suitable baffle is placed so as to direct the air stream. Automatic charging gear, in this case, comprises a hoist interlocked with the door gear, so that when the door lifts the charging cradle is hoisted and a billet is gently tilted into the furnace. At the discharge end a receiving cradle is provided inside the furnace, and this.

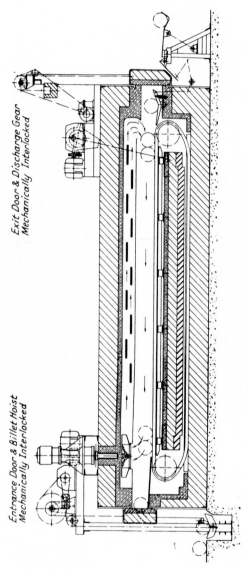

Exit Door & Discharge Gear
Mechanically Interlocked

Entrance Door & Billet Hoist
Mechanically Interlocked

Fig. 95.—G.W.B. conveyor-type furnace.

when depressed by a billet, automatically opens the circuit of the charging and conveyor gear.

The tilting cradle inside the furnace is interlocked with the discharge door. When the door, which is electrically operated, is opened, the tilting cradle discharges the billet which runs out into a receiving trough, whence it is picked up and transferred to the extrusion press. A furnace of this type, dealing with

FIG. 96.—Horizontal-type, low-frequency induction heater, by Loewy-Magnethermic.
(*Haffner and Elkan, ' Metallurgical Reviews '.*)

billets 20 in. in diameter, and 48 in. long, which is in operation, has an output of 3 tons per hour. Several other interesting forms of conveyor furnace have been brought into operation to which adequate discussion can not be given in a brief account.

In the most modern installations considerable use is being made of low-frequency induction heating for billets of all metals, a development which has been reviewed by Logan[20] and by Haffner and Elkan.[5] Among the economies which are claimed for this method of heating is the small space which the unit occupies, as is apparent from the example shown in Fig. 96. The method is capable of handling the largest billets, as is evidenced by its use in connection with the Heavy-Press Programme of the United States, although there is a minimum diameter of billet, ranging from about 2 in. in the case of aluminium to 5 in. in the case of titanium, below which the method is not satisfactory.[5] Even with the largest billets heating is quite rapid, a 32-in. diameter aluminium billet weighing over 2 tons being heated to 450° C. in less than 30 minutes. Where the alloy is of a type which requires structural homogenization prior to extrusion such rapid heating is of less value and batch type furnaces are then used for prior homogenizing, although it is claimed that the use of

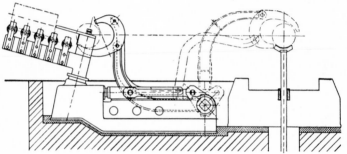

FIG. 97.—Mechanism for conveying billets from furnace to cradle of press.

induction heaters in addition to separate homogenizing furnaces may still be economical. The method is finding application also in die heating.

An interesting application of the low-frequency method is in taper-heating of billets to offset the temperature rise encountered during extrusion.[21] At high rates of deformation the back end of aluminium billets may pass through the die at temperatures as much as 60° C. higher than those obtaining when the front end is extruded, leading to various defects in the product.* By the use of a three-section induction coil a thermal gradient may be established in the billet during heating prior to extrusion such that the temperature rise during extrusion is offset and metal passes through the die at a constant temperature. The rapid

* See page 248.

heating associated with the induction method lends itself well to taper-heating.

In transferring billets from the furnace to the press container, the smallest ones are simply carried in hand tongs; rather larger ones requiring the aid of an overhead chain sling. With heavy billets some form of conveyor is necessary, of which there are several patterns in use. Inclined roll-ways are often used. The

FIG. 98.—Billet on conveyor about to be inserted into a 8000-ton Hydraulik press container.

sketch, Fig. 97, shows one of these in combination with a mechanical arm which places the billet on the press cradle in front of the container. In some modern plants, a bogie running on rails is used to carry billets weighing half a ton, as shown in Fig. 98. Another type of mechanical conveyor can be seen in Fig. 99. The handling of billets and of the extruded product, together with aspects of plant layout, are topics which are currently engaging much attention in the trend towards integrated and automatic presses, such as that shown in Fig. 100.

REFERENCES

[1] M. D. Stone. Design and Construction of Large Forging and Extrusion Presses for Light Metals. *Trans. Amer. Soc. Mech. Eng.*, 1953, **75**, 1493–1512.

FIG. 99.—Fielding and Platt press of 2000 tons, showing the billet conveyor.

FIG. 100.—Compact integrated extrusion press plant by Loewy.
(*Haffner and Elkan, ' Metallurgical Reviews '.*)

[2] G. W. Papen. Requirements for Large Light-Metal Forgings and Extrusions in the Aircraft Industry. *Ibid.*, 1953, **75**, 1483–91.

[3] T. L. Fritzlen. Metallurgy and Production of Suitable Aluminium-Alloy Ingots for Large Forgings and Extrusions. *Ibid.*, 1953, **75**, 1513–18.

[4] T. F. McCormick. Large Extrusion-Press Operation and Production Problems. *Ibid.*, 1953, **75**, 1525–33.

[5] E. K. L. Haffner and R. M. L. Elkan. Extrusion Presses and Press Installations. *Metallurgical Reviews*, 1957, **2**, 263–303.

[6] H. Lorant. Extrusion Method of Manufacturing Tubes. *Mech. Eng.*, 1947, **69**, 471, 1052.

[7] S. Plankensteiner. Metal Rod and Tube Presses and Their Tools. *Stahl u. Eisen*, 1936, **56**, 1497–1504.

[8] E. Loewy. Latest Developments in Extrusion of Metals. *Iron, Steel Eng.*, 1952, **29**, (4), 65–9.

[9] J. Witthoff. Carbide Tools for Non-Cutting Purposes. *Metal Treatment and Drop Forging*, 1954, **21**, 456–62.

[10] H. Assmann. Extrusion Press Mandrels. *Metal Ind.*, 1949, **74** (3), 46–50; (4), 69–72.

[11] F. Hemmerich. Containers for Extrusion Presses. *Metallwirtschaft*, 1944, **23** (27/30), 251–7.

[12] H. M. Hiller. Containers for Extrusion Presses. *Metallurgia*, 1953, **7**, 993–1000.

[13] M. R. Horne. The Elastic-Plastic Theory of Containers and Liners for Extrusion Presses. *Proc. Inst. Mech. Eng.*, 1953, **169**, 107.

[14] P. Bernhoeft. The Operation of a Directly-driven 1500-ton Press. *Z. fur Metallkunde*, 1932, **24**, 210–13, 261–3.

[15] R. Worsdale. *The Manufacture of High-Strength Light-Alloy Extrusions.* Assocn. of Engineering and Shipbuilding Draughtsmen. Pamphlet 1938.

[16] Huffman. *Machine Design*, 1956, **28** (22), 116.

[17] A. B. Graham. Developments in Alloy Sections and Tubes for Marine Engineering. *Inst. of Engineers and Shipbuilders of Scotland*, 1938.

[18] B. P. Brunt. Extrusion Presses: Electric Resistance Heating of Billet Containers. *Met. Ind.*, 1949, **74** (5), 91–3.

[19] H. G. Lindner. Developments in Electric Billet Heating Furnaces for Extrusion Presses *Metallurgia*, 1939, **20**, 53–6.

[20] J. A. Logan. 60-Cycle Induction Heating for Forging and Extrusion. *Metal Progress*, 1954, **66** (6), 94.

[21] A. J. Mueller. Taper Heating of Aluminium Extrusion Billets. *Ibid.*, 1957, **71** (2), 76–7.

[22] F. Rodgers. Steels for Extrusion Tools. *Met. Ind.*, 1958, **93** (22), 449–52 and (23), 469–73.

CHAPTER V

Flow in Metals during Extrusion

THE properties and, in particular, the quality of extruded metals are influenced in a decided fashion by the manner in which the metal flows during the process to take up its final dimensions in issuing from the die. By the study of this flow, and by observing how it is affected by variation in the conditions of operation, a great deal of valuable information can be derived regarding the degree and distribution of the deformation undergone by the metal in different parts: it is also chiefly by such means that it has been possible to assign the cause to certain of the defects which are peculiar to extruded metals. There seems no reason to doubt that metals undergoing all kinds of deformation adapt themselves to the new shape in a manner which resembles the flow in liquids, following a streamline course of flow determined in accordance with the geometrical conditions. The plastic deformation which occurs during extrusion is basically no exception to this, although the flow generally shows very considerable departures from a simple streamline form, partly owing to strong frictional effects, and partly because the billets, for various reasons, are not invariably in a uniformly plastic condition throughout. In the result, the flow sequences become extremely complex and are difficult to interpret, the more so because some of the factors to which they are subject are only imperfectly understood. However, there is sufficient data available from numerous investigations to make the main outlines of the problem reasonably clear, and to allow the flow which takes place in the extrusion of such simple shapes as plain cylindrical bars and tubes to be reasonably well understood.

Methods of Studying Flow

The investigation of flow phenomena in metals during deformation originated in the classical work of Tresca,[1] whose long series of experiments demonstrated the essential plasticity possessed by many crystalline bodies. His studies included the deformation of billets made up from superimposed lead discs when forced through a die. It is interesting, too, to record his attempt to extrude heated discs of wrought iron through a die by repeated blows from a steam hammer.

It was not until about the period of the war (1914–18) that serious attention was attracted to the course of flow in technical extrusion processes in the attempt to discover the origin of defects in extruded materials, then disturbingly frequent in their occurrence. In a research published in 1918 Schweissguth[2] gave what has turned out to be the proper explanation of one of the most serious of these troubles, though without being able to offer any satisfactory means of overcoming it. Since that time much ingenuity has been shown in devising improved methods of identifying the flow process.

One of the commonest methods is simply to macro-etch longitudinal sections of billets after they have been extruded to different residual lengths. This has the advantage of being easy and quick to do, but the picture presented by the distorted crystal structure leads to no more than a general qualitative understanding of the flow process. In an attempt to trace the actual path followed by individual parts of the original billet, Schweissguth prepared brass billets through which rods of brass of slightly different composition were inserted longitudinally, so that differentiation between the two could be obtained by etching subsequent to partial extrusion. Doerinckel and Trockels[3] also used composite billets, building them up from brass discs separated by thin sheets of a second brass, which was used, too, for the longitudinal bolts holding the discs together. Besides those consisting of transverse discs, Schmidt[4] had further resort to billets made up with concentric cylinders alternately of magnesium and 5 per cent zinc-magnesium alloy. In laboratory experiments composite billets have been much used. Several investigators[5, 6, 7] have recorded observations made from experiments with layered billets of coloured wax, and of plasticine; while Unckel,[8] using mixtures of chalk, beeswax and Vaseline, to which colouring matter was added, created billets consisting of cubical units of different colour, from the ultimate distortion of which in sectioned residues, deductions could be made regarding the distribution of flow. It would appear that the use of such simple materials in experiments designed to give an indication of the type of flow to be expected in the forming of complicated sections could be valuable, especially in view of the agreement which Green[9] has shown to exist between the deformation of plasticine and hot metal. Smith and Swindells[10] have also made a novel suggestion in

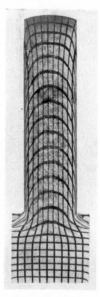

FIG. 101.—Flow shown by distortion of co-ordinate net pattern. Direct extrusion of tin at 100° C., using lubrication.

this connection, in which flow is simulated by constructing a model press with silver sand as the material being extruded, and gravity as the source of extrusion power. Although they are careful to point out that the analogy must not be carried too far, they claim that interesting ideas on how to design multi-hole dies may be obtained by varying the layout of the apertures in the die and observing the sinking surface of the silver sand.

By far the most satisfactory method is that by which an ordinary cast billet, after first being accurately cut longitudinally into two equal halves, has a co-ordinate net or other pattern inscribed on one of the cut faces (see Fig. 101). The two halves are then put together and secured, during preheating, by bands which are later removed when the billet is inserted into the press container. It is essential that the assembled halves fit the press closely so that the plane of separation lies in the axis of the container. For a die of circular aperture which is also axially placed, the conditions are symmetrical, and tangential displacement of metal across the plane of separation can not occur during extrusion; the billet therefore behaves as though it were uncut. After carrying extrusion to the desired amount, the remaining part of the billet can be removed from the press and both it and the rod extruded from it are then easily broken apart by a light blow. The distortion of the original pattern now affords a ready and accurate means of tracing the course of flow and one which is capable of quantitative examination. This important method appears to have been applied first to the study of the cold drawing operation by Zagorski,[11] and in the observance of geological phenomena by Riedel.[12] Its application to extrusion was made later by Siebel and Hühne,[13] and by Sachs and Eisbein.[14] Several means of applying the pattern have been adopted. Sachs and Eisbein cut a rectangular system of fine grooves on the prepared faces of copper and brass billets, which were filled in with a mixture of clay and graphite. On large billets of aluminium, Unckel[15] cut grooves 5 mm. deep, 2 mm. wide, and spaced 20 mm. apart, into which he hammered strips of 1 per cent copper-aluminium alloy, finally rubbing the prepared faces with graphite and clay to ensure their easy separation after partial extrusion of the billet. For the final examination of the flow, the residue of the half-billet carrying the inserted strip was smoothed with emery and then etched with concentrated hydrochloric acid to blacken the alloy strips. An adaptation of the method used by the author[16] for small billets of lead, tin, aluminium, etc., consisted in inscribing the required pattern with printer's ink on one of the billet halves, which were then wired together tightly. Even on aluminium billets heated to as high as 600° C. for extrusion, this has proved satisfactory, since the close contact between the surfaces preserved the pattern from destruction by heating.

Examples of Flow in Direct Extrusion

There will be considered first of all the results obtained from the extrusion of small billets in a laboratory type of press. This has the advantage that the conditions can be made fairly simple and are well defined. If attention is confined to the flow of metal through a cylindrical die with square shoulders, which is the one most frequently used in extrusion, then there can be selected for description three kinds of flow sequence which typify the behaviour in the direct process of extrusion.

Type A. Fig. 101 shows the distortion of the net pattern of a billet of tin after extruding by 66 per cent of its initial length. In producing this, it is to be noted that the billet and the press itself were heated to a uniform temperature of 100° C., and this was held while the extrusion was performed. The container had a smoothly finished surface and was lubricated with oil and graphite. The die aperture is large to help in following the distortion of the pattern but this does not affect the general features which are the same when a greater reduction is employed. It is apparent that the billet has moved easily through the container, undergoing no deformation until the metal comes within a short distance of the die. There the centre part travels forward more rapidly than the sides, which are held back under the shoulders of the die. Next to the latter, the units of the first outer ring of pattern elements have become stagnant, and between this dead zone and the outer elements further along the sides of the billet there has developed a funnel-shaped region in which deformation is severe. As the side units enter this zone, they are first of all compressed and then pass diagonally with heavy shearing into the die to constitute the outer part of the extruded bar. The general effect, therefore, is that whereas the centrally-lying elements undergo a minimum of deformation by pure elongation which corresponds with the actual change in cross-section between the billet and the bar, the outer units have experienced much additional working and are stretched out along the sides of the rod, lying well in rear of the centre ones with which they were initially horizontally aligned. It will be seen that the front end of the bar differs from the remainder in having received slight working. It consists of the pattern units which lay, to

146

begin with, directly opposite the die orifice and so have not had to pass through the deformation zone at the approaches to the die. This short length, in which the cast structure of the billet is more or less completely preserved, soon gives way to material which, in the longitudinal sense, has had approximately uniform working. Extrusion carried beyond the stage shown in Fig. 101 produces no new features until the back end of the billet comes within the deformation zone. This happens when the billet has been reduced to a disc of thickness about one-quarter of its diameter. The rapid inflow directly under the die aperture, made apparent by the upcurve of the transverse lines of pattern in Fig. 101, creates a tendency for a hollow funnel to be formed

FIG. 102.—Funnel formed in rear end of billet residue if extrusion is carried to full extent.

in the middle of the base, which develops increasingly if the extrusion is pressed as far as it will go: the back end of the bar thus becomes unsound over a short length (see Fig. 102).

Siebel and Hühne have applied a method of analysis based on the distortion of a co-ordinate net pattern to flow during extrusion of the type just described. This begins with the consideration that the deformation in an element bounded by mutually perpendicular faces can be resolved into a deformation normal to the faces, and superimposed shear strains. If the boundaries of the element are so selected that two opposite faces lie perpendicular to a direction of stress—as happens if a face lies in a plane of symmetry—then shear is only possible in planes normal to the limiting surfaces and investigation is made simpler. It has been seen in Fig. 101, that the deformation during extrusion is such that only in the vicinity of the axis of the bar has it occurred as a simple elongation, corresponding to the reduction in area from the billet to the bar. The pattern units lying off the axis must necessarily have undergone equal elongation, but have also experienced additional shear deformations which are very severe towards the outside of the bar. Thus a total deformation is produced in them which is considerably greater than that at the axis. Now the deformation suffered by an object during shaping

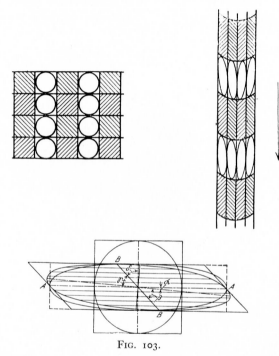

FIG. 103.

can be assessed from a comparison of the initial and final dimensions of the object only if parallel-walled elements continue to have plane parallel faces after deformation. The fact that here only the axially placed elements show such parallelepipedial deformation is an indication of extra deformation having occurred which can not be estimated from the external dimensions of the bar, and represents an internal loss of work which must have an effect on the force required to cause extrusion, making it greater than that theoretically required.

148

The extent of the additional deformations in extrusion has been calculated for some simple cases by reference to the deformation of spheres located within each cubical pattern unit, which participate in their distortion, becoming converted into ellipsoids, the principal axes of which characterize the changes in form which have been produced. The spheres can be regarded as being transformed first by a deformation which corresponds with the

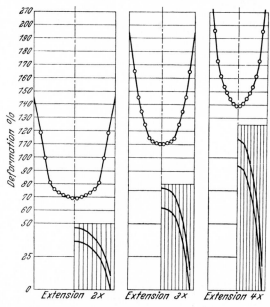

FIG. 104.—The amount and distribution of deformation in extrusion calculated by reference to the distortion of spherical units.

alteration of the external dimensions of the whole body into ellipsoids whose long axes coincide with the axis of the bar, and these then being converted into the final form by shear displacement through an angle which is greater the further the distance from the central axis of the rod (Fig. 103).

The results of their experiments along these lines on billets of lead, using different dies to give extrusion ratios of 2, 3 and 4, are reproduced in Fig. 104. The lower curves show the distortion of a transverse set of pattern elements in each case, while the upper curves show the calculated deformation undergone by

149

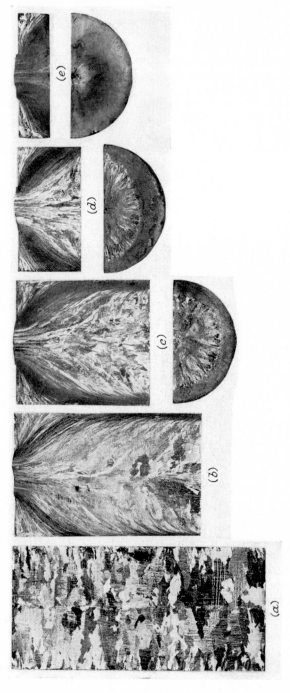

Fig. 105.—Etched sections of partially extruded billets. Direct method, showing flow of type B.

each element. The outstanding fact emerging from this is that even in these cases, where the flow is relatively simple, the deformation close to the surface of the extruded bar has been approximately double that required for pure stretching such as

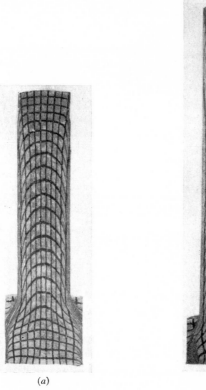
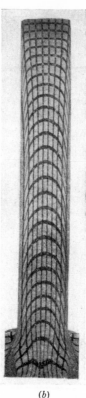

(a)   (b)

FIG. 106.—Tin billets partially extruded at 100° C. by the direct method without lubrication.

the centre has undergone. As it will be seen later, this lateral difference can be much greater in practice.

Type B. The etched billet residues in Fig. 105, and those in Fig. 106, on which the net pattern method was used, were obtained in experiments with bismuth and tin respectively, for which the only variant from the preceding case lay in the omission of lubrication; the container being used with a dry emeried surface. A uniform temperature was again held during extrusion. The general features of the last type are reproduced with the addition that the restraining effect of friction has led to heavy shear all along the sides of the billet close to its surface. This sheared region is continuous with that under the die shoulders.

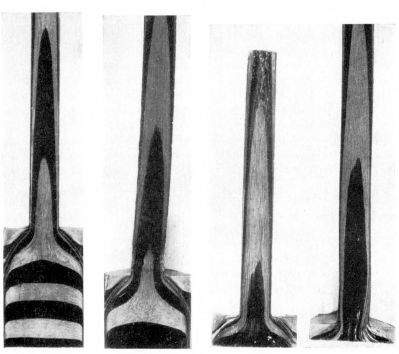

Fig. 107.—Flow in the direct extrusion of tin at 100° C. as shown by distortion of transverse banded pattern.

The effect is to increase the rate of travel of the centre part into the die relatively to the metal at the outside, and to augment the severe deformation of the outer layers of the bar. Apart from this, over the greater part of its length the extruded bar preserves the same general features as in the preceding type A. In the later stages, the effect of the continued shearing of the billet past its peripheral layers causes the latter to build up at the rear end of the billet in front of the advancing pressure disc, and, when the billet has become reduced to about one-third of its first length, this accumulated material bulges inwards and begins to affect the deformation of the metal in the centre (see Fig. 106 (*b*)). Ultimately the bulges come right in and, as shown in Fig. 105, reduce the more lightly worked core to a narrow cone, so that the last 10 per cent or so of the extruded bar has a heavily deformed outer ring which extends almost to the middle. A point to be noted here is that these changes do not, in this case, begin to effect the structure of the issuing bar before the billet has come down to a disc of roughly one-fourth of its diameter in thickness, as may be seen in Fig. 107. Now

FIG. 108.—Tube extrusion, direct method, using polished mandrel, but without lubrication.

it is important that the possible ways in which the displacement of the billet through the container may take place in direct extrusion should be clearly understood. It may occur, as seen in type A, by the overcoming of the interfacial friction between the billet and the container. This may be expected to depend on the conditions at the interface. With smooth, lubricated surfaces it occurs easily. Without lubricant, the roughness of the container and the coefficient of friction between the metals tend to control the facility of translation, and a point is reached at which the friction resistance exceeds the shear resistance of the hot metal. In that case part or all of the displacement of the billet occurs by shear in its surface layers leaving the skin clinging to the wall of the container. In the examples shown in Figs. 105 and 106 shearing has predominated over sliding, as it has also in Fig. 108, as can be seen by tracing the history of successive chequer units on the right-hand side. The left side of this billet was given a different pattern consisting of transverse bands. Incidentally this photograph, which applies to the extrusion of a tube, also shows some effect on the flow caused by the friction at the surface of the mandrel, which had been polished. Under practical conditions of extrusion, too, it is usual for the skin of the billet to be immobile, and it would seem more correct then to refer the force needed to move the billet through the container to that required for internal shear than for overcoming friction. This should be borne in mind where further reference to this question is made later and formulae are suggested in which friction coefficients are introduced. Nevertheless, flow of an

FIG. 109.—Irregular flow in direct extrusion caused by trace of lubricant.

intermediate type between A and B, in which sliding and shear are combined, can be produced experimentally and also occurs in practice. The extrusion of a metal which is stiff and has a high shear resistance will tend to lead to sliding. A trace of lubricant on one side of a billet is sufficient, as shown in Fig. 109, to alter the flow and leads to an eccentric pattern. The significance of the above remarks in relation to the origin of defects will appear shortly.

Two points to be mentioned are that the examples shown are the outcome of trials with metals of low melting-point, such as lead, tin, and bismuth, for all of which the flow under similar conditions was found to be identical. Moreover, the extrusion of particular metals at widely separated temperatures did not affect the manner of flow so long as the temperature in the billet was uniform.

Type C. The flow experienced in the previous cases is not representative of that which occurs in the majority of instances in technical extrusion, though it is typical of some, as will be seen later. A very significant difference which is generally found can be illustrated by considering the flow process of the hard

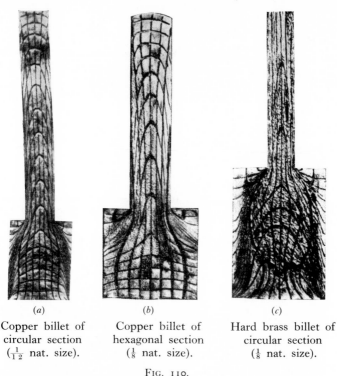

(a)	(b)	(c)
Copper billet of circular section ($\frac{1}{12}$ nat. size).	Copper billet of hexagonal section ($\frac{1}{8}$ nat. size).	Hard brass billet of circular section ($\frac{1}{8}$ nat. size).

FIG. 110.

brasses. Fig. 110 (c) shows the half-section of a large billet removed from an ordinary industrial press after partial extrusion, and Fig. 111 a similar billet which has been macro-etched. The first thing to notice is that the zone of shear formed by the displacement of the centre through the outer part retained by friction, is now at a greater depth below the surface and is more broadly diffused, leaving a fairly thick rim of dead material extending down the sides from the stagnant zone under the shoulders of the die to the back of the billet. As the extrusion ram advances

FIG. 111.—Etched section of hard brass billet, 40 per cent extruded.

FIG. 112.—Composite billets, showing enfolding at rear corners. Direct extrusion, flow of type C.

this rim is gathered up in front of the pressure disc and bulges in towards the centre to take the place of the rapidly flowing metal there. In a later stage this material is enfolded and projects tongues into the centre stream, which enter the die and form part of the bar over as much as 30 per cent of its length, at the back end. The whole sequence is very well shown in Fig. 112, for which Schmidt used billets 6 in. in diameter, made from concentric cylinders of magnesium and 5 per cent zinc-magnesium alloy. The accretion of the dark-etching outer zone at the back corners and its eventual intrusion into the bar is very apparent. It will be seen that the chief difference between types B and C consists in the retention, in the latter, of more material along the sides and its much earlier intrusion, from the back end, into the die.

The Extrusion Defect

The opportunity can be taken here to refer to a characteristic fault which, under the name of ' the extrusion defect ' or ' piping ', has long been well known in copper alloys, but to which other metals are also susceptible. This can definitely be associated with flow of type C, is slight or absent in type B, and does not occur at all in type A.

It is still sometimes confused with defects of a different origin, but its real nature, first explained by Schweissguth, and amply confirmed by Genders[17] and other workers, must be regarded as being beyond doubt. Although its incidence has been greatly reduced, constant vigilance is still needed to avoid its inclusion in material passing into service. The defect has its genesis in the oxidized skin of the billet. This constitutes part of the material which, as just described, becomes enfolded during extrusion at the rear corners of the billet. The actual path followed by the unsound metal can be seen in Fig. 113. It takes the form of a funnel closing in from the corners and continuing into the die as a tubular fault. In the bar, the defect appears in section as a partial or complete annulus which, wide at first, becomes of less diameter as the back end of the bar is approached. It is marked by the presence of drawn-out fragments of dross and oxide. Fig. 114 shows a bad case in which the core of the bar is detached from the outside. The defect is most apparent

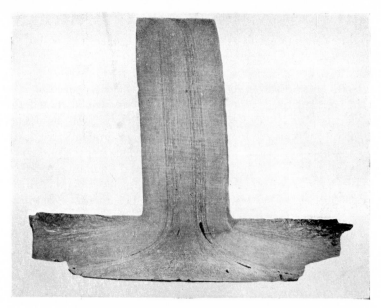

FIG. 113.—Extrusion defect entering at back end of an extruded bar.

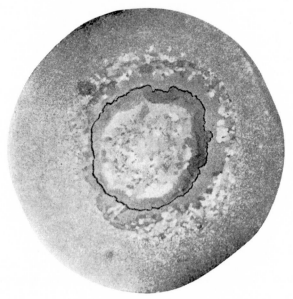

FIG. 114.—Section of fuse rod, with loose core resulting from extrusion defect (Genders).

in larger sizes of bar, and is more attenuated in thin sections and tubes. Its presence to any serious extent greatly impairs the quality of the metal for most purposes.

A further consequence of flow of type C, which should be mentioned here, although it will be referred to more fully in connection with the properties of extruded metals, is that the working of the product over its length is nowhere near as uniform as in the other types. At the back end, and extending roughly over a third of the total length, the metal is subjected to an intense and complex deformation except near the axis of the bar. As the back end is approached metal which has undergone very severe working, often, as mentioned below, at a lower temperature than elsewhere, comes to occupy more and more of the cross-section, extending finally almost to the centre of the bar.

Several explanations have been advanced to account for flow taking the course it does in type C, in contrast with type B in the experimental billets. An obvious difference lies in the temperature conditions. For instance, in the extrusion of copper alloys, the strongly heated billets are placed in a cooler container so that the outer layers are chilled and therefore become relatively stiff. This will accentuate the tendency for the centre part of the billet to be displaced through the outer portion and will therefore increase the liability of the harder chilled rim to be turned in at the back of the billet. The temperature gradient between the centre and outside will also cause the shearing displacement between the two parts to occur at greater depth below the surface, and so leave a thicker rim of metal along the sides. That such a modification of the flow can be caused by the temperature factor alone can be demonstrated. Fig. 115 represents a billet of tin, extruded at 100° C. from a cooler container at 30° C., the flow pattern of which is closer to Fig. 110 (c) than to Fig. 106 (a). In agreement with this result, it is a matter of experience that the proportion of defective material is lower when working with a hot press and when a rapid rate of extrusion is used. The defect is however encountered acutely in the extrusion of high strength aluminium alloys for which the press container is held at a temperature only slightly below that of the billet, and this points to the fact that variable plasticity arising from unequal temperature distribution is not the sole determining factor and that other causes must be found. In this connection,

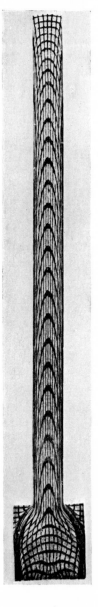

the very strong adherence of aluminium to the wall of the container, and the high co-efficient of friction of aluminium, may be significant. Although no evidence of it was found in experiments with pure metals, there is some reason to believe that under similar conditions of extrusion, some alloys flow differently from others. Sachs and Eisbein have demonstrated that, when extruded from the same press, hard brass showed flow of type C, and copper of type B (cf. (c) and (a), Fig. 110). This also receives support from Crampton's[18] statement that high copper alloys, consisting entirely of the a phase, are little subject to the central extrusion defect, but are apt instead to be unsound at or just below the surface skin of the extruded parts; the latter form of fault, as will be seen shortly, may originate when flow follows type B. It is possible that this difference has its cause in variability of properties within the billets. In alloys which have a heter-ogeneous structure, the constituents in the outer layers may differ in quantity and size from those in the core, due to the conditions of cooling in the mould. Unequal plasticity in working can also be expected where there is any degree of inverse segregation. On the other hand, Blazey *et al.*[19] have provided reasonably convincing evidence in connection with studies of tube extrusion that this differ-ence in behaviour may be ascribed to the different surface conditions of brass and copper

FIG. 115.—A billet of tin extruded at 140° C. from a cold container, bringing out the effect of a temperature gradient. (Cf. Fig. 88 *a*.)

billets as normally charged to a press (see page 171). Brass
billets may be made to show the lubricated type of flow if they
are plated with a layer of copper before preheating, while copper
billets can be made to flow like brass if surface oxidation is prevented during preheating. It is suggested therefore that copper
oxide acts as a lubricant.

In order to avoid the extrusion defect, one way is to leave
part of the billet unextruded and to treat this as scrap. As much
as 30 per cent of each billet may need to be rejected, but this
is very uneconomical and the better plan is to extrude further
and reject unsound material by inspection of fractures on the
back end of the bar. In brass extrusion, the practice most widely
adopted to overcome the worst of the trouble is to use a pressure
disc smaller in diameter than the container, so that a skull, about
$\frac{1}{8}$ in. to $\frac{3}{16}$ in. in thickness, containing the skin of the billet,
remains on the wall of the container. This is very largely effec-
tive, but is not altogether reliable. Its efficacy obviously depends
on the pressure disc being well centred, for if the skull is eccentric
or incomplete, a partial or semicircular defect is likely to appear
in the bar. Moreover, surface oxide carried in by the crumpling
of the skin when the billet is upset in the press before it begins
to extrude may lie too far in to be included in the skull. A
means of centring the pressure disc, assuming that the extrusion
ram enters the container axially, is afforded by providing a tapered
projection on the end of the extrusion ram which engages in a
recess in the back of the disc. The same purpose is fulfilled,
in the case where the ram and disc are hollow to allow the passage of a mandrel, by having a projecting ring on the ram face
engaging in an annular recess in the disc. An alternative to
cutting a skull which is almost invariably adopted with such
metals as 20 per cent nickel-silver, cupro-nickel, monel, and
pure nickel, is to turn the exterior of the billets to remove the
casting skin and surface blemishes. In the manufacture of high-
grade tubes it is also a fairly general practice to machine the
billets. The extrusion defect is not entirely obviated in this
way, since superficial oxidation of the turned surface occurs
during preheating, though it is possible to obtain some degree
of control over this by regulation of the furnace atmosphere.

The idea that the entry of impurities into the bar might be

prevented or delayed by the use of specially shaped pressure discs
has often been entertained, and various trials have been made
which have led to divergent opinions. The general plan has
been to use discs with concave, ribbed or roughened surfaces
with the purpose of trapping or immobilizing the enfolding defective metal. On the whole no success can be claimed for these
measures: the creation of a stagnant layer at the base of the
billet is ineffective in preventing the oxide, etc., from entering
at the rear edge of the billet since it follows a curved path over

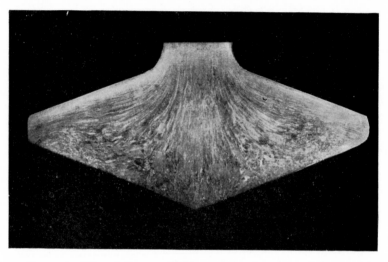

FIG. 116.—Discard from steel billet resulting from use of conical die
and recessed pressure disc.

this layer. The most that can be said is that a concave or conic-
ally recessed disc slightly delays the appearance of the defect.

Reverting in this connection, however, to the hollow funnel
which forms in the base of the billet when it has been reduced
to a thin disc, and which, incidentally, is not peculiar to any of
the above types of flow, this can be almost completely suppressed
by using a dished or conical pressure disc. Such a disc, in conjunction with a conical die, is sometimes used to reduce the weight
of the discard from the billet (Fig. 116).

In the course of their trials, Sachs and Eisbein obtained some
curious results by extruding billets of hexagonal cross-section in

an ordinary cylindrical container. The flow in copper in such a case was, as shown in Fig. 110 (b), considerably altered as compared with that in a round billet (Fig. 110, a). A change in flow, though not so pronounced, was also found with the brass billets which they tried in the same way. It is difficult to find a satisfactory explanation, unless it is assumed that the hexagonal billet does not become squeezed up under pressure to make even contact with the container, so that the friction surface is not as great as under ordinary conditions.

The position now reached is that it has to be recognized that in extruding most of the technically important metals some proportion of the material is liable to extrusion defect, and though by use of palliative measures it can be mitigated very largely, so that the scrap loss from this cause is probably not higher, on the average, than 12–17 per cent, it is not thereby avoided altogether. There still remains to consider the feasibility of inducing a radical alteration in the flow, and the question whether this, while providing a means of overcoming one trouble, will introduce new difficulties. The possibilities of modifying the flow lie in (a) reducing the interfacial friction between billet and container by using some suitable lubricant; (b) altering the form of the entry to the die to avoid the rapid inflow from the centre of the billet while the sides lag behind; (c) the use of the inverted method of extrusion.

Lubrication

In so far as the frictional conditions between the billet and the container in extrusion influences both the pressure requirements and the mode of flow, it is to be expected that lubrication, in an attempt to alter these frictional conditions, will be of importance. In practice, lubrication is widely used, although its application is not always simple. For copper alloys, graphite or graphite and oil, is applied thinly to the die entry (and to tube mandrels) in the interests of surface finish and to reduce wear. The container too is usually swabbed out cursorily between each extrusion. Aluminium alloys, on the other hand, are frequently worked without a lubricant, or with only a very little in the die. Graphite, if it is used, imparts a dark skin to these metals, which can not be got rid of. One of the difficulties in finding suitable lubricants for these and the harder metals is that, as Bowden and Tabor[28] show, such lubricants must remain solid at the temperature involved if boundary lubrication is to occur. This rules out the more usual organic lubricants and has led to the development of techniques employing rather unconventional lubricants. However, even when a material is available which produces boundary lubrication its use is not always straightforward.

It has been seen that, in the experiments with small billets, effective lubrication exercises a profound effect on the course of flow. A good deal of attention has been given to its possible advantages in practice, including a reduction in the power required to extrude long billets. Newson[20] has described trials in which a wash of graphite was applied to hot billets of P.M.G. alloy. These extruded more easily than usual, the view being taken that the billets slid through the container after the manner of that in Fig. 101. On extracting the unextruded discs of the billets from the press, they fell into two parts, the separate faces, seen in Fig. 117, being coated with graphite. The bars produced were unsound on the outside, having a wrinkled skin covering a laminated surface which was also coated with graphite. This provides a good example of the fact that when conditions of flow are such that the skin of the billet is not enfolded to give the central defect, it may be entrained elsewhere to give rise to a subcutaneous defect. This is not confined to the case where lubricant is used, but seems to be associated with flow of types A and B when some sliding occurs with the latter. Copper and high copper alloys are somewhat liable to show, usually over the final third of the extruded length, a rough bark-like skin which has to be cleaned up by scalping. Reverting to Fig. 107, to see the mechanism by which this occurs, the outer layers of the billet become concertinaed in the deformation zone near the die with the result that oxide, etc., is liable to be drawn in through this zone, passing out through the die at or just below the surface of the bar (see also Fig. 118). An almost identical defect can occur in inverted extrusion.

A development of far-reaching importance and concerned with the question of lubrication in extruding the high melting point metals, is the Ugine Sejournet* process.[21] The tendency of

* British Patents Nos. 607,285, 661,555 and 663,357.

many of these metals to seize on the die and mandrel, together with the difficulties which arise due to the formation of hard scale on others, are prevented by the use of glass as a lubricant. In order to reduce scale formation the billets are usually heated

FIG. 117.—Separation at flow surface in discard end of hard brass billet.

in a salt bath in which they rest in a basket. They are discharged on to an inclined surface on which a glass fibre mat, or a smooth bed of powdered glass, has been placed. As the billet rolls down to the press it acquires an adherent coating of glass. A glass cartridge is also placed against the face of the die; this may be in the form of a plate-glass pad, or glass-fibre pad in the case of a concave die. Similarly for tube extrusion in which prepierced billets are used, the bore is coated either by placing a glass-fibre sock over the mandrel or by placing a mound of powdered glass along the bore and causing this to be evenly distributed as the billet rolls down the inclined tray. Thus the hot billet is physically insulated from the tools by the glass,

FIG. 118.—Aluminium billet extruded 60 per cent at 500° C. Showing how entraining of oxidized surface layers can lead to subcutaneous defects. Direct extrusion.

which softens and acts as a lubricant, and which is much superior to graphitic and other types of dressing.

A modification of this procedure as practised at the Fiav Mazzacchera plant in Italy is to replace the salt bath heating by heating in a glass bath contained in a furnace of novel design,[22] which is gas-fired and of the rotary type. Considerable economies are claimed for this type of heating, following which the adhering glass is removed by mechanical scraping before being replaced by the glass coating which acts as the lubricant during extrusion. The removal of the glass carried over from the heating furnace is rather surprising, more especially since it is not necessary to remove the salt from the more usual salt bath heating before the glass lubricant is applied. Indeed it is claimed[23] that the presence of this salt assists the glass in promoting effective lubrication.

The advent of glass lubrication has occasioned the testing of other rather unconventional lubricants, such as lime feldspar, mica and various salt mixtures,[23] which, while not so effective as glass in the extrusion of higher melting point metals, may prove useful with other materials. Molybdenum disulphide and polytetraflorethylene (P.T.F.E.) are new lubricants that may also find applications in extrusion, particularly at the lower temperatures. The use of a thin film of a pure soft metal to separate the container and billet is another technique which is proving useful in some cases where frictional conditions make extrusion difficult. (See Chapter VIII.)

Conical Extrusion Dies

It is justifiable to feel that, so far as the flow of the metal is concerned, the square-faced type of die so far considered is not the most ideal shape. It is clear from the foregoing that it is one of the main factors in causing the deformation to be very unequal by its effect in holding back the inflow from the outer zone of the billet. A bell-shaped entry to the die, suggested by the flow surface which the metal creates for itself by the formation of the dead zones under the shoulders of the die, might appear to have merits, and this and other shapes have been tried from time to time. It has, however, to be borne in mind that regulation of flow is only one aspect to be taken into account, and that the strength of the die, and the effect of its shape on the extrusion pressure, have also to be considered. Dies of conical form are now often used in rod and tube extrusion. With soft metals, such as tin and lead, the effect in small-scale experiments of using polished, lubricated dies of varying conicity is as shown in Fig. 119. Even with the widest included angle, the dead zone is absent, and the outermost units of pattern pass out along the face of the die. As the angle is made more acute, the superimposed deformation towards the outside of the bar becomes less, and, in the final case, there is a fairly close approximation to uniform deformation by simple elongation. If the metal exhibits strain hardening, as when aluminium is extruded at room temperature, then dead metal zones are observed when the die angle is large.[24] Although the more uniform deformation observed with dies of small angle looks as if it might entail a reduction in the force needed for extrusion, the latter is not the case, as will be seen when this aspect of the matter is discussed in Chapter VI. Such a die as the last of the series shown in

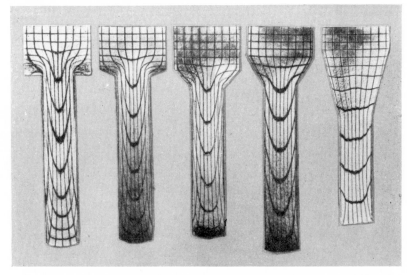

FIG. 119.—The effect on the distribution of flow caused by the use of dies of different conicity. Small-scale experiments with tin. (*Sachs and Eisbein.*)

Fig. 119 would also be quite unsuitable because it would not withstand the bursting stresses in use.

In so far as, with conical dies, the skin of the billet is caused to pass across the die face, the enclosure of impurities inside the extruded bar will tend to be avoided, and they will be apt to appear instead on its surface. In extruding nickel alloys, using conical dies and with a graphite lubricant, it seems probable that flow of this kind is brought about. Attention to adequate lubrication, and the use of turned billets, conduce then to the production of clean extruded surfaces.

FIG. 120.—Flow in the inverted process of extrusion.

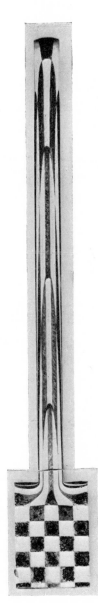

FIG. 121.—2·5 per cent copper-aluminium alloy extruded at 360° C. by the inverted method.

Flow in Inverted Extrusion

It is of interest to compare the flow in direct extrusion with that which accompanies the inverted method, wherein friction between the container and billet is altogether absent owing to there being no relative movement between them. Fig. 120 shows a series of etched billet residues, and Fig. 121 one of 2·5 per cent copper-aluminium alloy, the latter extruded at a uniform temperature of 360° C. The similarity with flow of type A is

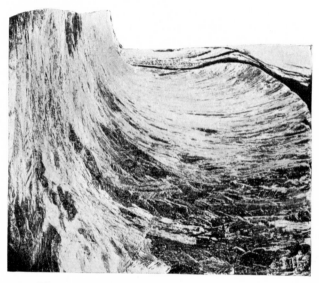

FIG. 122.—The enfolding of the skin of the billet in inverted extrusion.

striking. Deformation is confined to a zone near the die and, as the latter travels forward, the deformed zone moves with it into the unaffected metal. Up to the point to which extrusion has been carried in Fig. 121, five horizontal sets of the chequer pattern have been involved, and the sixth row is just beginning to be affected in the centre. Of these five rows, the three centre units in each have gone completely into the rod, while portions of the outermost units remain foreshortened under the die shoulders where they still contribute to the stream entering the die. The leading end of the bar shows, as before, only slight

working.   At the extreme back end the usual hollow funnel can
be made to form by pushing extrusion far enough.

It is generally agreed that notwithstanding some serious practical disadvantages of the inverted method, it gives a product
which is more uniformly worked in a lengthwise direction than
that made by direct extrusion, for which flow of type C is most
common, and this is seen to be so.   In the transverse direction
marked inequality of deformation as between centre and outside
persists.   The inverted process gives freedom from the central
extrusion defect, but as already mentioned, an alternative defect
is liable to occur close to the surface of the bar.   The origin
of this is clearly shown in Fig. 122.   It can be largely avoided
by providing a clearance between the die and container, so as
to cut a skull, just as in the direct process.

Flow in Tube Extrusion

Blazey, Broad, Gummer and Thompson[19] have studied the
flow of copper and copper alloy billets into tubes on an industrial
scale.   Using billets containing marker pins, inserted at intervals
along a length and diameter of the cylindrical billets, they observed only two types of flow while varying the material and
conditions of extrusion over wide limits.   In the absence of
lubricant between billet and container the normal type of flow
is as shown in Fig. 123, where the dark areas indicate the way
in which the marker pins, originally located at the surface, have
flowed during the extrusion.   Pins 1–5 were located on the side
of the billet and were drawn into the interior and ultimately
into the tube with pin 4 usually the first to reach the die followed
by 3, then 2 and 5 and lastly by 1.   Pins A and B were located
on a diameter on the back end of the billet and reached the die
only towards the end of the extrusion.   This diagonal flow towards the annular space between die and mandrel, which also
is apparent in Fig. 108, appears to be intermediate between types
B and C, although the authors state that there is no tendency
for the outer layer of the billet to fold in and produce a double
or blistered wall on the tube.

If relative movement between billet and container is facilitated,
by the use of lubricants in the case of brass or the presence of
an oxide film in the case of copper, the flow is as shown in

Fig. 124. Each pin in turn reaches the bottom of the billet, flows across the face of the die and enters the tube into which it finally disappears so that in no cross-section of the tube are all five pins to be seen together. This mode of flow has features in common with those of types A and B.

Since the two modes of flow are differentiated by the part

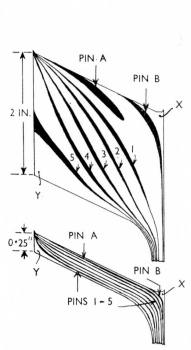

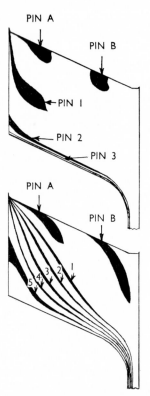

FIG. 123.—Vertical sections through discards of brass billets three-quarters extruded (*upper*) and fully extruded (*lower*) in a non-lubricated container, showing manner in which pins are drawn into the billet and down into the shell.

(*Blazey et al.*, ' *J. Inst. Metals* '.)

FIG. 124.—Vertical sections through copper billets three-quarters extruded in a non-lubricated container.

Upper: illustrates type of flow for a billet with an oxidised surface.

Lower: illustrates type of flow for a billet protected from oxidation.

(*Blazey et al.*, ' *J. Inst. Metals* '.)

played by lubrication Blazey and his co-workers consider the practical implications of their observations. The lower extrusion pressures needed in the presence of lubricant are offset by the fact that surface imperfections on the billet are likely to be extruded and appear as imperfections, either on the surface or in the interior of the wall of the tube. Providing the extent of the billet surface imperfection is not too great, this will not be the case in the absence of lubrication, as the skin of the billet is left in the container.

In the same paper it is shown, from studies of the structure of the plug produced by the piercing operation, that axial porosity in the billet, if not too widespread should be wholly pushed into the plug by a square ended mandrel. With a pointed mandrel part of the porosity should appear as spill and scale on the inner wall of the tube.

Unsymmetrical Flow

The flow of the metal in the extrusion of complicated sections has, so far, received hardly any attention, although the flow in forming tubes is not entirely dissimilar in that unsymmetrical deformation is involved in both cases. Green[25] has studied the flow of plasticine in unsymmetrical plane-strain extrusion by arranging that the die aperture was not central with respect to the container. This condition results in a larger dead region under the side of the die of greatest length, as shown in Fig. 125, with the result that flow is more restrained on this side and the transverse grid lines are no longer symmetrical about the centre line of the extruded rod. This effect becomes even more marked if the container has smooth walls, as shown in Fig. 126. Here, the material under the short side of the die comes through so readily in comparison with that on the opposite side that it causes the extruded product to rotate as it emerges from the die. Experiments of this nature may prove useful in those cases where it is necessary to design a die, such as that shown in Fig. 82, which will permit simultaneous extrusion through an additional aperture in order to balance the flow.

Northcott, McLean and Lee[26] have in fact used such experiments in determining an appropriate design for a multi-hole die to control the incidence of erratic circumferential strength in extruded aluminium alloy bar. Longitudinal streaks on the surface of the bar were found to result in low circumferential strength and laminated fractures and were due to strings of particles of intermetallic compounds. These originated in a

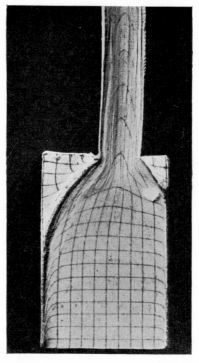

Fig. 125.—Unsymmetrical end-extrusion of Plasticine with rough container walls.
(*Green, ' J. Mech. Phys. Solids '.*)

central billet segregate and, in extrusion through multi-hole dies, appeared at the surfaces of extruded bars due to flow over the edges of the die holes at the positions nearest the billet axis. This point was shown in laboratory experiments using composite billets of lead and bismuth and of differently coloured plasticine to study the mode of flow. Using dies having 1, 2, 3 or 4 holes, all symmetrically disposed about the centre, the results shown in Fig. 127 were obtained and clearly indicate the formation of surface defects from a central billet segregate in the case of

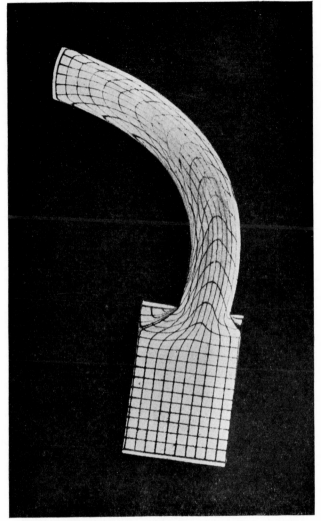

FIG. 126.—Unsymmetrical end-extrusion of Plasticine with smooth
container walls.

(*Green, ' J. Mech. Phys. Solids '.*)

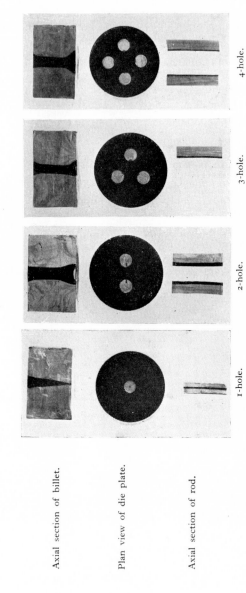

Axial section of billet.

Plan view of die plate.

Axial section of rod.

1-hole.   2-hole.   3-hole.   4-hole.

FIG. 127.—Extrusion of Plasticine billets through various die plates. (*Northcott et al., 'J. Inst. Metals'.*)

multi-hole dies. If the arrangement of the holes was altered so that one hole was central then, as shown in Fig. 128, the billet segregate was concentrated in the core of the central rod. When a similar experiment was made on an industrial scale using the aluminium alloy concerned an improvement in the circumferential properties was observed.

Axial section of billet.

Plan view of die plate.

Axial section of rod.

3-hole with central hole. 4-hole with central hole.

FIG. 128.—Extrusion of Plasticine billets through modified die plates.
(*Northcott et al.*, '*J. Inst. Metals*'.)

Johnson[27] has studied the flow patterns from extruding pure lead and tellurium lead rods of circular, square, rectangular, triangular and I-section form from cylindrical billets. He found that, for regular-shaped squat sections, originally transverse planes are so deformed that after emergence through the die orifice the most advanced points of the plane appear to be those which have passed through the orifice centroid. The general shape of the deformed patterns on planes of symmetry could be anticipated by reference to plane-strain or axi-symmetric extrusions, the orifice width in the flow plane considered seeming to determine the overall pattern in that plane, regardless of other transverse dimensions. The I-section grid distortion showed two peaks on the transverse lines running parallel to the web, each peak emerging near the junction of the web and a flange, where flow may be expected to be less restrained. The somewhat surprising result was obtained in this work that for all the shapes, with the exception of the I-section, the load was independent of the shape and wholly dependent on the reduction in area. The I-section required a 5–10 per cent higher load than the other sections, for the same reduction.

Dodeja and Johnson[29] have also studied the flow patterns produced by the cold extrusion of various soft metals through multiple-hole dies having the holes arranged in different patterns. With holes of the same area arranged in-line and with a disposition balanced about the die centre line, lubrication resulted in the highest rate of extrusion through the holes nearest to the container wall, whereas in the absence of lubricant the rate of extrusion is greatest through the inner holes. As may be expected, the extrusions from different holes showed varying degrees of inhomogeneity of deformation.

REFERENCES

[1] H. Tresca. On the Flow of Solid Bodies under High Pressure. *Comptes Rendus*, 1864 (2), **59,** 754–8; 1867 (1), **64,** 809–12. *Mem. Sav. Ac. Sc.*, 1868, **18,** 733–99; 1872, **20,** 75–135.

[2] P. Schweissguth. The Course of Flow in Extruded Brass Billets during the Hydraulic Extrusion of Bars. *Z.V.D.I.*, 1918, **62,** 281–310.

[3] F. Doerinckel and J. Trockels. Processes of Flow in Brass Ingots during Extrusion. *Z. fur Metallkunde*, 1921, **13,** 466–73.

[4] W. Schmidt. The Extrusion of Elektron Metal. *Ibid.*, 1927, **19,** 378–84.

[5] R. J. Redding (discussion). *J. Inst. Metals*, 1921, **26,** 246.

[6] W. Rosenhain and F. S. Tritton (discussion). *Ibid.*, 250.

[7] R. H. Greaves (discussion). *Ibid.*, 254.

[8] H. Unckel. *Z. für Metallkunde*, 1921, **13,** 466.

[9] A. P. Green. *Phil. Mag.*, **42,** 1951, 365.

[10] C. Smith and N. Swindells. *J. Inst. Metals*, 1953–4, **82,** 323.

[11] J. Zagorski. *Diss. T.H.*, Berlin, 1929.

[12] W. Riedel. *Neues Jahrb. Mineral*, 1929, B, **67,** 151.

[13] E. Siebel and H. Hühne.   Investigation on the Course of Deformation during Technical Forming Operations.   *Mitt. K.W. Inst. Eisenforschung*, 1931, **13,** 43–62.

[14] G. Sachs and W. Eisbein.   Power Consumption and Mechanism of Flow in the Extrusion Process.   *Mitt. Material*, S. **16,** 1931, 67–96.

[15] H. Unckel.   The Heterogeneity of the Material as it Affects the Flow Process in the Dick Extrusion Method.   *Z. für Metallkunde*, 1936, **28** (6), 151–4.

[16] C. E. Pearson.   A Comparison of the Extrusion Properties of Some Aluminium Alloys.   *J. Inst. Metals*, 1939, **64,** 299–310.

[17] R. Genders.   The Extrusion Defect.   *Ibid.*, 1921, **26,** 237–45.

[18] D. K. Crampton.   The Extrusion of Metals.   *Trans. A.S.M.*, 1936, 55–79.

[19] C. Blazey, L. Broad, W. S. Gummer and D. B. Thompson.   *J. Inst. Metals*, 1948–9, **75,** 163.

[20] J. E. Newson (discussion).   *Ibid.*, 1931, **45,** 378.

[21] J. Sejournet.   *Iron Coal Trades Rev.*, 1952, **165,** 963.

[22] —— *Machinery*, 20 April and 4 May, 1956.

[23] K. A. Wilhelm and G. A. Moudry.   *Iron Age*, 1954, **173,** 29 April.

[24] W. Johnson.   B.I.S.R.A. Report, MW/E/55/54.

[25] A. P. Green.   *J. Mech. Phys. Solids*, 1955, **3,** 189.

[26] L. Northcott, D. McLean and O. R. J. Lee.   *J. Inst. Metals*, 1948, **74,** 81.

[27] W. Johnson.   *J. Mech. Phys. Solids*, 1958, **7,** 37.

[28] F. P. Bowden and D. Tabor.   *The Friction and Lubrication of Solids*. Clarendon Press, Oxford.   1950.

[29] L. C. Dodeja and W. Johnson.   *J. Mech. Phys. Solids*, 1957, **5,** 281.

CHAPTER VI

The Pressure of Extrusion

APART from certain impact processes carried out with cold blanks, extrusion forms one of a group of technical hot-working operations, including hot rolling and forging, in which very extensive deformation is brought about in the upper working ranges of the metals. Regarding the conditions which govern such shaping operations at high temperatures, accurate knowledge is still somewhat incomplete and is not comparable with that which has been accumulated in respect of the behaviour of metals when subjected to cold-working operations. Research in relation to high temperature deformation has been concerned for the most part with the ability of materials to endure stress in service, and with the development of alloys capable of bearing continuous loading when heated without undergoing ' creep '. The converse properties which involve the workability of metals in relation to technological shaping in the course of manufacture have been less fully examined, and have only recently been studied to any extent. The high degree of practical success with which the present great variety of technical alloys are extruded has been attained, for the most part, on the basis of empirical knowledge, using experience to discover the limits within which satisfactory working can be obtained.

The force which it is necessary to apply to cause the continuous discharge of a metal through an extrusion die will obviously be affected by a variety of circumstances. Primarily there will be involved the nature of the metal concerned and the manner in which its properties are influenced by the temperature and the speed at which the work is carried out. Besides these, there must enter into account the amount of deformation involved, as an index of which can be taken the dimensions of the billet in relation to those of the section which is being produced. Additional factors are the shape of the section and the design of the die used in forming it. While the problem is thus one of considerable complexity, the derivation of systematic data from which it can be studied is rendered very difficult, under industrial conditions. For apart from the cost which is involved and the need to avoid interference with production programmes, there is also the fact that these conditions, especially as regards temperature, but also in other respects, are usually insufficiently constant to allow of accurate mensuration.

Just as in the study of flow phenomena, the resort to experiment with suitable apparatus has provided a means of overcoming some of the practical obstacles, and, by breaking down the problem and examining the variables independently, some light has been cast on the fundamental aspects of the process. Such studies have, of course, their limitations and it is necessary to exercise caution and to avoid a too literal interpretation in seeking to apply the results, since the dissociation of the various factors necessitates experimental procedure which departs from ordinary practice. Nevertheless, there are many points at which a direct comparison between the experimental work and its practical counterpart can be made, and at these a remarkably high measure of agreement is obtained.

Tammann[1] appears to have been the first to attempt to ascertain what pressures are required in extrusion. In his apparatus, the metal to be examined was placed in a cylinder closed at one end, and a ram of smaller diameter than the cylinder bore was forced into the open end so as to cause the metal to flow out through the annular space between the two. The principle is therefore essentially that of inverted extrusion. Several metals were examined at different temperatures, though the effect on the egress velocity of only two pressures was measured in each case. Among his main conclusions were that, for constant pressure and temperature, the rate of extrusion is uniform, and that, for a given pressure, an increase of $10°$ C. nearly doubled the rate of flow through the same aperture, although as the melting-point was approached, the increase was found to be somewhat greater. He placed the metals which he used in order of decreasing ease of extrusion as follows K, Na, Pb, Tl, Sn, Bi, Cd, Zn, Sb. Portevin,[2] working mainly with magnesium alloys, concluded that for a metal under given conditions, the speed and pressure of extrusion form only one variable, the one determining the other.

The important series of investigations into processes involving plastic deformation pursued at the K.W. Inst. für Eisenforschung of which a review has been given by Körber,[3] and at the K.W. Inst. für Metall-Forschung under Sachs, have gone a long way in elucidating many of the problems encountered in the working of

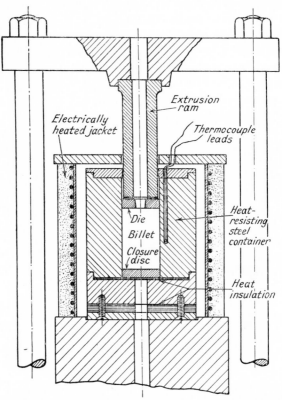

FIG. 129.—An apparatus for experimental extrusion adaptable for the direct or inverted method.

metals. As part of these researches Siebel and Fangemeier,[4] and Sachs and Eisbein[5] studied the extrusion process, using the metals lead and tin at the ordinary temperature. The latter, in particular, took account of a large number of relevant factors, and also extended their work to cover some aspects of the extrusion of copper and brass on an industrial scale. Using a heated press,

Pearson and Smythe[6] examined the relation between extrusion pressure and speed, and the influence of temperature for a number of soft metals. The former has done the same for certain aluminium alloys.[7] The diagram shown in Fig. 129 provides an example of an apparatus for extrusion which has been found very suitable for small-scale experiment, and which is convertible for either direct or inverted working. In order to conduct an extrusion at a predetermined temperature the whole of the press body, which is made from special heat-resisting steel, is enclosed inside an electrically heated jacket, by which means temperatures up to 600° C. can be uniformly maintained. With this apparatus, the power for operation is obtained from a single lever hydraulic testing machine arranged for compression. In working, it is possible, alternatively, to fix the load and measure the speed of extrusion by observation of the rate at which the ram enters the container, or, to ascertain the load required to maintain a selected rate of extrusion. Unless specifically mentioned all speeds of extrusion referred to below are measured at the ram, and are not the efflux velocities, which are, of course, dependent also on the reduction which is being effected. Pressures are quoted in tons per square inch on the extrusion ram.

Extrusion-Pressure Curves

By making observations in an apparatus of this kind of the pressure changes which take place during the extrusion of a billet at a predetermined rate, and with the metal in a uniformly heated condition, curves such as are shown in Fig. 130 are

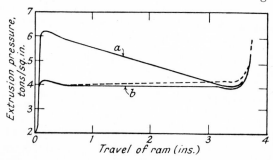

FIG. 130.—Pressure curves for the extrusion of aluminium by direct (a) and inverted (b) methods to rod, involving a reduction of 90 per cent; ram speed 0·2 in./min. Temperature held at 450° C.

obtained. Of these, (*a*) represents the direct method of extrusion, and is a typical pressure record for the case where a dry unlubricated container is used; it corresponds therefore with flow of the type B in the preceding chapter. The pressure rises sharply while the billet is being compressed to fill out the container, and is at a maximum as extrusion starts. As the stroke continues, the pressure falls progressively until, when only a thin disc of the billet is left, it increases rapidly again due to the increasing resistance to the radial inflow of this residue to the die aperture. The difference between the maximum and minimum pressures can be attributed to the force which is required in moving the billet through the container against the frictional impedance which, as we have seen, has generally to be overcome by severe deformation in the peripheral zone of the billet. The actual pressure which has to be exerted on the ram at any moment is therefore not only that which is required to bring about the deformation at the die, which is the real pressure of extrusion, but is greater by an amount which depends on the residual length of the billet, and only falls to the true extrusion pressure as this length approaches zero. It is easily seen that the maximum pressure will vary also according to the amount of friction between the billet and the container: when the latter is smooth and adequately lubricated, so that the flow follows type A, the initial pressure is very little greater than that towards the end of the extrusion.

For the case of inverted extrusion, in which the billet has not to be displaced relatively to the container, the pressure curve, (*b*) has a different form. Deformation inside the billet is now confined entirely to a zone in the neighbourhood of the die entry, and the pressure recorded is solely that required to induce it to flow through the die. Once, therefore, the zone of deformation has been created at the beginning the pressure remains substantially constant throughout the operation until the end of the billet is approached.* The value of this steady pressure cor-

* As indicated by the broken curve in Fig. 130, the pressure in inverted extrusion frequently rises slightly as extrusion proceeds, the increase being usually not more than 5 per cent. This is brought about by metal becoming interposed between the die and the container and obstructing the movement of the former.

responds very well, as might be expected, with the minimum value in the direct method. Where figures for the extrusion pressure are given in succeeding pages they refer either to the constant pressure in the inverted, or the equivalent minimum pressure in the direct process.

The start of the formation of a hollow funnel in the middle of the base of the billet (Fig. 102) is usually marked on the pressure record by a drop in pressure just before the sudden rise which results from the increasing resistance to radial inflow of the thin disc. This is particularly apparent in curve (b) of Fig. 130, and is due to the fact that the pressure pad is no longer supporting the middle of the base of the billet.

The Degree of Deformation

The extent of the deformation which is entailed in an extrusion operation must obviously be one of the decisive factors in regard to the force which it is necessary to apply. The deformation is ordinarily given in terms of the percentage reduction based on the cross-sectional areas of the container and the die aperture, $\dfrac{A - a}{A}$. 100. The term 'extrusion ratio', taken from the ratio $\left(\dfrac{A}{a}\right)$ of the above areas, is also frequently referred to. The question of how the pressure of extrusion is affected by the reduction can be approached by observing the pressure to cause extrusion at a predetermined rate through a series of dies of different size but otherwise of standard form. This has been done by several workers[8, 9, 10] using for the most part flat dies having a constant bearing length. The results of experiments on lead at the ordinary temperature using the inverted method, and with the ram advanced at 0·1 in. per minute, are given in Table 3, and a similar series for brass, at a much higher rate, in Table 4.

From the graph, Fig. 131, plotted from these data, it is seen that the pressure increases rather slowly to begin with until the reduction is about 90 per cent, after that it shows an increasingly sharp rise, especially when it exceeds 97 per cent. This brings out very clearly the greater difficulty that there is in extruding

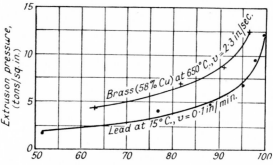

FIG. 131.—The extrusion pressure in dependence on the degree of deformation.

very small sizes from a large diameter billet, and emphasizes the need, in case of the stiffer metals, for using a container of suitable size in relation to the section which is to be made. With the more easily extrudable metals reductions are frequently given which exceed 99 per cent. On the other hand, the reduction on some of the harder materials can not be taken beyond about 95 per cent, corresponding to an extrusion ratio of 20.

TABLE 3

THE EXTRUSION PRESSURE IN RELATION TO THE DEGREE OF REDUCTION FOR LEAD AT 15° C.

Inverted Method. $v = $ o·1 in. per minute.   Flat-faced die

Reduction by Extrusion per cent $\left(\dfrac{A-a}{A}.100\right)$	Extrusion Ratio $\left(\dfrac{A}{a}\right)$	Extrusion Pressure tons/sq. in.	$\log_e \dfrac{A}{a}$	βY tons/sq. in. (vide p. 202)
99·1	112	13·0	4·71	2·53
98·2	55·6	10·25	4·02	2·34
95·0	20·0	7·25	2·99	2·22
88·2	8·5	5·25	2·13	2·30
81·0	5·3	4·2	1·67	2·31
52·4	2·1	1·9	0·73	2·42

Sachs and Eisbein have shown that if the extrusion pressure is plotted against the logarithm of the ratio $\dfrac{A}{a}$, straight lines are

TABLE 4

THE EXTRUSION PRESSURE FOR DIFFERENT REDUCTIONS (Sachs and Eisbein)
Brass (58 per cent Cu; 2·7 per cent Pb). Direct Extrusion from
1000-ton Press

Diameter of Billet in.	Diameter of Rod in.	Reduction per cent $\frac{A-a}{A}.100$	Extrusion Ratio $\frac{A}{a}$	Extrusion Pressure tons/sq. in.		Mean Temper- ature ° C.	Ram Speed in./sec.
				Initial	Minimum		
7·25	1·22	96·6	28·2	17·7	12·5	640	2·3
7·25	2·05	90·7	10·7	15·5	8·3	640	2·3
7·25	2·8	82·2	5·6	14·2	6·4	650	2·6
7·25	4·0	63·8	2·8	12·3	3·9	660	2·9

obtained which pass through the origin (Fig. 132), indicating a
relation given by

$$P = c.\log\frac{A}{a} \qquad . \qquad . \qquad . \qquad . \qquad (1)$$

in which ' c ' is a constant involving the resistance to deformation
of the metal.

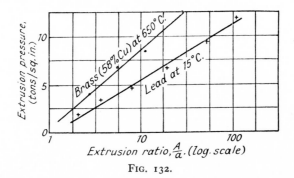

FIG. 132.

The Influence of Speed on the Extrusion Pressure

The extrusion process is significantly affected in several ways
by the speed at which it is conducted. For the moment we shall
be concerned only with the bearing which this has on the pressure
requirements. The rates used in extruding metals vary a good
deal, and although there are reasons for this which are not

187

governed by the pressure requirements, it is nevertheless a matter of decided interest which calls for examination.

TABLE 5

Extrusion Pressure tons/sq. in.	Corresponding Speed of Extrusion
0·60	1
0·69	1·8
0·92	10
1·15	35
1·38	86
1·60	175

The data in the above table are derived from tests in which lead billets kept in a heated press at 200° C. were subjected to extrusion by the inverted method under constant loads, and the uniform rates at which the ram moved into the container were measured. Similar results have been obtained in numerous experiments at other temperatures and using several of the soft metals. Summarizing those for lead only, which are typical of the remainder, it is found that to bring about a tenfold increase in speed, the pressure has to be increased as follows: at 17° C. by 36 per cent: at 100° C. by 44 per cent: at 166° C. by 50 per cent: and at 325° C. by 55 per cent.

When we come to consider how the pressure is affected when, say, brass is extruded under technical conditions, at different rates, the matter is complicated by a factor, namely the cooling of the billet, the extent of which is greater the lower the rate of extrusion and the hotter the billet in relation to the press container. Thus, the pressure curve taken in direct extrusion is similar to the experimental curve (a) in Fig. 130, only when extrusion is completed in a matter of 3 to 4 seconds, so that hardly any loss of heat occurs; at lower rates the pressure shows less fall during the working stroke, and it may, in fact, be found to rise as a result of the increasing stiffness of the cooling metal. Evidence of this is afforded by the records made by Sachs and Eisbein which are reproduced in Fig. 133. The upper set refers to brass billets inserted at 650° C. into a container well warmed from previous working, and for these it may be seen that the pressure at the beginning is higher the greater the rate used, but that because of the greater opportunity for cooling at the lower speeds, the final pressures approach the same value for all of them. The lower graph was obtained when the container was comparatively cold, with the result that the more slowly extruded billets became severely chilled, and that the final pressures of this series are in the reverse order to what they were to begin with. It was obviously useless to compare the final pressures in order to assess the effect of extrusion speed, and they had to be content to do so therefore by comparing the initial pressures for billets which were all of equal length, concluding therefrom that to

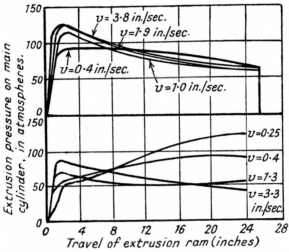

Fig. 133.—Pressure records taken during the extrusion of brass billets.

increase the speed of extrusion by ten times the pressure at 650° C. and 700° C. must be raised by 30 and 60 per cent respectively. The extremes of speed normally used on brass presses can be taken as being certainly not less than 0·5 in. per second, or more than 5 in. per second, and are generally well within these limits, and it would seem therefore that, leaving aside its consequential effect on the cooling of the metal, the rate at which extrusion is conducted has, *per se*, only a moderate effect on the pressure which is required.

There are ample experimental data relating to the soft metals from which to derive an expression for speed and pressure of extrusion. When values for these are plotted logarithmically the points fall on a series of straight lines according to the temperatures at which they were determined, their relationship being given by:

$$v = b \, P^a \qquad . \qquad . \qquad . \qquad . \qquad . \qquad (2)$$

in which a and b are constants for any temperature. The index a, giving the increase in the rate of extrusion with increasing pressure, shows little variation in the higher range of temperatures,

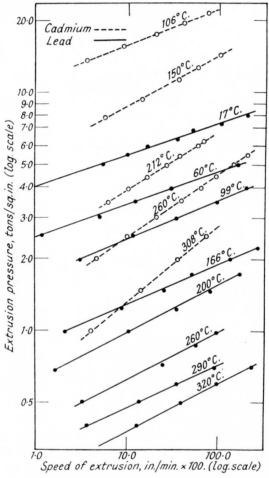

Fig. 134.—The relation between the speed and pressure of extrusion.

as may be seen in Fig. 134, from the fact that the lines are approximately parallel, but at lower temperatures *a* increases in value, and the lines incline more steeply to the pressure axis. In explanation of this, it can be suggested that at low temperatures a certain threshold pressure has to be exceeded before continuous flow can occur. Thus a given percentage increase in the pressure will produce a greater effect on the speed than it does at high temperatures where the limiting pressure for flow is very low or no longer exists. The mean value of the index for several metals in the high ranges where it continues to be fairly constant are as follows:

Lead	(200°–325° C.)	.	.	.	5·2
Tin	(100°–220° C.)	.	.	.	5·3
Cadmium	(200°–300° C.)	.		.	3·5
Bismuth	(100°–250° C.)	.	.	.	8·3

These high values bear out the observation made above for lead and brass that variations in speed of the order usual in practice have, in themselves, a rather minor influence on the pressure for extrusion.

The Influence of Temperature

The temperature of extrusion, like speed, has implications in the process other than its effect on the pressure, but these can be left aside for the time being. The essential features of all hot-working processes are that the work should be carried out in a range of temperature in which the metal has sufficient plasticity to allow the shaping process, usually severe, to be conducted with the power which is available; a range, too, in which the effects of the deformation are dissipated rapidly enough to prevent the resistance of the material from being affected, at all events to any serious extent, by work-hardening such as occurs at lower temperatures. It is an almost invariable rule that the resistance to deformation of metals and alloys falls off as the temperature is raised and tends often to become very small as the melting-point is approached, though there are considerable differences both in the rate at which this change occurs and in the ultimate degree of softness which is attained. By taking advantage of this increasing softness working operations can be made easier, but a limit to the temperature which it is possible to employ is reached owing to the loss of cohesive strength which ultimately leads in all materials to intergranular disintegration. The temperature at which hot shortness sets in depends not only on the particular metal, but also on the nature of the deforming process, and can also be influenced by the rate of deformation. Some forming processes lead more readily than others to hot failure, according to the kind and intensity of the stresses to which they give rise. It happens that the forces in extrusion are predominantly compressive, thus permitting rather higher working temperatures than are possible in rolling or forging. All the same differential stresses are present in metal as it leaves the die, due to unequal flow throughout the section, and these are greater the more intricate the shape, so that hot tears and cracks develop at lower temperatures than with products of simpler form. So far as the metals themselves are concerned, hot shortness does not generally appear in pure metals until they are close to their melting points, but the presence of a small amount of a more fusible phase, due in some cases to particular impurities, or in alloys, to a small amount of a eutectic constituent which causes a long freezing range, leads to its earlier incidence and often has the result of seriously restricting the range in which work can be performed, confining it to one in which the general matrix of the alloy is still very stiff. Where this occurs the difficulties of working are greatly enhanced. Thus the hot-working range of a metal can be regarded as lying between limits set by hot shortness on the one hand and by growing stiffness at low temperature on the other, and to assess its capacity for undergoing a particular shaping operation it is important to know the resistance of the material and the effect on it of temperature, and also its ability to hold together without rupture. There are several ways of determining the resistance to deformation of metals in the cold, as by hardness, tensile and compression tests, some of which can be made applicable to show its variation in the high temperature ranges. These, however, do not cover the second point. Tests have also been introduced to measure the forgeability of metals at different temperatures, both as regards the power which is required and the liability to failure by cracking, but these, especially as regards the latter, do not form a reliable guide to the extrusion characteristics. All the same, qualitative data derived in this way afford an interesting comparison with the relative behaviour of metals in their extrusion. For instance, Doerinckel and Trockels,[11] and Genders,[12] whose results are reproduced together in Fig. 135, have examined the properties of different brasses in hot forging trials. Their results give numerical expression to differences which are already well recognized in the extrusion of these alloys. Undoubtedly the effect of temperature on the behaviour in extrusion can best be determined under actual conditions of extrusion, indeed the process lends itself rather well to this in an experimental sense in those cases where the temperature of the metal under test can be maintained during the trial, and where other causes of pressure fluctuation can be excluded. In Fig. 136 are shown the results of experiments in which the extrusion pressures required to maintain a particular rate of flow through a standard die orifice, at different temperatures, was measured. It will be seen that the general temperature-plasticity relationship is the same in each case, though the rate at which the stiffness increases with reduced extrusion temperature differs considerably. Using similar data Schishokin[13] has derived the formula

$$P = A \cdot e^{-\lambda T} \qquad . \qquad . \qquad . \qquad . \quad (3)$$

where T is the temperature of extrusion and λ is a coefficient for the metal. This formula has been confirmed by Pearson in working with aluminium alloys for which λ had the following values

Aluminium (99·5 per cent)	.	.	0·0082
2·5 per cent Cu-Al alloy .	.	.	0·0064
5·0 per cent Cu-Al alloy .	.	.	0·0064
5·0 per cent Zn-Al alloy .	.	.	0·0078
11 per cent Zn, 1·3 per cent Cu	.		0·0068
rem. Al			

Similar temperature-plasticity curves for technical alloys would be of great interest since those above do no more than indicate the general relationship which may be expected. Experimental difficulties preclude this at present in the case of copper alloys, but a comparison of the relative extrusion properties of some high-strength light alloys is shown in Fig. 137. One of the advantages of examining metals thus by actual extrusion is that it also affords

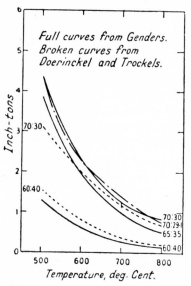

FIG. 135.—The work required in forging various brasses.

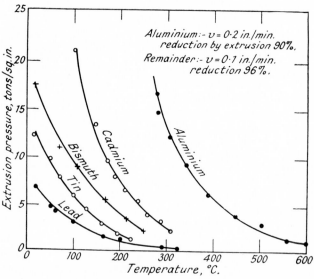

FIG. 136.—The effect of temperatures on the pressure of extrusion.

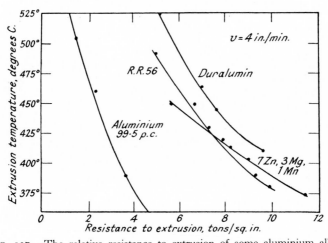

FIG. 137.—The relative resistance to extrusion of some aluminium alloys.

some evidence of the practicable limits such as are caused by hot shortness.

An interesting correlation of data such as that given in the preceding pages, with values calculated by the methods outlined in Chapter VII has been given by Hirst and Ursell.[14]   For lubricated extrusion they define the maximum possible extrusion ratio as a function of preheat temperature for a given pressure, according to an equation similar to that developed in Chapter VII. The extrusion ratio is also limited at any given preheat temperature due to the heat generated by the deformation (see page 248), and this too may be derived from a knowledge of the extrusion conditions and certain properties of the billet material. These two limiting conditions serve to define an area in which extrusion is likely for a given set of press conditions.   The authors show that there is reasonable agreement between the predicted and observed limitations of extrusion for a high-strength aluminium alloy.

Pressure and Die Shape

It has been indicated already that while the majority of extrusion dies used for round bars are of the plain cylindrical type without lead-in, and with sharp or only slightly radiused edges to the aperture, various other shapes are also used. These special forms usually serve some definite object such as controlling the flow of the metal, securing better surface finish on the extruded stock or the avoidance of cracking. There is some evidence that metals which are sensitive in respect of the speed at which they are extruded can be taken at higher speed through suitably shaped dies. This is a matter which could probably be profitably examined more fully. How the pressure of extrusion is affected (in the case of different technical alloys) by die shape is an interesting question to which there is frequent reference in the literature,

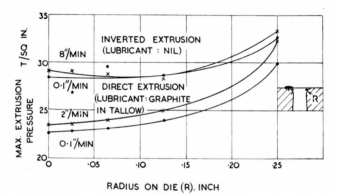

FIG. 138.—Effect of die radius on maximum extrusion pressure for extrusion of super-pure aluminium at different speeds.
(*Johnson, British Iron and Steel Research Association.*)

though not as a rule in very precise terms. A considerable amount of experimental work on it has been done, mostly on lead and tin.

For dies with a radiused lead-in, Siebel found that for lead at room temperature, increasing radii gave a progressive reduction in extrusion pressure, amounting finally, with a very large fillet, to about 10 per cent. This is contrary to the general experience. Sachs and Eisbein recorded, also with lead, a pressure increased by 15–20 per cent over that for a sharp-edged die. In trials at high temperature with several soft metals Pearson obtained results which disfavour the use of large radii. Johnson[15] has produced similar evidence from experiments on the extrusion of lead and aluminium at room temperature. Fig. 138, taken from his work, shows that the maximum pressure may be increased by as much as 38 per cent for a die with a radius of 0·25 in. as compared with a sharp-edged die. The effect of a radius on the die produces interesting changes in the shape of the extrusion-pressure curve. Fig. 139 shows that the presence of a radius causes the initial rise of the curve to be more gradual but that, since the radius also increases frictional effects by increasing the area of contact between metal and die, the maximum extrusion pressure eventually rises above that observed with a square die. Johnson also observed the flow patterns of aluminium billets cold extruded through dies of different radii and found that as the die radius

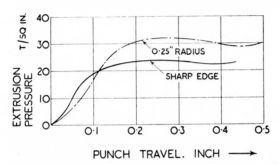

FIG. 139.—Effect of die radius on extrusion pressure curves for direct extrusion of super-pure aluminium.

(*Johnson, British Iron and Steel Research Association.*)

increases the distortion of the metal becomes more uniform with a smaller flow gradient between the metal at the axis and that at the outer surfaces. This will decrease the tendency for end piping but the advantage is outweighed by the increased extrusion pressure. Evidence from technical practice also supports the conclusion that this form of die puts up the pressure. Bernhoeft,[16] for example, gives figures showing that for some brass alloys a radiused die such that $\frac{b}{a} = 2$ (Fig. 140) increased it by 25 per cent, and the same tendency has been observed with aluminium alloys. The slight radiusing adopted in most practice has only a small effect.

On the other hand, there is almost unanimous agreement that from the pressure point of view, an advantage is derived from the

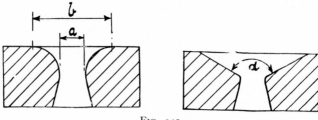

FIG. 140.

use of dies with a conical lead-in. From the reduction in the amount of deformation undergone by metal with dies of increasing conicity, as shown in Fig. 119 also, it might seem that the extrusion pressure would be diminished. Actually the lower force required in the working of the metal as the die angle is reduced tends to be offset by the greater area of the friction surface in the die. That is to say, that reduction in the amount of work expended internally is accompanied by an increase in the external losses at the tool surface. Experiments by Sachs and Eisbein with lead and tin indicate that the best compromise between these opposing factors is reached with a cone angle around 90° at which there is a definite minimum in the pressure, showing a reduction over the flat die of about 30 per cent. Where conical dies are used in practice they are usually of wider angle than this, between 120° and 160°, but even so the general concensus of opinion is that they effect a lowering of pressure in the region of 10–20 per cent. Exceptionally, Löhberg[17] has reported that, for zinc-base alloys, conical dies bring about a slightly increased pressure.

A characteristic of a die which has some influence on the pressure is the length of the cylindrical bearing in the aperture before it is relieved at the back side. This has been referred to earlier as affording a means by which the tendency for unequal flow through an irregularly shaped die can be controlled by varying the bearing length so as to retard flow at some points and accelerate it elsewhere. In extruding cold lead billets through carefully polished dies, Sachs and Eisbein found little difference in pressure with bearing lengths varying in the ratio 15 : 1, but drilled, unpolished, dies showed a difference in pressure of ×2 for the same variation. Considering the extremely wide difference in the bearing length, this change in pressure seems, perhaps, rather small, but the frictional effects in the case quoted may well be dissimilar to those in hot extrusion practice with other metals. There is, for instance, a strong tendency with aluminium alloys for the hot metal to bite on to and adhere strongly to a steel surface. Another point to be remembered in connection with the control of flow in a die is that, as shown above, the rate of extrusion is strongly affected by small changes in pressure, so that quite a small change in bearing length at some point in a die will have a marked influence locally on the rate of flow.

Multiple-hole dies are often used in extruding small sections. It is obvious that the pressure required when several holes are provided will be greatly reduced over that for one hole of the same size. Actually the pressure when using several holes is reduced almost to that for one large hole with a sectional area equal to the sum of the smaller ones. Thus, with lead, a three-hole die called for only 10 per cent, and a four-hole die for 22 per cent, more pressure than a single hole of the same total area.

REFERENCES

[1] G. Tammann. On the Rate of Extrusion of Crystalline Substances. *Ann. Physik.*, 1902, **7**, 198; 1903, **10**, 647.

[2] A. Portevin. Experiments on the Compression and Extrusion of Metals and Alloys at High Temperatures. *Rev. de Metallurgie*, 1929, **26**, 435–43.

[3] F. Korber. The Plastic Deformation of Metals. *J. Inst. Metals*, 1932, **48**, 317–42.

[4] E. Siebel and E. Fangemeier. Researches on Power Consumption in the Extrusion and Punching of Metals. *Mitt. K.W. Inst. für Eisenforschung*, 1931, **13**, 29–43.

[5] G. Sachs and W. Eisbein. Power Consumption and Mechanism of Flow in the Extrusion Process. *Mitt. Material*, **S. 16**, 1931, 67–96.

[6] C. E. Pearson and J. A. Smythe. The Influence of Pressure and Temperature on the Extrusion of Metals. *J. Inst. Metals*, 1931, **45**, 345–69.

[7] C. E. Pearson. *Ibid.*, 1939, **64**, 299–310.

[8] E. Siebel and E. Fangemeier. *Ibid.*

[9] G. Sachs and W. Eisbein. *Ibid.*

[10] V. A. Bobrov. The Relation between Specific Pressure, Temperature and the Elongation Factor (in the Extrusion of Light Metals). *Trans. Sci. Res. Inst. Light Metals—' Nüsalumini '*, 1933 (1 and 2), 63–73; (3), 31–51; 1933 (5), 32–43.

[11] F. Doerinckel and J. Trockels. The Hot Working of Brass. *Z. für Metallkunde*, 1920, **12**, 340.

[12] R. Genders. The Aluminium Brasses. *J. Inst. Metals*, 1930, **43**, 163-80.

[13] W. P. Schishokin. The Extrusion Properties of Metals and Alloys at Different Temperatures. *Zhur. Priklad. Khimii*, 1929, **2**, 663.

[14] S. Hirst and D. H. Ursell. Some Limiting Factors in Extrusion. *Met. Treatment*, 1958, **25**, 409-13, 416.

[15] W. Johnson. B.I.S.R.A. Report, MW/E/55/54.

[16] P. Bernhoeft. The Operation of a Directly-driven 1500-ton Press. *Z. für Metallkunde*, 1932, **24**, 210-13, 261-3.

[17] K. Löhberg. *Ibid.*, 1939, **31**, 279-83.

CHAPTER VII

Theoretical Analysis of Flow in Extrusion

It is clear that it would be of considerable value if the plastic strains which occur in extrusion could be expressed mathematically and in a form which would allow an assessment of the contribution of each of the extrusion variables in terms of the power required to effect the deformation. For certain given conditions of press operation it would then be possible to arrive at the overall optimum conditions of extrusion ratio, temperature and speed, in terms of the properties of the metal to be extruded and the extrusion pressure. The problem has received a considerable amount of attention, particularly in recent years with attempts to apply plain strain theory in place of the semi-empirical approach of the earlier dimensional theories in which homogeneous deformation was assumed, and the field has been reviewed by Bishop.[1]

The work required to be done in deforming a plastic material was deduced by Fink[2] as early as 1874 from observations on the rolling of metals. Siebel[3] has applied the same approach in calculating the force required in carrying out extrusion. The work done, dW, in extruding a bar of length L and of cross-section A by an amount dl is

$$dW = Y.A\,dl$$

where Y = yield stress (assumed constant). With a constant volume $V = A.L$

$$A = \frac{V}{L}$$

and hence

$$dW = Y.V\frac{dl}{L}$$

$$\therefore\ W = Y.V \log_e \frac{l}{L} \qquad .\qquad .\qquad .\quad (1)$$

If the extrusion pressure is P then the work done in extruding is

$$W = P.A.L = P.V$$

$\therefore$ the work per unit volume

$$\frac{W}{V} = P$$

Hence, from (1)
$$P = Y \log_e \frac{l}{L},$$

$$= Y \log_e \frac{A}{a} \qquad . \qquad . \qquad . \qquad . \qquad (2)$$

where a is the cross-section of the extruded rod.

This relationship takes no account of the effect on the extrusion pressure of non-homogeneous flow in extrusion, or of friction at the die surfaces, and can serve therefore only as an approximation. In practice the forces necessary, and the amount of work requiring to be performed in metal-forming processes are always greater than the theoretically calculated values. This is because the deformation which is effective in producing the required change in shape is always accompanied to a greater or less extent by further deformation which contributes nothing to the change and represents an internal loss in the process. As already seen in Chapter V, this supplementary deformation is very extensive in extrusion, where it causes a marked departure from uniformly distributed flow of a parallelepipedial kind. Besides such internal losses, work is also consumed in overcoming friction between the material and the deforming tools.

The usefulness of the theoretical equation can be tested by measuring the values of P for different die sizes and comparing these with the results obtained from calculation according to equation (2). In doing this, using values for Y obtained from compression tests at appropriate speeds of deformation, Sachs showed that the actual values of the extrusion pressure are considerably in excess of those calculated. The extent of the deviation is shown in Fig. 141, from which it is evident that the observed extrusion pressures are about 45 per cent above those calculated. The actual extrusion pressure is therefore given by

$$P = \beta . Y \log_e \frac{A}{a} \qquad . \qquad . \qquad . \qquad . \qquad (3)$$

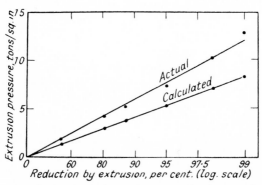

FIG. 141.—The calculated and observed pressures for the extrusion of different sizes of bar.

in which β is a constant which measures the efficiency of the process for a given set of conditions.

i.e.
$$\beta = \frac{P'}{P}$$

where P' is the extrusion pressure in the actual working process.

Equation (3) has some practical value since the efficiency is not likely to vary significantly within any one production unit and a little experience should enable it to be estimated with sufficient accuracy for normal production requirements. If, however, it is required to assess the effect of some considerable departure from normal production the efficiency method may not be applicable and the calculations must be based upon a more accurate model of the process. This will entail allowing for friction, for inhomogeneous deformation and for the fact that Y, the resistance to deformation or yield stress, is not necessarily a constant.

For extrusion by the direct process, on the assumption that the drop in the power required during the extrusion of long billets is ascribable entirely to reduced friction between the billet and the container, the additional force which this entails can be evaluated as follows. If a thin slice of the billet, of thickness dx, is in equilibrium, then

Force on face of slice = Frictional force acting at the cylindrical
nearest the ram   surface of the slice

203

i.e. $$A \cdot dp = 2\pi r \cdot dx \cdot \mu p$$

where p is the pressure, r the radius of the billet and μ the co-efficient of friction between the metals concerned.

$$\therefore \frac{dp}{p} = \frac{2\pi \cdot r}{A} \mu \cdot dx$$

$$= \frac{4}{D} \mu \cdot dx$$

where D is the billet diameter. On integration between O and L, where L is the length of the billet, this gives

$$p = p_0 \cdot e^{\frac{4\mu}{D} L} \qquad . \qquad . \qquad . \qquad . \qquad (4)$$

where p is the maximum pressure, at the beginning of the extrusion, and p_0, the minimum pressure, exerted at the end of the ram stroke. If the curvature of the line joining these two values is small, so that it can be replaced by a straight line of slope represented by the tangent of the exponential curve at the end of the ram travel, then (4) becomes

$$p = p_0\left(1 + \frac{4\mu L}{D}\right) \qquad . \qquad . \qquad . \qquad (5)$$

Somewhat similar expressions have been suggested by Siebel[3] and by Sachs and Eisbein.[4] Siebel gives as the additional force (R) due to friction between billet and container

$$R = \pi \cdot D L \mu \cdot Y \qquad . \qquad . \qquad . \qquad . \qquad (6)$$

where L is the length of the billet at any instant. The total pressure exerted in direct extrusion is then the sum of (2) and (6)

i.e. $$p = Y \log_e \frac{A}{a} + \frac{Y \cdot 4\mu \cdot L}{D} \qquad . \qquad . \qquad . \qquad (7)$$

Sachs and Eisbein have proposed a slightly modified form in

$$p = (P + Y)e^{\frac{4\mu L}{D}} - Y \qquad . \qquad . \qquad . \qquad (8)$$

where P is the extrusion pressure given by equation (2).

The maximum value which μ can have in the above equations is 0·5. This arises from the fact that when the frictional drag reaches a value of 0·5 Y the material will yield in shear, since, adopting Tresca's yield criterion,

$$Y = 2k$$

where k = maximum shear stress. Although it is doubtful whether such high values of μ will be encountered, it seems likely that some shearing will occur near the surface of the billet in industrial extrusion because of the desirability of leaving a skull of metal in the container. However, even when a skull is left in the container, there may be some motion of the surface of the billet relative to the container, as is indicated by the work of Blazey et al.[5] on tube extrusion (see page 171). The relative amounts of sliding and shearing will again depend upon the coefficient of friction, but the general effect will be to cause the pressures estimated from the above equations to be too low.

This also will be the effect of assuming the yield stress to be constant, although two opposing effects will tend to minimize the error introduced from this source. Thus, since recovery from work hardening is a rate process, the speed with which the billet passes through the zone of deformation will determine the extent to which the yield stress recovers to the non-work hardened value and if the extrusion rate is high Y will increase during extrusion. (Recovery may be completed after the material has passed through the die but this will have no effect upon the extrusion.) Opposing this increase is the effect of the increased temperature, which results from the fact that about 90 per cent of the plastic work appears as heat. Where there is evidence of a net change in yield stress during extrusion, Johnson and Collins[6] have shown that the use of an averaged value is satisfactory for practical purposes.

The assumption of homogeneous deformation in the derivation of the previous equations is clearly the most unreasonable of those simplifications which are necessary to yield a model capable of mathematical expression. Sachs and Eisbein have offered a tentative model, based on a die with a conical lead-in, from which to evaluate the contribution of the friction at the die to the total power requirement. With dies of different conicity increasing steepness causes a gradual change in the flow of the metal, which, as seen from Fig. 119, becomes much more nearly uniform across the section. When the die angle is made very small, the problem becomes identical with that for a drawing die. For the case of drawing, it has been possible to devise experimental methods by which all the essential relationships, including the measurement of the internal and friction losses, have been established, with results that have been of great value in assessing the results of variations in drawing technique, and in arriving at the best working conditions in regard to the optimum die angle, etc. Taking the theoretical equation (2), they propose a modification to bring in the friction at the die surface for a conical die on the basis of knowledge derived from drawing, so that the extrusion pressure becomes increased, for a die of angle α to

$$F = Y\left(1 + \frac{\tan \alpha}{\mu}\right)\left[\left(\frac{D}{d}\right)^{\frac{2\mu}{\tan \alpha}} - 1\right]$$

This formula, however, involves assumptions which are only strictly justified when the die angle is very small. Even if it proved possible to allow for the effect of friction at the die when the die angle is large this approach would not be entirely satisfactory, since the lack of uniformity in the deformation is as much a result of the constraint on the flow by the shape of the die as it is a result of friction in this region.

The extrusion pressures calculated from equations (4), (7) and (8) for a given set of conditions will have the smallest value when derived from equation (7) and the largest when derived from (8). Since it is clear from the above that each of these estimates is likely to be low when compared with the pressures measured under industrial conditions, it is to be expected that equation (8) is likely to be the most satisfactory and Zholobov[7] has shown this to be the case. The greatest difficulty which he found was in regard to the coefficients of friction, the previously assigned values for which were unsuitable. This is not to be wondered at, for as shown earlier, the displacement of a billet through the container does not involve a straightforward friction problem, and in any case, a good deal must depend on the surface condition of the container. However, by substituting values for μ as follows

$1000°-900°$ C. $= 0·10-0·15$: $900°-800°$ C. $= 0·15-0·18$ for copper; and $850°-725°$ C. $= 0·15-0·18$: $725°-650°$ C. $= 0·18-0·20$ for brass

and taking the true resistance to deformation (Y), from compression tests, as being

Temp. °C. . . .	900°	850°	800°	750°	700°	650°
Copper Y
(tons/sq. in.) . .	0·95/1·14	1·27/1·4	1·46/1·6	1·9/2·2	—	—
Brass (58/42) Y
(tons/sq. in.) . .	—	—	—	0·8/0·9	0·9/0·95	1·0/1·14

he obtained results of which a selection taken at random is shown in Table 6. It will be seen that, with these various adjustments, it is possible to obtain a fair measure of agreement between the observed and derived extrusion pressures.

Plane Strain Theories

The appearance of Luders lines in annealed mild steel test pieces stretched slightly beyond the yield-point is well known, as is the fact that with uniaxial tension they are inclined at about 45° to the axis of the specimen. This relationship to the direction of stressing is due to the fact that they are the traces of the surfaces of maximum shear stress along which there is relative movement of the adjacent material. With more complex stress systems imposed they still appear, as is apparent from Fig. 142, which

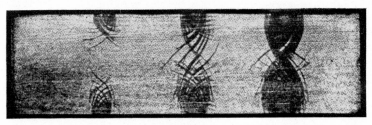

FIG. 142.—Luders lines in a mild steel bar pressed on both sides with narrow faced tools.
(*Körber, 'J. Inst. Metals'.*)

shows the distribution of Luders lines in a prismatic test-piece which has been pressed on both sides beyond the yield point by means of narrow-faced tools. The symmetry of the flow lines is clear, as also is the fact that the deformation extends deeper into the metal as the pressure is increased, i.e. the slip lines define the shape of the plastic region for a given stress system.

Two families of slip lines (labelled α and β) are usually observed, emanating from opposite corners of the same tool in the case shown in Fig. 142. The laws governing the properties of these slip-line families were derived by Hencky[8] (stress equations) and

TABLE 6

Dimensions of Billet		Extruded Bar or Tube Diameter in.	Extrusion Ratio $\frac{A}{a}$	Speed of Extrusion in./sec.	Extrusion Temperature °C.	Observed Maximum Extrusion Pressure tons/sq. in.	From Equation (8) using Corrected Values of μ		Calculated Extrusion Pressure tons/sq. in.
Diameter in.	Length in.						μ	k	
Copper									
7·1	15	2·75	6·6	0·8	850°	**13·2**	0·16	1·4	**14·2**
7·1	21·5	2·36	9·0	1·1	860°	**26·3**	0·15	1·27	**21·0**
10·0	15·8	3·0	11·0	1·4	760°	**31·0**	0·21	2·2	**30·5**
16·0	21·5	8·3 × 9·0	17·5	0·4	910°	**18·4**	0·14	1·15	**21·0**
7·1	14·8	1·58 × 2·15	22·0	2·0	880°	**23·6**	0·15	1·27	**27·5**
7·1	14·0	2·36 × 2·68	28·8	3·0	860°	**33·7**	0·15	1·27	**34·5**
7·1	14·0	1·75 × 2·1	38·0	2·0	850°	**39·0**	0·16	1·4	**38·2**
58/42 Brass									
16·0	21·5	7·1	5·1	0·4	725°	**11·2**	0·18	0·89	**6·2**
12·0	18·5	5·5 × 7·0	6·8	1·2	730°	**15·0**	0·18	0·89	**17·9**
16·0	25·0	4·5 × 7·0	7·9	0·6	730°	**12·7**	0·18	0·89	**13·2**
12·0	20·5	3·75 × 5·0	13·0	1·2	720°	**14·3**	0·18	0·89	**18·9**
7·1	13·0	1·6 × 2·25	18·7	3·0	700°	**27·5**	0·20	0·95	**25·4**
7·1	14·0	2·0 × 2·28	35·5	2·0	730°	**40·6**	0·18	0·89	**31·6**

Geiringer[9] (velocity equations), the former expressing the variation of stress and the latter the variation of the velocity components along the slip lines; they are strictly applicable only in the case of plane strain, i.e. when the flow occurs in parallel planes without a normal component. Fig. 143 shows a system

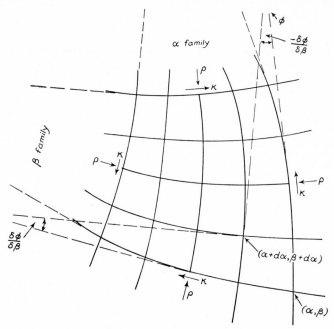

FIG. 143.—Slip-line system for compressive stress p.

of slip lines associated with a mean compressive stress p and shear stress K, in which case Hencky's equations are:

$$p + 2K\phi = \text{constant along an } \alpha \text{ slip-line}$$
$$p - 2K\phi = \text{constant along a } \beta \text{ slip-line} \qquad \cdot \qquad (9)$$

the significance of which is that the variation of p along a slip-line is simply related to the angle turned through by the slip-line. The analogous velocity equations of Geiringer are

$$du - vd\phi = 0 \text{ along an } \alpha \text{ slip-line}$$
$$dv - ud\phi = 0 \text{ along a } \beta \text{ slip-line} \qquad \cdot \qquad (10)$$

where u and v are the velocity components referred, at any point, to the directions of the α and β slip-lines respectively. These enable the directions of flow to be determined relative to the motion of the die or ram in extrusion.

If this slip-line pattern is known the stress and velocity equations can be readily applied in determining the pressure and direction of flow. Since it will not usually be possible to determine this pattern experimentally (its appearance in the form of Luders lines is peculiar to the cold working of mild steel) it will be necessary to use other methods and these will generally involve trial and error until a solution is found which simultaneously

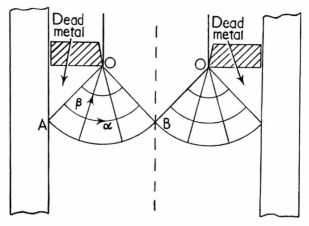

FIG. 144.—Inverted extrusion with 50 per cent reduction, showing slip-line field and plastic region.

(*Hill, 'J. Iron and Steel Inst.'.*)

satisfies the stress and velocity equations. This and other aspects of slip-line theory have been discussed fully by Hill,[10] to whom the following example[11] is due.

The slip-line field and plastic region for inverted extrusion involving a 50 per cent reduction in area and the use of a square die are shown in Fig. 144. The corners of the die at O will be stress singularities and the β slip-lines will be radii through these points, which will be foci for the α slip-lines in the form of concentric circular arcs. In inverted extrusion there is no relative motion of the undeformed billet to the container and therefore no friction between them, so that the slip-line at A will make an angle of 45° to the wall. For reasons of symmetry the slip-lines will also intersect the central axis at B at 45°. OAB is, therefore, one-half of the plastic region and OA is the boundary of the dead metal zone. The remaining boundary conditions which must be satisfied if this slip-line field is correct concern velocities. On OA the normal component of velocity must be zero; across AB and OB the normal components of velocity must be compatible with the rigid motions of the undeformed billet and extruded material respectively. It is easily shown from (10) that with the slip-line field of Fig. 144 the speed of extrusion from the die is twice the rate at which the die moves relative to the container which, since the calculation is for a 50 per cent reduction, is clearly correct and can be taken as indicating that the slip-line field satisfies the velocity equations.

The stresses are determined from equations (9), from the second of which it can be seen that p is constant along each radius and equal to k on OB. On OA, integration of the first relation gives

$$p = k(1 + \pi)$$

The total force on the die per unit width normal to the plane is

$$k(2 + \pi) \times \text{die width}$$

assuming there is no friction between the dead metal and the container wall. The extrusion pressure, P, defined as extrusion force/area of billet, is then

$$P = k\left(1 + \frac{\pi}{2}\right)$$
$$= 1 \cdot 28 \times 2k$$
$$= 1 \cdot 28 \ Y \quad . \qquad . \qquad . \qquad . \quad (11)$$

If this result is compared with that derived from equation (2), which assumes homogeneous deformation, then for a 50 per cent reduction

$$P = Y \log_e 2$$
$$= 0 \cdot 7 \ Y$$

which is less than (11) by about 45 per cent, the extent of the deviation observed in Fig. 116.

Hill[11] has calculated also the deformation of a square grid ruled on a cross-section of the original billet for a 50 per cent reduction. Purchase and Tupper[12] have compared this result with one they obtained in a plane-strain extrusion with a 46·7 per cent reduction, the two being compared in Fig. 145. The

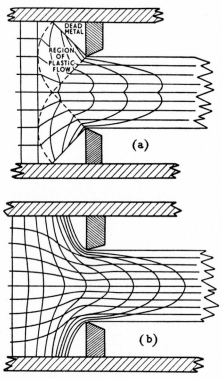

FIG. 145.—Comparison of flow patterns for plane strain extrusion.
(a) Theoretical solution—50 per cent reduction.
(b) Experimental—46·7 per cent reduction.
(*Purchase and Tupper, 'J. Mech. Phys. Solids'.*)

extent of the correspondence is quite reasonable, as also is that when the comparison is made with grids inscribed on cylindrical billets, as in Chapter V. A feature of the deformed grid calculated from slip-line theory which is not shown in experimental results is the kink near the central axis.

The analysis has been extended[13] to reductions other than 50 per cent, where the slip-line fields, shown in Fig. 146, are slightly

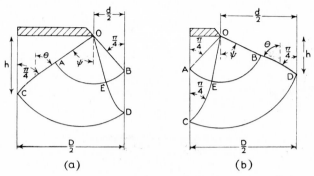

FIG. 146.—Slip-line fields for (a) greater than 50 per cent, (b) less than 50 per cent reduction in inverted extrusion.

(*By permission of the Controller of H.M. Stationery Office.*)

different from that for an extrusion ratio of 2. For reductions under 50 per cent

$$P = k\left(1 - \frac{d}{D}\right)\left(1 + \frac{\pi}{2} + 4\psi + \frac{2h}{d} - \frac{4\int\theta\sin\theta\ ds}{d}\right) \quad (12)$$

where D and d are the initial and final widths of the billet and h the depth which the deformed zone extends into the billet at the axis from the plane of the die. θ is the angle between the tangent at any point on BD and the axis and ψ is the constant value of θ along OB. It is apparent from Fig. 146 (*a*) that ψ must be less than $\pi/2$ so that a lower limit is set to d/D corresponding to a reduction in area of about 8 per cent.

For the case of a reduction in excess of 50 per cent, integration is carried out on OAC (Fig. 146 (*b*)), so that θ is the angle between the tangent at any point on AC and the axis and ψ is the constant value of θ along OA; h is the depth of C below the plane of the die. The extrusion pressure is then

$$P = k\left(1 - \frac{d}{D}\right)\left(1 + \frac{\pi}{2} + 4\psi + \frac{2h}{D - d} - \frac{4\int\theta\sin\theta\ ds}{D - d}\right) \quad (13)$$

In this case there is an upper limit upon the reduction since ψ will again be less than $\pi/2$. Equation (13), together with the addition of an expression representing the friction between the billet and wall (see page 204), will give the pressure for direct extrusion through a square die.

The results given by equations (12) and (13) are, of course, equal to that given by (11) for a reduction of 50 per cent. Purchase and Tupper[12] have compared the values given by these equations with those determined in the plane-strain extrusion of lead and, if the von Mises criterion of flow is adopted ($Y = \sqrt{3}.k$), the results are remarkably consistent, as shown in Fig. 147.

The solutions given above are strictly only applicable to plane-strain, no solutions existing for axisymmetric extrusion where the hyperbolic relationships of the plane-strain case are no longer applicable. It is somewhat surprising therefore to find such a

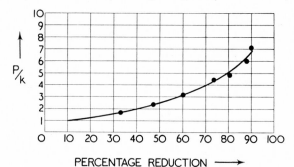

FIG. 147.—Comparison of theory and experiment in plane strain extrusion with various reductions.

(*Purchase and Tupper, 'J. Mech. Phys. Solids'.*)

high degree of correspondence between the predictions of plane-strain theory and experimental observations made under axisymmetric conditions. The similarity between the distorted grids predicted by Hill on the one hand and observed with cylindrical billets on the other has already been mentioned, but probably even more remarkable is the observation made by Purchase and Tupper[12] that the extrusion pressure in inverted extrusion is the same for equivalent reductions whether observed under axisymmetric or plane-strain conditions. Using the results of Table 3 (page 186) they have produced Fig. 148, from which it may be deduced that, even though unexpected mathematically, plane strain theory gives a reasonable representation of the conditions which exist in axisymmetric extrusion.

Johnson[14] has extended the analyses of Hill to include larger

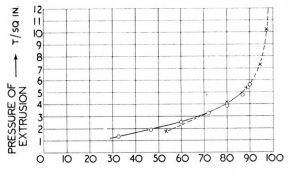

FIG. 148.—Comparison of extrusion pressures for plane strain and axisymmetric extrusion.

(O—Purchase and Tupper, plane strain; X—Pearson, axisymmetric.)

(*Purchase and Tupper, ' J. Mech. Phys. Solids '.*)

reductions and also the effects of friction at the die and container wall in direct extrusion. He finds that the curves calculated from plane-strain theory may be expressed empirically in the form

$$p/2k = a + b \log_e \frac{1}{1 - r} \qquad . \qquad . \qquad . \quad (14)$$

where a and b are constants and r is the reduction. Hill[13] has indicated that the equation to the curve shown in Fig. 147 is similar to (14) and for large reductions may be represented by

$$p = 1 \cdot 45 \, Y \log_e \frac{D}{d} \text{ for plane strain}$$

$$= 1 \cdot 45 \, Y \log_e \frac{A}{a} \text{ for axisymmetric strain}$$

This also is the form of equation (3) and when this is applied to the results shown in Fig. 141 the value obtained for β is precisely 1·45.

Johnson[15, 16] has given a solution to the problem of direct extrusion through a smooth wedge-shaped die over a range of reductions for plane-strain conditions, a problem also considered by Hill.[11] The result depends upon the conditions of friction existing at the die face and upon the semi-angle of the die, these factors determining whether the metal slides over the die face

P

or forms a dead metal zone for a particular reduction. Johnson[15] has analysed these two conditions and when the metal slips along the die the variation of the extrusion pressure/yield stress ($= 2k$) with reduction for various die angles is as shown in Fig. 149. The lowest curve is that for homogeneous deformation, given by equation (2), and the upper curve is that for a square die ($\alpha = 90°$). It will be seen that, for a given reduction, the extrusion pressure is reduced with a die having a conical lead-in, in agreement with the observations made in Chapter VI, but that the extent of any power saving resulting from the use of such dies will be reduced

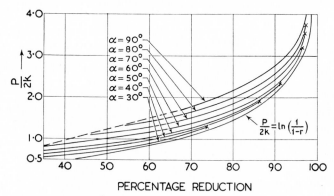

FIG. 149.—Extrusion pressures for various reductions through smooth conical dies of various semi-angles α.

(*Johnson*, ' *J. Mech. Phys. Solids* '.)

as the reduction is increased. When a dead metal zone forms on the die face the slip-line field is somewhat different from that for slipping along the die. Fig. 150 shows the predicted variation for extrusion pressure/yield stress against reduction for a square die when a dead metal zone is present, curve *AB* representing a lower limit for frictionless extrusion and curve *DC* an upper limit, corresponding to the slip-lines meeting the container wall at 45° for *AB* and 0° and 90° for *DC*. There is no reason why dead metal zones should be uniquely associated with square dies, and in fact it has been shown[17] that such zones are nearly always associated with 90° and 75° dies while slip occurs over the die face with 30° dies. Curves similar to those shown in Fig. 150 may be determined for die angles other than 90°, and in a further

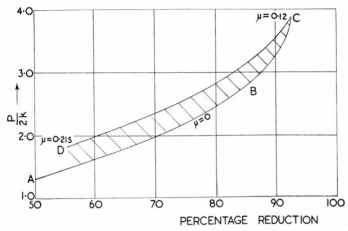

FIG. 150.—Extrusion pressures for various reductions when dead metal zone forms on die face.

(*Johnson, British Iron and Steel Research Association.*)

publication[18] Johnson compares these with the results of experiments carried out under plane strain conditions. Typical of the results obtained are those shown in Fig. 151, which refers to the

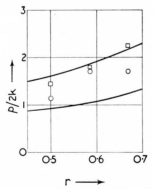

FIG. 151.—Extrusion pressures for lead reduced varying amounts through 45° dies. Upper curve calculated assuming friction exists, lower curve when friction absent. Points refer to experimental measurements.

(*Johnson, ' J. Mech. Phys. Solids '.*)

extrusion of pure lead through a die of semi-angle 45°. The upper curve refers to a perfectly rough container wall and a rough die face supporting a small dead metal zone, while the lower

217

curve refers to slip along a smooth die face, i.e. frictionless extrusion. As may be expected, almost all the results are bounded by these curves, with a tendency to approach the upper curve at higher reductions, which is indicative of the difficulty of obtaining frictionless conditions even in laboratory extrusion.

Both Hill[11] and Johnson[16] have shown that slip-line theory indicates that, for a given reduction, there is an optimum die angle for which the power consumption is a minimum, in agreement with the experimental findings of Sachs and Eisbein.[4] The theory indicates also that the optimum angle increases with increasing friction and with increasing reduction.

The valuable contribution which Johnson has made to both the theoretical and experimental aspects of extrusion has recently been extended[19] to an experimental justification of equation (14). From measurements of p and Y at various values of r on pure lead he finds that

$$\frac{p}{Y} = 0.8 + 1.5 \log_e \frac{1}{1 - r}$$

The results of applying this expression to the evaluation of $p/\overline{Y}$ and the comparison of this quantity with the experimentally determined value for various metals is shown in Table 7. When the metal work hardens $\overline{Y}$ is taken as the average value of the true stress over an appropriate range of logarithmic strain. The pressure can be predicted to better than 7 per cent. Dodeja and Johnson[20] have pointed to the necessity for determining the constants a and b on a non-hardening material for the case of axisymmetric extrusion, and not using the values obtained under plane-strain conditions.

In connection with the problems of extruding complex sections, and the difficulty of ensuring symmetrical flow into the die, the work of Green[21] on unsymmetrical extrusion under plane-strain conditions is of interest (see Chapter V). A slip-line field for an unsymmetrical extrusion from a container with rough walls is shown in Fig. 152. The increase in extrusion pressure due to marked eccentricity can be considerable when the deformation is large, as shown in Fig. 153. Eccentricity is here defined as

$$\varepsilon = \frac{b - c}{+ cb}, \quad 0 \leqslant \varepsilon \leqslant 1$$

TABLE 7

EXPERIMENTAL RESULTS FOR THE EXTRUSION OF LEAD, TIN AND
ALUMINIUM

Material	Fractional Reduction, r	Load, tons	Pressure, p tons/ sq. in.	$\overline{Y}$, tons/ sq. in.	Experimental Value of $p/\overline{Y}$	Predicted Value of $p/\overline{Y}$
Pure Lead .	0·75	2·78	3·54	1·30	2·72	2·88
	0·86	3·8	4·85	1·31	3·71	3·75
	0·938	5·15	6·55	1·31	5·00	4·97
Tellurium	1·75	4·5	5·75	1·94	2·96	2·88
Lead	0·86	5·9	7·5	1·96	3·83	3·75
(0·065% Te)	0·938	7·95	10·1	1·97	5·12	4·97
Pure Tin	0·75	5·6	7·15	2·41	2·96	2·88
	0·86	7·55	9·63	2·54	3·79	3·75
	0·938	11·0	14·0	2·72	5·11	4·97
Super-pure	0·75	15·0	19·1	6·44	2·95	2·88
Aluminium	0·86	21·25	27·1	6·80	3·97	3·75
	0·938	31·0	39·5	7·35	5·33	4·97

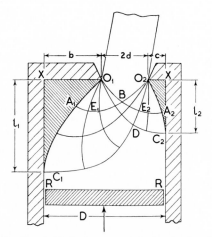

FIG. 152.—Slip-line field for unsymmetrical extrusion from container
with rough walls.

(Green, 'J. Mech. Phys. Solids'.)

where *b* and *c* are the parameters shown in Fig. 152. It is interesting to note that these curves can be represented, to within $2\frac{1}{2}$ per cent by equation (14). As Jordan and Thomsen[22] have pointed out, tube manufacture will involve unsymmetrical flow of this kind if the geometric centre of the extruded tube wall coincides with a line in the billet along which radial flow occurs. It may be expected, therefore, that extrusion pressures in tube manufacture will exceed those estimated only from considerations of the reduction in cross section and the effect of friction.

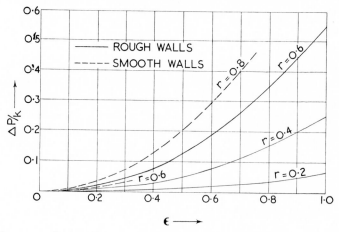

FIG. 153.—Increase in extrusion pressure due to eccentricity at various reductions.

(*Green, ' J. Mech. Phys. Solids '.*)

Thomsen and his co-workers[23] in the last few years have made an interesting approach to the problem of determining the boundary conditions which must be established in conformity with the stress and velocity equations if slip-line theory is to be applied; the method supplements the analytical approach, used by Hill, with experiments. The instantaneous velocity vectors are determined from the observation of an inscribed grid during incremental steps in the deformation, and from the velocity field the stress field is calculated. The technique, which has been called *visioplasticity*, has, so far, merely confirmed that slip-line theory gives a reasonable approximation to the deformation under actual conditions, and also that the discrepancy between these is largely due to the assumption of a plastic/rigid solid in slip-line theory.

Because of the necessity, for mathematical reasons, to make simplifying assumptions of this nature extrusion theory can hardly be considered to be complete. From the practical viewpoint, however, the theory, at least in certain of its aspects, appears to be quite adequate, since under practical conditions it is extremely doubtful whether there is anything to be gained from a theory which estimates pressure to a greater accuracy than that given by, say, Johnson.[19] Thus, while it is true that the theory allows for strain hardening in only a crude fashion and is quite incapable, at present, of allowing for the complex effects of variations in strain rate, there will be a number of sources of random error under production conditions which will prevent a high degree of reproducibility of the power requirements even for apparently identical extrusions. Therefore, for simple extrusions the theory may be regarded as adequate and the line of theoretical approach which probably would now prove most useful to extrusion practice would be in the direction of unsymmetrical deformation.

REFERENCES

[1] J. F. W. Bishop. The Theory of Extrusion. *Metallurgical Reviews*, Inst. Metals, 1957, **2**, 361–90.

[2] C. Fink. *Z. Bergwes. Prevsz*, 1874, **22**, 200.

[3] E. Siebel and E. Fangemeier. Researches on Power Consumption in the Extrusion and Punching of Metals. *Mitt. K.W. Inst. für Eisenforschung*, 1931, **13**, 29–43.

[4] G. Sachs and W. Eisbein. Power Consumption and Mechanism of Flow in the Extrusion Process. *Mitt. Materials*, S. **16**, 1931, 67–96.

[5] C. Blazey, L. Broad, W. S. Gummer and D. B. Thompson. The Flow of Metal in Tube Extrusion. *J. Inst. Metals*, 1948–9, **75**, 163–84.

[6] W. Johnson and A. G. Collins. The Plane Strain Extrusion of Lead and Aluminium through Wedge-shaped Dies. B.I.S.R.A. Report MW/E/54/54, 1955.

[7] V. V. Zholobov. The Pressure of Flow in the Hot Extrusion of Non-Ferrous Metals. *Metallurg*, 1937, **8**, 77.

[8] H. Hencky. *Zeitschrift für angewandte Mathematik und Mechanik*, 1923, **3**, 241.

[9] H. Geiringer. Proc. Third International Congress for Appl. Mech. Vol. 2. Stockholm, 1930.

[10] R. Hill. *Mathematical Theory of Plasticity*. Clarendon Press. 1950.

[11] —— A Theoretical Analysis of the Stresses and Strains in Extrusion and Piercing. *J. Iron Steel Inst.*, 1948, 1, **158**, 177–85.

[12] N. W. Purchase and S. J. Tupper. Experiments with a Laboratory Extrusion Apparatus under conditions of Plane Strain. *J. Mech. Phys. Solids*, 1952–3, **1**, 277–83.

[13] R. Hill. The Theory of the Extrusion of Metals. Selected Government Research Reports, Vol. 6. Strength and Testing of Materials, Part 1, 191–204. H.M.S.O. 1952.

[14] W. Johnson. Extrusion through Square Dies of Large Reduction. *J. Mech. Phys. Solids*, 1955–6, **4**, 191–8.

[15] —— Extrusion through Wedge Shaped Dies. Part 1. *Ibid.*, 1954–5, **3**, 218–23.

[16] —— Extrusion through Wedge Shaped Dies, Part II. *Ibid.*, 1954–5, **3**, 224–30.

[17] —— The Cold Extrusion of Rod and Tube at Slow Speeds. B.I.S.R.A. Report MW/E/55/54, 1955.

[18] —— Experiments in Plane-Strain Extrusion. *J. Mech. Phys. Solids*, 1955–6, **4**, 269–82.

[19] —— The Pressure for the Cold Extrusion of Lubricated Rod through Square Dies of Moderate Reduction at Slow Speeds. *J. Inst. Metals*, 1956–7, **85**, 403–8.

[20] L. C. Dodeja and W. Johnson. *J. Mech. Phys. Solids*, 1957, **5**, 281.

[21] A. P. Green. An Unsymmetrical Extrusion in Plane Strain. *Ibid.*, 1954–5, **3**, 189–96.

[22] T. F. Jordan and E. G. Thomsen. Comparison of an Unsymmetric Slip-Line Solution in Extrusion with Experiment. *Ibid.*, 1955–6, **4**, 184–90.

[23] E. G. Thomsen, C. Yang and J. G. Bierbower. *Univ. Calif. Pub. Eng.*, 1954, **5**, 89.

CHAPTER VIII

Metals and Alloys for Hot Extrusion

THERE are wide differences in the facility with which metals can be extruded: while certain ones lend themselves readily and present few problems, others are, in varying degree, more difficult and make special demands on technique and equipment. Among the reasons which contribute to this are differences in the stiffness of the metals and the length of their extrusion range, and also the position on the temperature scale of these ranges. In a number of cases trouble mainly arises from the susceptibility to speed effects shown by some metals. It is, of course, with the difficult materials that the operating conditions become of chief concern, since for those that are soft and have a long plastic range no closer control is required than will suffice to give ready extrusion and the attainment of suitable properties and structures.

The Extrusion Range

The full range for hot-working a metal can be regarded as lying between temperature limits at which, on the one hand, it becomes hot short, and, on the other, marked work-hardening sets in or the force required to deform it becomes excessive. Thus, for extrusion, it extends from a temperature at which the metal cracks or breaks up as it leaves the die down to one at which, under the full power of the press, the billet fails to extrude and becomes a ' sticker ' in the container. This interval depends primarily on the metal itself, and may be long or short, depending on the softness and plasticity which it acquires and retains with altering temperature, scme metals being inherently stiff by comparison with others. The length of the working range is also reduced, as already mentioned, in alloys in which, from their constitution, hot shortness persists to low temperatures. Various types of test have been devised to enable a rapid and preliminary assessment to be made of the hot-workability of alloys without

223

having to resort to the costly process of extensive plant trials. Hot tensile, notched-bar impact, bending and flattening tests[1] are all capable of providing useful indications, if the results they yield are interpreted with due consideration to the fact that they do not reproduce all the various conditions obtaining in industrial extrusion. Clearly such tests cannot be regarded as substitutes for plant trials but at least they may be used as sorting tests in indicating temperature ranges for working, and even in measuring resistance to deformation within such ranges, where large numbers of experimental materials are under consideration.

The limitations of such tests in defining an extrusion range arise largely from the system of stressing imposed on the test piece usually being different from that obtaining in extrusion and from the scale of operation, so that the limits of extrusion of an alloy must be defined by reference to additional factors than those concerned only with the properties of the alloy. For instance, it is obvious that the stalling point in a given case will depend on what pressure can be applied to the billet. It will depend therefore on the total power of the press in relation to the size of the container and the dimensions and shape of the product to be made. In direct extrusion the length of the billet, too, will be material, since it affects the pressure which is required. Within limits, the fitting of a container of smaller diameter, where the overall dimensions of the required section permit this to be done, confers a twofold advantage in extending the range and easing extrusion because less pressure is needed for the lower reduction which is then involved, and also because greater pressure is available on the smaller sectional area (Table 8). A resort to this expedient can only be taken so far, for when extrusion temperatures are high a contrary influence arises from the rapidity with which a small billet loses heat: while the cooling surface of a billet decreases with reduction in its diameter, its total heat capacity varies as the square of its diameter. There is, besides, a limit to the stress that can be imposed on the extrusion ram; this is not usually taken above 75 tons per square inch, although ram pressures up to 100 tons per square inch are sometimes employed. Moreover billets of small diameter, by causing a reduction in the amount of work put upon the metal, may adversely affect its mechanical properties.

TABLE 8

Capacity of Press tons	Diameter of Container in.	Corresponding Maximum Pressures on Extrusion Ram tons/sq. in.	
1000	5, 6, 8, 9	51, 36, 20, 15·5	Screwing, stamping and high-tensile brass, 70/30 brass, copper, and up to 12 per cent nickel-silver
2000	5, 6, 7	100, 72, 55	Nickel, cupro-nickel, monel, inconel, etc.
5000	12, 15, 20	44, 30, 16	Duralumin and high-strength light alloys

The question of the cooling of the billet during the extrusion operation is an important one, for the possible working range becomes reduced by the amount of the temperature fall, and the initial temperature of the billet must be high enough to allow for the loss. In cases where the cooling is considerable the latitude left for the conduct of the extrusion may become very small. For this reason one is often concerned in practice not so much with the interval in which the working of a metal would, theoretically, be possible under steady temperature conditions as with the permissible variation in the temperature at which billets are fed into the press, and it is with the latter connotation rather than the former that the term ' extrusion range ' is ordinarily used. The extent to which heat is lost during extrusion depends on the relative temperatures of the billet and its surroundings, its dimensions, and the time it is in the press. With metals such as lead, magnesium and aluminium, extruding at fairly low temperatures, the container can be kept hot enough to minimize any change, but when extrusion temperatures from 900° C. and upwards to 1200° C., many hundreds of degrees above the press components, are necessary, serious chilling is liable to occur. Thus the higher the temperature required for extrusion the shorter the effective range tends to become.

For metals possessing only a short working range, and especially one lying at high temperatures, it is clear that the speed of extrusion becomes of paramount importance. To extrude such materials from a press in which the ram speed is limited may be impossible or require the most critical control of preheating temperatures, whereas a press with a rapid stroke allows comfortable latitude. At the highest temperatures, a serious problem is to find tool materials that will stand up to the work. In this connection, also, rapidity of operation is a vital consideration both to avoid excessive damage under the heavy pressures that are occasioned if the temperature is allowed to fall, and to prevent long exposure of the tools to the hot metal. The most durable and resistant steels yet available lose strength and undergo rapid destruction by abrasion if they are permitted to rise above 600°–700° C.

From the foregoing it is evident that an exact extrusion range for a metal applicable in all circumstances can not be specified. For the readily extrudable materials this is of no particular consequence, and it is only necessary to select a mid-range which will give the required results. Where stringent limits are put forward for an especially difficult alloy, covering perhaps as little as 10° C., it will be seen that they bear strict reference only to certain sizes, and to particular plant conditions which involve the power of the press and the rate at which it is operated, the container size, and the precautions taken to conserve heat by heating the container, etc. One result of this is that it is not uncommon to find temperature limits designated from one source for an alloy which are less stringent than those insisted upon from another. It also occurs sometimes that the temperatures proposed cover slightly different ranges. The latter is not surprising in view of the real difficulty that there is in measuring the true temperature, where this is high, of the billets leaving the preheating furnace. Apparent temperatures observed by optical pyrometer, or those measured by contact instruments, are satisfactory for control purposes but are not readily converted into true figures.

The sensitivity of some metals in regard to the speed of their extrusion is referred to later in this chapter.

Brass and Other Copper Alloys

The extrusion process is probably still most familiarly associated with its application to various brass alloys, for not only were they the first of the harder metals to be used in this connection, but they continue, in a multitude of extruded forms, to occupy a position of the highest industrial importance; this being especially the case for those ranging in composition from 55 to 65 per cent of copper, which easily predominate in terms of quantity over the other members of the series. In general, the ease with which they can be extruded and the number and intricacy of the shapes it is possible to produce falls off as the copper content increases, so that, although the whole range of commercial brasses can now be extruded without much trouble, by far the greatest choice of manufactured forms is to be had between the above limits. The reason for this lies in the fact that alloys belonging to the β and $\alpha + \beta$ series, the latter reverting to β at high temperature, are characterized by their extreme plasticity, which they retain between 600° C. and 800° C. With slightly more difficulty, due to their greater stiffness, and the rather higher temperature which is needed, as already indicated by Fig. 135, the α brasses, the more important lying about 70/30 in composition, are now available in all but the most complex shapes. To be capable of hot working the lead content of these alloys must be low (0·05 per cent max.)

Smith and Swindells[2] have stated that, as a general rule for copper alloys, the lowest extrusion temperature consistent with the alloy, extrusion ratio and power available is preferred for the following reasons:

1. The tendency for deterioration of the surface of the billet during preheating is reduced.
2. Liquid phases at grain boundaries are avoided. Even if these are not sufficiently serious to cause cracking during extrusion, they may impair the impact-resistance of the finished product.
3. A finer structure is obtained in the extruded condition.
4. The mechanical properties throughout the extrusion are more uniform.
5. The tendency for grain growth to occur on reheating is considerably reduced.

The purposes to which extruded brass products are put may be roughly classified as follows: (i) For use as extruded in the form of channels, tees, box, girder and such-like sections for constructional applications; and as tubes, for condensers, heat exchangers, distillation plants, and so forth. (*ii*) For further fabrication in the engineering industries, extruded material forms a convenient starting-point. Instances are to be found in rod and

FIG. 154.—Selection of extruded brass sections.
(*Courtesy of Delta Metal Co.*)

wire made in free-machining alloy for high-speed automatic machines; stock for forging and hot stamping; blanks in high-tensile alloys for gears and pinions; tube for roller and ball-bearing cages. (*iii*) In a variety of special shapes and hollow forms for electrical and architectural purposes, shop fronts, doors, stairways, decorative trimmings in transport vehicles, etc. A small selection from the many thousands of current brass sections are illustrated in Fig. 154.

It would serve no useful purpose to attempt an exhaustive catalogue of the various brass alloys which are used in these ways, and mention must be confined to a few representative examples. A large percentage of the output consists of free-cutting brass with 57–60 per cent of copper—or rather higher in American specifications—and 2·5–3·5 per cent of lead, employed for rapid screw-machine work. Hot stamping brass, with 57–59 per cent copper, generally with lead up to 2 per cent, is an important product, as, too, is naval brass. High-tensile brasses, or, as they continue to be better known, manganese bronze alloys, which, due to high mechanical properties combined with good resistance to corrosion have many applications, and are very serviceable under marine conditions and for certain types of chemical plant, are commonly produced in the extruded form. Smith and Swindells[1] have discussed the extrusion practice for some of these alloys in some detail.

Copper, while it is capable of being hot-worked over an extensive range of temperature, is distinctly harder when hot than most brasses. It can, however, be obtained in all the common extruded forms, as round, hexagon and flat sections, and is produced in large quantities as tubing. Production is made in the arsenical, high-conductivity, deoxidized and tough grades.

Tables 9 and 10, compiled by Crampton,[3] give a convenient summary of copper alloys used in the form of extrusions, and of their average properties. Cook and Davis[2] have quoted extrusion temperatures for copper and copper alloys which show some differences from those quoted in Table 9 and may be more representative of British practice. Table 11, derived from data given by Bernhoeft,[4] gives some indication of the relative extrusion pressures for different brasses. These were obtained from a directly driven 1500-ton press working at a speed of 0·5 in. per second, which, though rather below what is now a normal rate for such alloys, was constant for all, so giving them a comparative value. The figures are comparative also in that they refer to the extrusion in each case of 1-in. diameter rods from billets 6·5 in. in diameter (extrusion ratio 42). Similar data has been given by Cotter and Clark[5] for rod and tube extrusion. As material comes from the press, it is liable to show some deviation from the nominal dimensions to which it is being made. This arises

TABLE 9
COPPER-BASE EXTRUDED ALLOYS —ROD

Alloy	Approximate Composition * Cu	Pb	Sn	Ni	Mn	Al	Misc.	Approximate Temperature Range for Extrusion °C.	Mechanical Properties as Extruded — Tensile Strength lb./sq. in.	Elongation percentage in 2 in.	Most commonly used Temper	Mechanical Properties for such Temper — Tensile Strength lb./sq. in.	Elongation percentage in 2 in.
Free-cutting brass	61·5	3·5						700–760	48,000	45	Drawn	55,000	30
Forging brass	60	1·75						680–730	50,000	45	As extruded	50,000	45
Architectural brass	58	3						650–730	54,000	45	As extruded	54,000	45
Naval brass	60		0·75					650–730	55,000	45	(Light drawn)	63,000	25
											(Hard drawn)	70,000	25
Free-cutting naval brass	60	1·5	0·75					650–730	55,000	45	(Light drawn)	63,000	35
											(Hard drawn)	70,000	25
Manganese bronze	57·5		1		0·05		1 Fe	620–700	65,000	35	Drawn	80,000	20
Muntz metal	59							680–730	52,000	45	Drawn	62,000	30
Rivet metal	63							700–760	46,000	50	(Rivet temper)	60,000	35
											(Hard drawn)	80,000	10
Free-cutting commercial bronze	89	2						700–820	36,000	50	Drawn	45,000	30
Copper	100							820–900	32,000	40	Drawn	42,000	25
Leaded copper	99	1						820–900	32,000	40	Drawn	42,000	25
Silicon bronze	96						3 Si	790–840	53,000	70	(Drawn half hard)	73,000	45
											(Drawn hard)	90,000	35
											(Drawn extra hard)	108,000	25
10 per cent nickel-silver	45	2		10	0·5			700–760	80,000	10	As extruded	80,000	10
13 per cent nickel-silver	41	1·25		13	0·5			700–760	90,000	7	As extruded	90,000	7
Nickel-aluminium bronze	91			7·5		1·5		760–820	50,000	45	Quenched and aged	100,000	20
Nickel-aluminium bronze	85			12·5		2·5		870–930	60,000	35	Quenched and aged	125,000	10
Aluminium bronze (5 per cent)	95					5		820–870	50,000	60	Drawn	70,000	30
Aluminium bronze (8 per cent)	92					8		730–790	60,000	60	As extruded	60,000	60

* Properties shown are *average*. Balance in all cases is zinc. Includes all types of copper.

(Reproduced by courtesy of the American Society of Metals.)

TABLE 10

COPPER-BASE EXTRUDED ALLOYS—TUBE

Alloy	Approximate Composition						Approximate Temperature Range for Extrusion °C.	Approximate * Mechanical Properties			
								As Extruded		After Final Condenser Tube Anneal	
	Cu	Ni	Al	Sn	Pb	Zn		Tensile Strength lb./sq. in.	Elongation percentage in 2 in.	Tensile Strength lb./sq. in.	Elongation percentage in 2 in.
High brass . . .	66·5				0·5	33	660 690	45,000	65	50,000	55
Admiralty brass . .	70			1		29	650-680	46,000	65	52,000	60
Red brass . . .	85					15	775-800	38,000	50	44,000	42
Aluminium brass . .	76		2			22	730 760	48,000	65	52,000	60
Ni silver, 18 per cent .	65	18				17	870 900	55,000	45	60,000	40
20 per cent Cupro-nickel	75	20				5	980 1010	48,000	40	53,000	35
30 per cent Cupro-nickel	70	30					1010 1050	54,000	35	63,000	30
Silicon bronze . .	96		3 Si			1	730 760	53,000	65	60,000	60
Nickel-aluminium bronze	92	4	4				820-850	50,000	45	60,000	30
Aluminium bronze .	95		5				800-830	50,000	55	58,000	35

* Properties shown are average.

(Reproduced by courtesy of the American Society of Metals.)

for such reasons as gradual alteration in the die during use, and the thermal contraction of the metal in cooling from the working temperature. In the case of brass an allowance of 0·02 in. per inch is usually provided when the die is made, to offset the latter.

TABLE 11

Material						Usual Extrusion Temperature ° C.	Minimum Extrusion Pressure tons/sq. in.
Cu	Zn	Pb	Sn	Al	Mn		
100	–	–	–	–	–	870–910	19·4 (880° C.)
62·5	37·5	–	–	–	–	780–790	—
58	40	2	–	–	–	760–780	13·5 (750° C.)
56	40·5	–	–	1·5	2	730–780	11·9 (760° C.)
67	33	–	–	–	–	790–810	25·4 (790° C.)
60	39	–	1	–	–	750–780	14·9 (770° C.)
48	41	1	nickel 10%			760–780	23·9 (770° C.)

More difficult to eliminate entirely is the variation in size which is apt to occur between the leading and back ends of an extruded length owing to the alteration in the temperature at which the metal passes through the die. In an actual example quoted by Wragg,[6] for a bar for which the specified diameter was 1 in. ± 0·004 in., the first 3 ft. were just on the lower limit, over the next 34 ft. the bar was inside the top limit of 1·004 in., while the last 21 ft. were above this, with a maximum diameter of 1·006 in. For many purposes the order of accuracy obtainable is sufficiently near for the intended application, and no further processing other than straightening is required, but a bar such as the above can be brought within finer limits and made serviceable over its full length at little additional cost by light drawing, which also has the advantage of sharpening up the profile of sections to which it is applied. The exacting specifications needed for engineering work must be met by drawing or reeling or both.

Smith and Swindells[1] have indicated the necessity for care to avoid damage to the hot metal as it emerges from the die. Good surface finish can only be obtained if adequate clearance is allowed in the back die and die-holder and if the run-out table is kept smooth and clean. Occasionally, small hard white particles are found on extruded brass strip and which have been shown to be zinc picked up after the strip leaves the die. At high temperatures zinc volatilizes from the brass and condenses on the relatively cool support behind the die. If this zinc is allowed to build up, it may melt as the back die warms up during extrusion and fall on to the strip, or the strip itself may touch the deposit. The removal of the ' pick-up ' which develops on dies during use is clearly important for good surface finish and dimensional tolerance. It is therefore interesting to note the use of vapour blasting in the United States for such die maintenance.[7] Essentially the method consists in projecting into the die orifice under high pressure a fluid containing suspended fine abrasive; the slightly matt surface imparted to the die is stated not to impair its performance and may even prolong die life by providing a key for lubricants. Apart from the dangers of surface damage certain brasses containing lead require careful handling whilst they are cooling after extrusion since they are inclined to be brittle in the range 250°–500° C.

Extruded brass rod can be obtained in all sizes from $\frac{3}{16}$ in. to 5 in. diameter, tubes up to 5 in. o.d., with wall thicknesses ranging from $\frac{1}{20}$ in. on small sizes up to $\frac{3}{4}$ in. A few of the usual manufacturing limits are given below, though somewhat closer tolerances than these can be worked to, the cost being increased in order to provide for a greater proportion of reject.

Examples of normal manufacturing limits:

Round bars $\frac{3}{16}-\frac{7}{16}$ in. diameter inclusive $\pm$ 0·002 in.
   ,,   ,,   1–1$\frac{3}{8}$ in.   ,,   ,, $\pm$ 0·004 in.
   ,,   ,,   above 2 in.   ,,   ,, $\pm$ 0·008 in.
Tubes and hollow sections
    on outside diameter up to 3 in. $\pm$ 0·003 in.
    on inside diameter up to 3 in. $\pm$ 0·010 in.

Concentricity
    Tubes up to 1$\frac{1}{2}$ in. o.d. 0·01 in. out of centre
          above 2 ,, ,, 0·02 ,, ,, ,, ,,
          above 3 ,, ,, 0·025 ,, ,, ,, ,,

Aluminium Bronze

This is an important series of alloys which can be taken as

falling into two main groups. In the first the principal alloys, containing 4–8 per cent of aluminium, while considered primarily as cold-working alloys, can also be extruded at about 850° C., and are now used extensively in the making of condenser tubes. Their working behaviour is similar to that of 70/30 brass, than which, however, they are rather stiffer. The second group of alloys, running mostly from 9 to 11 per cent of aluminium, are the more widely used for extrusion. Alloys in this range of aluminium content usually carry other alloying elements, especially nickel, manganese and iron, and sometimes lead and zinc.[2] The effect of these elements is to require the use of higher temperatures and pressures for extrusion, but this can be performed satis-factorily even when lead is present to the extent that the alloy would crack if rolled. Their working qualities are excellent and a very full range of sections can be made, extruding at 850°-900° C., where they are only little less plastic than is 60/40 brass at 750°-800° C. They are attractive on account of their high strength associated with the ability to withstand electrolytic and direct corrosion and also behave well under erosive conditions.

The Tin-bronzes

These alloys are particularly sensitive in their hot working characteristics to the effects of porosity, tin sweat and impurities.[8] Until comparatively recently, the application to these of extrusion had made very little progress, and only those containing up to 4 or 5 per cent of tin were a practicable proposition. The chief difficulty in hot-working those of higher tin content lay in the presence, in the cast alloys, of excessive amounts of the hard δ constituent and in its uneven distribution owing to inverse segregation to which these alloys are especially susceptible. While this could be overcome to a limited extent by annealing so as to bring about the absorption of the δ phase, the degree of hetero-geneity made this an inordinately long process, and the extrusion of bronze containing up to 9 per cent tin, after homogeneizing them in this way, was of no great practical significance. As the result of modifications in foundry technique, a remarkable change has been brought about. Lepp[9] has shown that, by steps taken to eliminate the gas absorbed in the molten alloys, a nearer approach to an equilibrium structure in the cast ingot is obtained, less δ is formed, and segregation becomes inappreciable. The degassing is accomplished by a process* known as selective oxidation in which a controlled addition of copper oxide is made to a neutral or basic slag as it lies on the alloy. Extrusion billets of bronzes with 10–14 per cent of tin, prepared in this way, become homogeneized sufficiently to enable them to be extruded after an annealing period of only about 4 hours at 650° C. Although these improvements in casting technique have resulted in higher tin bronzes being extruded, these alloys are intrinsically stiff and can only be worked in narrow temperature ranges. Relatively little published data is available on the properties of these alloys at high temperatures or even on the more technological aspects of their extrusion.

Phosphor-bronzes

The situation in respect of these is similar to that of the ordinary bronzes, and it would seem that somewhat parallel progress has been made. Lepp[10] has given figures for the properties of an extruded bronze with 8 per cent of tin, and various amounts of phosphorus, as follows:

TABLE 12

Phosphorus per cent	E.L. tons/sq. in.	U.T.S. tons/sq. in.	Elongation per cent
0·33–0·36	13·3–14·0	28·5–29·8	62–58
0·39	14·6	29·6	57
0·44–0·54	14·0–14·6	29·8–31·0	63
0·64–0·80	14·0–15·2	31·7–32·8	61–59
0·80–0·90	15·2–19·0	33 –34·5	53–48

Among comparative new-comers in the field of extrusion are the *nickel-aluminium bronzes*, from which, when advantage is taken of their capacity for undergoing precipitation hardening, extremely good mechanical properties are obtainable.

The Silicon-bronzes have assumed importance in recent years and have found considerable application in the U.S.A. Although consisting essentially of copper alloyed with 2–4 per cent of silicon, other metals as, for example, iron, manganese, zinc, tin,

* British Patent No. 436,204.

aluminium, and lead are frequently also present in small amounts. They can be extruded in the majority of forms, and are in demand for their strength and non-corrodible properties.

Nickel-silvers

The ternary alloys of copper-nickel-zinc may be divided into two classes. The better known of these, the nickel-silvers, contain from 8 to 30 per cent nickel; 10 to 30 per cent zinc, and come within the limits of the α solid solution range. Mainly regarded as cold-forming alloys, they can also be hot-worked by rolling and extrusion. The latter is relatively easy if the nickel content lies not higher than 10–12 per cent, but above this they become increasingly stiff, and this calls for progressive raising of the extrusion temperature as the percentage of nickel is increased. The range for satisfactory working becomes short, and demands careful control of preheating and press operation. By reason of their more silvery colour and greater freedom from tarnishing, the high nickel members of the series have come into prominence, notably for decorative and architectural work, a typical alloy for this purpose containing 18–20 per cent nickel, 20 per cent zinc. For ordinary sections this material is extruded at 870°–890° C.

The second group, often referred to as nickel brasses, are those which consist of the α and β phases of the system in proportions varying according to their composition, which is found between 8 and 18 per cent nickel, and 38 to 45 per cent of zinc. These are hot-working alloys which lend themselves to extrusion rather more readily than the nickel-silvers, at temperatures in the neighbourhood of 800°–850° C., in the production, chiefly, of forging stock.

Cupro-nickel

The straight copper-nickel alloys, or cupro-nickels, constitute an important group in connection with their use for condenser tubes. The alloys first employed for this purpose about 1922 were of lower nickel content than the 70/30 mixture, which has now been found to be the most satisfactory. To begin with, the tubes had to be made by boring out the cast billets and subsequently drawing them. This was a most tedious and costly method of manufacture. However, the excellent properties of the alloys provided a stimulus to the solution of the, at first, serious problems encountered in extruding them. One of the main obstacles to be overcome lay in the inability of the press tools to withstand the pressures and temperatures involved, and this was only finally remedied by the advent of tungsten-chrome steels for these parts. In the manufacture of 70/30 cupro-nickel tubes, the billets are turned to remove surface blemishes and skin defects. The practice widely followed is to extrude tubes close to the final size, about 1 in. o.d., $\frac{1}{8}$ in. thick in the wall, so leaving a minimum of cold drawing to be done. For this purpose, the billets are bored out, since piercing mandrels of this size are not robust enough to stand up to the operation. As mentioned earlier, the alternative method of piercing and extruding thicker shells of larger bore from horizontal presses, and bringing these to the required dimensions in tube-reducing machines, has lately been found advantageous.

High-Nickel Alloys

The progress made in widening the range of extrudable copper alloys, made it possible to contemplate the extrusion of more refractory materials, and for many years now it has been a commercial proposition to deal in this way with a number of nickel alloys. Among these is monel metal, containing 65–70 per cent nickel, about 27 per cent copper, with small amounts of other elements, such as iron, manganese, and silicon, which has a high repute because of its immunity from attack by sea water and in a great many other media, in addition to having good strength properties at high temperatures. It will be well understood that the toughness and resistance to deformation possessed by this alloy when hot is not conducive to its easy extrusion. However, both monel and the related dispersion-hardening alloy, K-monel, are being made in the form of a number of the more simple engineering sections and as tube. Certain of the nichrome alloys, such as inconel, with 80 per cent nickel, 12–14 per cent chromium, remainder iron, which possess to a degree even more marked than monel the property of heat resistance, are now being extruded with success in the range 1150°–1200° C., even though production is limited as yet to rounds, hexagons, squares, and some tubes. A description of the extrusion of these has been given by Graham.[11]

With the advent of glass lubrication it is now possible to extrude even the harder nickel alloys, such as those in the Nimonic series.

The Extrusion of Steel

The term extrusion has frequently been used in connection with the fabrication of steel by certain press-forging operations, such, for example, as the manufacture of automobile valves, in which the extrusion principle is also involved. A description of these is included in Chapter XI. They are, however, quite distinct from extrusion proper in which the product is usually of constant dimensions determined by the form of the die orifice through which the metal flows. The extrusion of steel in this conventional sense is relatively new and has been revolutionized by the introduction of the Ugine Sejournet process* of glass lubrication, although the practicability of extruding steel tubes was demonstrated in England in 1928 and regular commercial production was under way in 1937.

The earliest applications of steel extrusion were in tube making, with mechanical presses, finding favour in Germany because of the advantage of giving a very rapid stroke but comparing less favourably in other respects with hydraulic machines. Evans[12] has described the method developed at the Mannesmann works for making tubes of small bore, which is applicable to low-grade Bessemer steels as well as to special alloy steels. The process is fundamentally the same as in non-ferrous tube extrusion. A solid billet at 1250° C. is placed in the container, where it is pierced and then extruded in one stroke. The very heavy press shown in Fig. 155 will extrude at the high rate of two billets a minute. Actual extrusion occupies only 3-4 seconds, the remainder of the time being taken in cutting off, cooling the tools, and in inserting a fresh billet. The billets are prepared from long steel bars which are nicked and broken into suitable lengths. After preheating they are passed rapidly through a descaling mill, the rollers of which detach the oxide scale, before they are transferred to the press. The hot tubes, up to 40 ft. in length, are at once fed into reducing rolls arranged in sequence to give the required diameter and wall-thickness. Finally they are passed to travelling

* Page 164.

cooling racks which carry them to the automatic machines which screw the ends. The tubes produced are up to 65 ft. long, in diameters of $\frac{3}{8}$ in., $\frac{1}{2}$ in. and $\frac{3}{4}$ in., with the usual wall-thicknesses.

Fig. 155.—Heavy mechanical press used in the extrusion of steel tubes.
(*Courtesy of 'Iron and Steel Industry'.*)

As compared with methods involving cross-rolling, which tends to open out and extend defects present in the original steel, the production of tubes by extrusion has the merit that such defects are closed up by the action of the all-round pressure in the latter process.

239

The predominantly compressive nature of the forces involved in extrusion is probably the reason why it is now possible to extrude tubes in steels which could not be made into tubes, or at least only with considerable difficulty, by conventional rotary piercing.[13] Indeed this may be regarded as one of the principal reasons for the development of steel extrusion, as also is the infinite variety of accurately profiled shapes which may be produced at lower cost than by rolling or forging followed by machining. The greatest difficulty in the way of these developments undoubtedly has been the much higher temperatures which are needed to bring steel to a sufficiently plastic state for extrusion, as compared with the general run of non-ferrous metals. The pressures which are necessary vary with the composition, but in most cases are not excessively high. The resistance to deformation of the majority of steels in the region of 1100°–1250° C. is actually not so high as for some of the nickel alloys and is roughly 50 per cent above that for most of the copper alloys. The real difficulties are in minimizing the time of contact between billet and tools and in restricting the wear suffered by the latter. A high rate of working, of 4 in. or more of billet length a second, is essential so as to avoid the damage which the tools would sustain if their contact with the highly heated metal were prolonged. In its modern form the hydraulically operated press, both vertical and horizontal, can be made to fulfil this requirement, and this type has now found preference over the mechanical press. Additionally, the modern high-speed press lends itself well to fully automatic operation, so that the operational sequence necessary for the performance of a single extrusion cycle is completed automatically once it is initiated, a feature which is highly desirable if the time of contact between billet and tools are to be kept to a minimum. Wear and tear suffered by the tools—to which oxide scale on the billets is a contributory factor—has been much reduced, and the process made economically feasible to a much wider range of products, since the introduction of glass lubrication.

In its essentials the technique of press operation in steel extrusion is not different from that employed in the case of other metals. The application of the glass lubricant (see page 164) and keeping the time during which the working tools are in contact with the hot steel to an absolute minimum, by using very rapid rates of deformation, are the two features which characterize steel extrusion and which raise their own problems. Thus, the use of glass necessitates special precautions being taken to ensure the complete protection of all sliding surfaces on the press from the abrasive particles which may be deposited and the thin film of glass which remains on the extrusion must be removed by pickling, either in molten caustic soda or in a mixture of sulphuric and hydrofluoric acid.[14] The glass adhering to the container is removed by an ejecting disc passed through the container to remove the discard, whilst the die is cleaned with the aid of pneumatically-powered hand tools and shot blasting. Even with modern high speed presses it may still be necessary to employ some means of mandrel cooling.

The steels which have been extruded into tubes and sections of varying degrees of complexity range from plain carbon steels[14] to highly alloyed material[12] including high speed steels, in which the carbide distribution may be superior to that obtained from forging and rolling.[60] Many of these are readily worked by processes other than extrusion, but Evans[13] mentions some materials, such as a steel containing 19·25 Cr, 9 Ni, 1·25 Mo, 1·25 W, 0·3 Ti, 0·4 Cb and 0·3 C and a nodular cast iron, which can be made into tubes only by extrusion. The tolerances which can be maintained on these sections are influenced by a number of factors of which die-wear is the most important.[14] The amount of wear that can be tolerated will depend on whether or not the section is to be cold-drawn after extrusion. For sections that are subsequently cold-drawn, the tolerances on the extruded section range from 3 to 10 per cent of the section thickness. If, on the other hand, extrusion only is employed, sections can be produced with a total tolerance on any dimension of 0·025 in., or, if specially required, a tolerance of about 0·010 in. can be maintained.

The British Iron and Steel Research Association are actively engaged in the field of steel extrusion, to which they have already made some valuable contributions,[15] particularly towards the development of a method of extrusion without a discard. This method, which is the subject of a patent application, involves the use of a friable dummy block between the ram and the billet. The dummy block which has been developed is a composite one made up of a body of compressed graphite powder with two thin pieces of asbestos at the front and rear. This not only provides adequate sealing against backward extrusion past the dummy, but is capable also of withstanding pressures of about 50 tons per square inch peak ram pressure. Preheating the dummy to some 800° to 900° C. is necessary and the design of the die is important with respect to ejecting the tail end, which contains a remarkably small amount of piping if the die shape is appropriate.

The effects of die shape on lubrication were studied in a simple experiment involving the extrusion of a $1\frac{1}{8}$ in. $\times \frac{3}{16}$ in. rectangular stainless steel section through two different dies. One die had a 180° face, $\frac{3}{8}$ in. inlet radius and $\frac{1}{4}$ in. parallel throat and the other a sloping face, specially shaped to smooth the flow, and again a $\frac{1}{4}$ in. parallel throat. The glass pads, of plain sheet glass, were shaped to fit the die and were very thin so that the flowing metal could take full advantage of the die shape. The surface finish of the bar extruded through the shaped die was superior to that produced by the flat-faced die, and the lubricant was more evenly distributed round the section.

In the same paper[15] some work is described on the composition of the glass lubricant as it affects the quality of the extruded bar. It is suggested that the probable requirements of a glass for a good surface finish on the extruded steel include satisfactory wetting of the surface of the steel (low surface tension), a viscosity with a specific range and minimum glass attack on the metal scale. This latter property is probably important in assisting the removal of glass from the bar, although it is suggested also that a glass of very low coefficient of thermal expansion would be beneficial in this direction, presumably because of the generation of higher thermal stresses on cooling. It is interesting to note that, generally, different results were obtained with stainless steel and mild steel, suggesting that different glasses should be used for different steels.

The possibility of using cast billets with very little surface preparation, as opposed to the pre-worked, machined, billets now commonly used in steel extrusion is being considered in these extensive investigations. Cast billets, in which severe internal piping was known to be present, showed a very high degree of closure of internal defects. Only the front 6 in. to 9 in. of the

bar showed signs of incomplete closure even though holes over
1 in. in diameter were known to be present. Extruded bars from
machined and unmachined billets showed no difference in surface
finish, suggesting that there is no need for machining, other than
that necessary for the removal of local imperfections, which may
be ground out by hand. This is not to imply that the surface
finish of extruded steel sections is generally of the standard
achieved with the lower melting point non-ferrous metals. On
the contrary, and particularly with highly alloyed steels, the finish
is sometimes so poor as to be unacceptable,[61] probably as a result
of certain inadequacies in glass lubrication as currently practised.

The Extrusion of Aluminium Alloys

The earlier preoccupation of extrusion with copper alloys has
been modified in a striking fashion by the employment of the
process on a quickly growing scale for the light alloys. Besides
the fabrication of sections in almost the finished form, extrusion
has an extremely valuable function to perform in converting the
rather fragile cast structures into a stronger fine-grained condition,
so rendering them better able to withstand further working in
the forge or rolling mill. In many works dealing with the high
strength alloys of both groups, pre-extruded material is used for
all subsequent shaping operations. Pre-extruded billets made
in a large press are, in fact, sometimes extruded in a second stage
into the final shapes in which they are required. All the same,
extrusion is not an invariable preliminary to the working of all
light alloys and some of the aluminium and magnesium alloys
can be rolled satisfactorily from the ingot.

The equipment required for extrusion is essentially similar to
that in use for copper alloys, the principal differences arising out
of the need for speed and temperature control in the presses; in
the types of billet preheating furnaces; and from the somewhat
different work requiring to be done after extrusion in heat-
treating and straightening. Aluminium alloys in particular are
required in the form of large engineering sections, and to obtain
them in the gauges and in the lengths, up to 70 ft., which are
called for in aircraft spars, etc., it has been found necessary
to lay down very heavy presses. Press capacities usually vary
from 500 to 6000 tons, but larger presses are in existence and are

being contemplated, particularly in connection with the United States Heavy Press Programme. The smaller presses are only capable of handling billets of about 3 in. diameter in extruding to sections of about $\frac{3}{4}$ sq. in., but the heaviest presses (12,500 tons) can accommodate billets up to 44 in. diameter, 70 in. long and weighing $2\frac{1}{2}$ tons, producing a multitude of section shapes and sizes, a selection of which is shown in Fig. 156.

The low throughput consequent on the very limited rates of extrusion which it is possible to use has made it desirable to fit

FIG. 156.—Extruded sections in aluminium alloy.

hydraulic speed indicators, covering the ranges from 0·01 in. per second to 1 in. per second, so as to enable the maximum safe speed, once this has been determined in any given case, to be maintained. Since, for the above reason also, a single extrusion may occupy as much as 20 minutes, the adoption of special methods of container heating, already described, is required in order to maintain the metal within what is often a narrow extrusion range. In addition, a small automatically regulated furnace or induction heater is generally provided adjacent to the press to preheat dies, mandrels, and pressure-discs ready for use.

The importance of supplying billets as homogeneous and free as ever possible from casting defects of all kinds as a prerequisite to the production of sound extrusions, is certainly no less for these alloys than for any others, and calls for the adoption of suitable technique in melting and casting procedures. Several types of melting furnace are in use, of which the electrical resistance or low-frequency methods are preferable owing to reduced danger from turbulence, and of gassing from the presence of water vapour which is apt to arise in other types. Staples and Hurst[16] have considered the question of melting and casting aluminium alloys for subsequent extrusion and have discussed the relative merits of the various casting techniques, particularly that which is now used in most modern plants, the direct-chill or continuous-casting process. If the billet shows surface exudations it is necessary to machine the surface, but machining is not applied to billets of all alloys and sizes indiscriminately.

Until relatively recently it was usual in making tubes and hollow forms in aluminium alloys to begin with hollow billets, made by casting round steel cores in the moulds or by boring from solid billets; more recently, continuously cast hollow billets have become available. The high-strength alloys in particular are not well suited to piercing on account of their stiffness, leading to damage to the piercing tool and giving it a tendency to wander. Moreover, there is considerable risk in making a quick piercing stroke in these materials of forming cracks and tears along the bore, leading to internal defects in the tube when it is formed. However, piercing is practicable with some alloys and some of the modern heavy presses are equipped for such operations. A more recent innovation in the production of tubes in the softer aluminium alloys is the use of bridge dies (see page 22) in conjunction with solid billets,[17] similar in principle to those used in lead pipe extrusion.

The preheating of aluminium alloy billets must be carried out with a greater degree of control than is usually necessary with other alloys. Electrically-heated furnaces are normally preferred, although gas- and oil-fired furnaces are also used successfully. Alloys of the aluminium-magnesium type should not be preheated in gas- or oil-fired furnaces unless they are of the true muffle type, since the products of combustion may react with the alloys to the detriment of their welding characteristics.[18] For some alloys, it is necessary to use very prolonged preheating times in order to homogenize the structure. In such cases preheating periods as long as 24 hr. may be required, but for normal purposes 4 hr. is usually sufficient.

A difficulty in regard to aluminium and its alloys is that of removing the layer of metal remaining on the wall of the container after extrusion. This layer, the thickness of which depends on the annular clearance round the pressure disc, can not, as in the case of the skull which is often cut when extruding copper alloys, be completely detached, since it alloys with the container. A tight-fitting clearing disc is used to eject most of it, leaving a thin smeared layer behind. The extent of this problem is increased as the container becomes warm, since it then frequently assumes a barrel-like shape and the clearing disc can no longer be tight-fitting along the whole of the length of the container.[18] In some works the disc is put through after each extrusion; in other cases the layer is left to accumulate during several operations. Its frequent removal is of considerable importance since it will embody the outer skin of the billet which must always be oxidized to some extent, and this may contribute, if left, to the formation of the familiar extrusion defect in the following extrusions. In discussing this question, Colombel[19] states that failure to clear the container can give rise to blisters on extruded material, and that responsibility for this has been established by the fact that the skin of such blisters has been shown to have the composition of the preceding billet, where this has been of a different alloy.

The use of lubricants, such as graphite and molybdenum disulphide, has not met with a great deal of success in reducing the tendency of aluminium alloys to adhere to the container or in reducing frictional effects in general.[1] The main reason for this is that such lubricants become embedded in, or just below, the surface of the extruded section, giving rise to non-metallic inclusions and blisters. So far as simply reducing friction is concerned, some success has been achieved in the case of the strong light alloys by interposing a layer of pure aluminium between the billet and container.[20] By this device, which demands some modification of the technique and is difficult to apply to sections of complicated shape and thin cross-section, extrusion pressures are reduced by about 35 per cent. The mode of flow is entirely modified to the lubricated type, with the elimination of shear strains and of the extrusion defect.

There is need now to discuss the question of the rate of extrusion in some additional aspects to those already touched upon. So far the general influence of it on the pressure for extrusion has been dealt with, and the necessity when working at very high temperatures for extremely rapid operation has also been stressed. It is not uncommon to find rates being used for some copper alloys as high as 8 in. per second, with small sections leaving the press at velocities up to 2000 ft. a minute in vertical working. In contrast with this there are many metals belonging to diverse groups of alloys, such as those of aluminium-, magnesium-, lead-, and zinc-base which are distinctly sensitive in respect of the rate at which deformation is carried out on them. If certain critical speeds, which depend on the alloy, the temperature, and the size and shape of the extruded part, are exceeded, characteristic faults ranging from roughened, torn or repeatedly cracked surfaces to more complete disintegration are exhibited.

It can scarcely be said that the cause of this is understood with certainty in every case, but there are several factors which can be regarded as possibly contributing. Among these are (a) differential stresses set up owing to unequal distribution of flow through the die aperture, (b) a rise in the temperature of the metal due to the heat generated by internal and external friction in the course of deformation, (c) strain hardening caused by working which may not be removed sufficiently rapidly by recrystallization: thus in magnesium alloys, in which relief occurs somewhat slowly, it is possible for the capacity of the metal for deformation to become exhausted if work is applied rapidly. The first of these has already been discussed: liability to cracking from hot shortness arises in all metals when the attempt to work them is made at excessively high temperature, but its onset is naturally earlier in those alloys in which either from their constitution or due to lack of equilibrium in the cast condition, a liquid phase occurs at low temperatures. When this is combined with inherent stiffness so that extrusion must be confined to a narrow range close to the point of incipient fusion, the likelihood of trouble becomes greater. The second factor above has a bearing on this. It is not difficult to show that the temperature of metal may rise considerably during extrusion.[5, 21]. For instance, it has been observed in the laboratory that lead extruded cold at a fairly high rate emerges from the press at over 100° C. A similar observation can often be made in ordinary practice where the egress temperature of aluminium alloys may be found to be as much as 60° above the billet temperature. It is evident that

FIG. 157.

most of the heat generated will be in the zone where deformation is most severe, in the region near the entry to the die, and is likely to be marked in the very heavily worked zone near the surface of the section, where there is also friction at the bearing surface of the die. When extruding slowly, the generation of high local temperature tends to be prevented by the dissipation of heat into the surrounding mass, and into the tools, but at high rates, when moreover the heating is greater on account of the enhanced pressure which is required, the temperature may easily be raised far enough to bring the surface layers to the point where hot ruptures develop. Fig. 157 shows typical examples of the cracking which is encountered. All the cases of this kind examined by the authors have shown that the path of rupture is intergranular. The same fault may on rare occasions be met with in brass, but, partly because the heat engendered by working tends to be more than counterbalanced by the effect of the cooler container and die, and also because most of the alloys allow of being extruded at temperatures well below the danger-point, it does not ordinarily interfere with the use of high extrusion rates. It is usually due, when it occurs, to the billets being too hot, and it is then sufficient when the front end of the bar is seen to be cracked, to ease back the pressure on the press for a few moments.

It is clear, however, that, while temperature effects are of prime importance in peripheral cracking, such cracks would not develop if longitudinal tensile stresses were not generated at the surface of the extrusion as it passes through the die. The fact that peripheral cracking can be produced in relatively difficult materials like magnesium when extruded at normal temperatures indicates the importance of the stress component. The variable flow velocities between material at the centre of the die and that which is held back at the periphery results in the tensile stresses which cause the cracks to open. It may be expected, therefore, that modification of the stress pattern may prevent cracking and Unckel[22] has had some success in extruding hot-short alloys to which an envelope of plastic metal was applied so as to facilitate flow at the periphery. In the same field, Pugh and Green[23] have shown that a super-imposed fluid pressure prevents cracking in the extrusion of difficult materials, such as bismuth and magnesium.

In the extrusion of aluminium alloys, indication that the rate is on the high side is first given by a scored, broken surface on the material. This is due to fouling of the die apparently as the result of alloying between it and the metal, occurring, maybe, when a critical temperature is attained. 'Pick-up' of this kind constantly tends to occur when working close to the maximum permissible speed, and makes it necessary to dress up the die with emery cloth between operations. Interesting experiments* have been made by the Aluminium Company of America to avoid

* U.S. Patents Nos. 2,047,237 and 2,135,193.

pick-up, and so make possible a higher rate of output. In one method, the die is cleaned, and incidentally cooled, by spraying it with 10 per cent caustic soda solution after each extrusion, a rejection of a few inches from the leading end of the bar being made to avoid danger of later corrosion from the surplus reagent which may be carried through. Alternatively, an attempt is made to prevent the die from reaching the critical temperature by spraying it externally with water during extrusion. Both methods are claimed to permit several-fold increase in the rate of extrusion, though it is easy to foresee difficulties in applying them.* More recently extrusion dies have been designed with internal water-cooling channels and have proved successful in permitting the use of higher extrusion rates.[24]

For any alloy it is a matter of trial to determine the actual conditions of speed and temperature which will give the best results. Container and tool temperature and the form of size and section also enter into this: thus, for example, squares need to be extruded at a lower speed than round sections. Generally speaking, the temperature and speed will have to be chosen so as not to approach the point where overheating and cracking occur, while avoiding the lower temperatures and speeds which promote excessive grain-growth (see page 284) during subsequent reheating. Smith[18] has stated that this choice presents no difficulty so far as the non-heat-treatable alloys are concerned, since these alloys are usually of the solid-solution type free from low-melting-point compounds and having relatively low re-crystallization temperatures. With the heat-treatable alloys the lower solidus temperatures and the need for solution treatment after extrusion both have to be considered. The condition most favourable to the retention of fine grain in the heat-treated product is that in which an extrusion temperature has been used sufficiently high to enable recrystallization to occur during the actual extrusion operation, or immediately after the section issues from the die. In some cases this temperature is found to be so high as to be impracticable, since it approaches that at which incipient melting occurs. If a lower temperature is selected, a very fine balance of temperature and speed of extrusion has to be maintained if

---

* Mr. Dix, Jr., in a private communication, states that some practical success has been obtained with the former of the above methods.

satisfactory results are to be achieved. Since it is clearly the temperature of the section as it emerges from the die which is really important, control by water cooling at the die should allow greater flexibility of other process variables. Fritzlen[25] has discussed another possible means of control, in the form of maintaining the container temperature at a fixed value below that of the billet.

It is apparent from a consideration of the factors mentioned above as influencing extrusion conditions, that it is difficult to generalize on the subjects of temperature and speed in the extrusion of aluminium alloys, since each extrusion represents a separate problem. In what follows on the extrusion of specific alloys it must be remembered, therefore, that the figures quoted may be altered according to the size of the extrusion, the amount of the reduction and to various factors associated with the particular press used.

Ordinary commercial grades of aluminium extrude readily, requiring only low pressures, and having a long plastic range upwards from about 370° C.; the usual limits employed being from 450° to 500° C. Regulation of the extrusion rate is of little consequence with aluminium itself, for which it can be as high as 1 in. per second, giving egress speeds up to 50 ft. per minute. A few of the softer alloys, such as the Al-Mn, Al-Si and Al-Mg$_2$Si series, also may normally be extruded at high temperatures and speeds (480°–500° C. and 30 ft. per minute). With the copper bearing alloys, such as duralumin, temperatures and rates have to be reduced to about 450° C. and 8 ft. per minute respectively. Even greater difficulty is experienced with the very strong alloys of the aluminium-zinc-magnesium type, which are normally extruded at about 420° C. where they offer considerable assistance to deformation. Speeds of 3–4 ft. per minute are common, since break-up occurs at slightly higher speeds. Smith[18] refers to the satisfactory extrusion of these alloys at a critical speed in the range 40–80 ft. per minute and at a temperature of 360° C., but he states that it is very unlikely that such conditions would be practicable in production.

Table 13 gives some typical figures which may be taken as a general guide to the conditions frequently used in fabricating aluminium alloys by extrusion.

TABLE 13

TYPICAL EXTRUSION TEMPERATURES AND SPEEDS FOR
SOME ALUMINIUM ALLOYS [18]

Designation	Composition				Extru-sion Range ° C.	Optimum Temp. ° C.	Con-tainer Temp. ° C.	Extru-sion Speed ft./min.
	Cu %	Mg %	Si %	Zn %				
B.S. No. HE14	4	0·6	0·6	–	400–480	450	420	6–8
B.S. No. HE11	2	0·6	1·0	–	400–480	460	420	15–20
B.S. No. HE10	–	0·6	1·0	–	400–520	500	420	30–50
D.T.D. No. 683	1	2·0	–	6·5	380–440	420	420	3–4
B.S. No. NE4	–	2·0	–	–	380–440	420	420	14–18
B.S. No. NE6	–	5·0	–	–	400–460	440	420	8–14
B.S. No. NE7	–	7·0	–	–	400–460	440	420	4–6

The following data, given by Zeerleder,[26] indicate the normal working conditions for different types, and afford a comparison of power requirements.

TABLE 14

Extrusion Temperature ° C.	Aluminium 450°/500°	Al-Mg-Mn 450°/500°	Al-Mg-Si 450°/500°	Al-Cu-Mg 380°/460°	Al-Mg 380°/420°
Dimensions of sections (in.) which can be extruded from a con-tainer 15·5 in. dia. under pressure of 16 tons per square inch	$\frac{5}{16}$ × 4	2 × 4	$1\frac{1}{4}$ × 4	3 × 4	5 × 4
Pressure in tons per square inch required to extrude a section of $\frac{1}{8}$-in. wall thickness from billets 8 in. dia. 30 in. long	20–25	45–65	22–48	54–70	76–95

A determination made in the laboratory of the relative specific extrusion pressures of several alloys has already been shown graphically in Fig. 137.

Finishing Treatment

The greater number of extruded aluminium alloys which are intended for structural uses require to be heat-treated after they leave the press in order to develop the maximum properties of which they are capable. Briefly, this treatment of age- or precipitation-hardening involves in the first place a period of soaking at a high temperature somewhat below the solidus curve of the alloy concerned, to cause the entry into solid solution of the hardening compounds; this is followed by rapid cooling, usually by quenching in water, with the object of retaining these in a condition of supersaturation, and is completed finally by a precipitation stage which is brought about in some materials by a period of ageing at the ordinary temperature, but is induced in others as the result of heating at comparatively low temperatures. Some alloys are prone to harden considerably on air cooling after extrusion, and, in the case of tube shells or other sections which have to be cold drawn, it may be necessary to soften them first by annealing. Tube-reducing machines, giving reductions up to 85 per cent in one operation, are now being increasingly used for aluminium alloys.

Since the extruded product leaves the die at a temperature which approximates to the solution heat-treatment temperature, attention has naturally been directed to the possibility of achieving solution-treatment by quenching the extruded lengths directly as they come from the press. Originally this was achieved by passing the bar into water troughs, but greater success has now been obtained by water spraying as the product leaves the die. Quite a large quantity of material is produced in this manner, which has the advantage that the development of large grain, associated with reheating (see page 285), may be avoided. It is necessary to preheat the billets to a temperature which ensures that under the extrusion conditions obtaining the temperature of the issuing extruded section lies within the solution-treatment range. In view of the other considerations, already mentioned, which govern the choice of extrusion temperature, this may clearly give rise to difficulties with certain alloys, although others, such as the aluminium-zinc-magnesium types, are ideally suited to die-quenching, because their optimum solution-treatment temperature

253

lies near to the optimum extrusion temperature. In the case of complicated sections great thought has to be given to the arrangement of the spray, not only to provide a water supply sufficient for rapid quenching of sections up to 2 in. thick, but in order to avoid twisting and distortion arising from the development of thermal gradients. The mechanical properties of die-quenched sections are entirely satisfactory, being as good as, and in some cases better, than those of sections in the same alloys produced by a separate heat-treatment process. The method has the further advantage that, since the sections are rapidly cooled, they are less sensitive to damage on the press run-out table. For this reason also, the technique may be useful when applied to non-heat-treatable alloys, provided that the quenching does not affect the characteristics of the alloy. In Germany, the technique of die-quenching has been applied to alloys in which the extrusion temperature had to be appreciably lower than the solution treatment temperature.[27] This is achieved by flash heating the extrusion as it emerges from the die, by passing it through a small furnace prior to being quenched. By holding the furnace at about 800° C., and with the particular rate of extrusion used, the temperature was raised the 40°–60° C. to the solution treatment temperature.

The methods adopted in bringing sections, many of which are very intricate, into a serviceable condition have been described in some detail by Worsdale.[28] As extruded, the lengths are reasonably straight, but severe distortion and warping is found to take place on quenching after the solution treatment. The latter is carried out generally in salt baths fired by gas or oil, or in electrically heated furnaces provided with air-circulating fans. The cradle with its load is withdrawn mechanically from the furnace and immersed as quickly as possible in the quenching tank. After quenching the sections are treated to remove the distortion to which it has given rise. This is done first of all in hydraulic stretching machines in which a strictly limited amount of extension* is given to straighten the lengths without reducing them below the permitted dimensions, or unduly decreasing their ductility. Stretchers capable of exerting a pull of up to 1000 tons on 80 ft. long and 40 sq. in. sections have now been built,

* Usually about 2% permanent extension.

with their gripping heads able to rotate to facilitate detwisting. Some channels and **I** beams, in which local warping is not always removed sufficiently by stretching and hand straightening to bring them within specification, are corrected by careful pressing at the points which require it. Worsdale points out that much improvement in avoiding distortion has been effected by the use for solution heating of vertical electric furnaces in which the extruded sections are suspended, being ultimately allowed to drop into deep water-tanks placed underneath, this method giving very good results with large and complex sections. Smith and Swindells,[1] however, have stated that a great deal of the distortion on quenching from horizontal furnaces may be avoided by proper loading practices.

Magnesium Alloys

Technical difficulties in the removal of chloride inclusions from the manufactured metal delayed progress in the development and engineering uses of magnesium and its alloys in the period when a great advance was being made in the application of aluminium-base alloys. With the eventual solution of this problem the way became clear, and an impetus was given to the discovery and exploitation of new alloys, which, once again, has been reinforced by the requirements of the aircraft and nuclear power industries in the current period. The particular merits of magnesium alloys are similar to those which give aluminium alloys their chief value, and consist primarily in the advantages derived from the association of low specific gravity with satisfactory strength figures; the advantage being increased by the still lower density (approx. 1·8) of the former than the latter (about 2·8), despite the fact that the mechanical properties of magnesium alloys are below those of the strongest of the aluminium alloys. A particular attraction of magnesium alloys, however, lies in their extraordinarily good machining properties, in which respect they are superior even to screwing brass. There is perhaps no group of alloys to which extrusion is of more importance than it is to these, since the comparatively coarse-grained structure of the cast material causes most of them to be too susceptible to cracking to be worked by an alternative means until sufficient deformation has been imparted to refine the grain: except, therefore, for one or two soft alloys, it forms an invariable preliminary to other shaping processes.

No great amount of pure magnesium is extruded for it has somewhat poor properties, especially as regards its proof stress. The alloying elements of chief concern at present are aluminium, zinc, cerium and zirconium; manganese is usually also present, since, though it has little effect on the strength, it has a valuable function in improving corrosion resistance. One important binary alloy, containing up to 2·0 per cent manganese, is used extensively for the manufacture of rolled sheet. It is comparatively soft and easier to extrude than other alloys, and is also one of the few which are capable of being rolled directly without pre-extrusion.

In the U.K. extrusions are made from billets of $2\frac{7}{8}$–12 in. dia. on presses varying in power over the range 600–3500 tons; normal maximum pressures on the billet are 30–50 tons/sq. in.[29] In the U.S. the Dow Chemical Company have recently installed a 13,200-ton press capable of handling billets up to 32 in. dia.[30] Extrusion technique is generally similar to that for aluminium base alloys but, according to Wilkinson and Fox,[29] die design requires special consideration and, in their opinion, should incorporate short bearing lengths and sharp die entries. Tube extrusion in alloys AM503, ZW2 and ZW3 is now made with bridge dies. (The aluminium-bearing alloys do not weld satisfactorily.) In contrast to the previous practice of using bored billets, mandrel piercing is now used in the extrusion of large diameter tubes in ZW3 alloy. The stiffness of the alloys towards extrusion is increased in proportion to the amount of hardening elements which they contain, and the temperature employed is generally higher the greater the quantity of these. Billet temperatures are also affected by the size of the sections, being higher for heavy reductions, but are usually in the range 250°–450° C. Container temperatures should be identical with, or only slightly higher than, billet temperatures.

Pre-heating of the billets requires to be carried out uniformly to promote as far as possible a homogeneous structure by absorption of compounds, such as Mg_4Al_3, present in the alloys. Fox[31] points out, and this is also applicable to aluminium alloys, that the initial structure of the billet has an important bearing,

TABLE 15

Designation	Composition					Mechanical Properties as Extruded		
	Al %	Zn %	Mn %	Ce %	Zr %	0·1 per cent Proof Stress tons/sq. in.	Ultimate Tensile Strength tons/sq. in.	Elongation per cent on 2 in.
Magnesium	—	—	—	—	—	—	12·0	8
Elektron AM503 / A.S.T.M.-M1.BSS-1355	—	—	1·5	—	—	8–13	15–20	4–10
Elektron AZ31 / A.S.T.M.-AZ31X	3·0	1·0	0·3	—	—	11	18	15
Elektron AZM / A.S.T.M.-AZ61X.BSS-1354	6·0	1·0	0·3	—	—	11–14 / 9–12	17–22 / 14–19	10–18 (3 in.) / 8–16 (3 in.)
Elektron AZ855 / A.S.T.M. AZ80X.BSS-1351	8·0	0·4	0·3	—	—	10–14	18–22	8–14
Elektron AM537	—	—	2·0	0·5	—	12	17	23
Elektron ZW2 (Tube)	—	2·0	—	—	0·7	11–15	17–22	3–8
Elektron ZW3	—	3·0	—	—	0·7	14–17	20–23	10–25 (simple sections)
DTD. 622 and 733	—	—	—	—	—	17–21	23–26	8–14 (3 in.)

and casting methods which lead to a fine grain are well worth adoption,[32] since if it is coarse, larger particles of the compounds are present which are less readily dissolved, and tend to give rise to a solution gradient. In magnesium alloys this results in internal stress, since solution is accompanied by a small contraction, and it can also influence the evenness of response to heat treatment later.

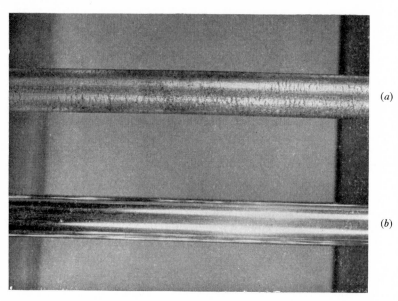

(a)

(b)

FIG. 158.—AM503 alloy bar extruded at 8 ft./min. (a) and 60 ft./min. (b) showing the resultant difference in surface condition.
(*Wilkinson and Fox, 'J. Inst. Metals'.*)

The binary magnesium-manganese alloy (AM503) is readily extruded at low pressures in the temperature range 250° to 350° C., the actual temperature used depending upon the reduction and billet length rather than the properties desired, which are relatively insensitive to extrusion conditions. Good surface condition of the extrusion is achieved only with high speeds, of the order of 50–100 ft. per minute, Fig. 158 showing the surface conditions due to speeds of 8 and 60 ft. per minute.

With the aluminium and zinc containing alloys, and particularly those with the higher aluminium contents such as AZM and

AZ855, difficulties arise at high speeds due to hot-shortness. Under conditions approaching equilibrium magnesium is capable of dissolving about 12 per cent aluminium, but in cast billets 4–5 per cent usually represents the limit of solubility.[33] Alloys containing 6 per cent Al or more therefore contain Mg_4Al_3, which forms a eutectic melting at 435° C. The extrusion temperature may vary from 250° to 400° C., but at the higher values speeds are restricted to about 12 ft. per minute. Continuous casting improves the homogeneity of these alloys and water cooling of the dies or taper heating of the billets further facilitate their extrusion.

The introduction of the magnesium-zinc-zirconium alloys, ZW2 and ZW3, has constituted a considerable advancement in the magnesium alloy technology for a number of reasons. They are high strength alloys, as the figures quoted in Table 14 show, but, since they do not contain aluminium, the cast billet contains only very small quantities of the second phase. Since the solidus temperature is raised by about 100° C. also, the risk of hot-shortness at relatively high extrusion speeds is very much reduced. However, the mechanical properties are sensitive to billet pre-heating time, temperature and extrusion speed, the effect of the latter being shown in Fig. 159. Long preheating times and high temperatures and speeds result in properties similar to those obtained with the older aluminium containing alloys, times having to be short and temperatures and speeds low if high properties are to be obtained. Increasing the zinc content to 5 or 6 per cent, as in the American alloy ZK60 and ZK61, reduces the sensitivity to extrusion speed in respect of mechanical properties. The alloying of the zirconium bearing materials has probably constituted one of the major problems associated with their development. It is usual to add the zirconium from a salt, and with careful control good results can be obtained[32], although Dominion Magnesium Limited in Canada have developed a method whereby the addition is made in the conventional manner through a master alloy.[33]

Although the explanation of the low extrusion rates necessary for the successful extrusion of some magnesium alloys does not appear to lie outside the reasons put forward for other metals, Altwicker [34] considers that the most significant cause is connected

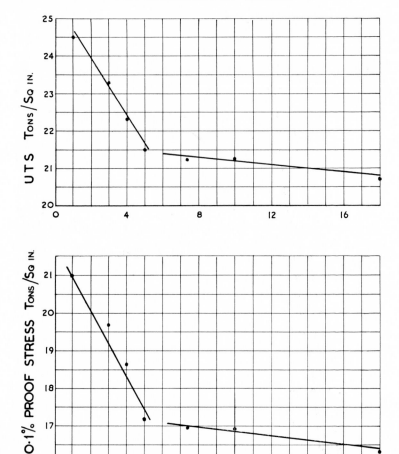

FIG. 159.—Effect of extrusion speed on the tensile properties of ZW3
$\frac{3}{4}''$ dia. bar extruded at 320° C.
(*Wilkinson and Fox, ' J. Inst. Metals '.*)

with the degree of recovery from crystal deformation, which is
less complete when work is applied quickly, causing higher
stresses and the exhaustion of the capacity for slip in the crystals.
This is worthy of consideration, for the speed with which recrystallization takes place varies from one metal to another, and

according to the temperature prevailing. It is also a fact that metals worked in what are considered to be their hot working range can frequently be made to show marked work hardening if they are quenched immediately following deformation, showing that temporary loss of plasticity can easily accompany rapid working.

Zinc-base Alloys

Virtually all the zinc and zinc alloy billets now extruded in the U.K. are for subsequent drawing to wire,[35] although, arising out of the policy of seeking substitutes for copper alloys, a number of additional applications were developed in Germany during the war years. Among the principal applications were tubes for cold-water systems, inflator pump bodies, hand rails, and as fittings in the electrical industry. A summary of the fabricating qualities and mechanical properties has been given by Kastner,[36] while problems connected with extrusion at the origin of faults in the latter have been discussed by Löhberg[37] and Wolf.[38]

TABLE 16

Composition of Alloy			Properties in Extruded Condition		Extrusion Temperature °C
Al	Cu	Mg	U.T.S. tons/sq. in.	Elongation per cent	
3·8/4·2	0·9/1·2	0·02/0·05	27	7	200
			25	10	320
9/11	1·8/2·0	0·02/0·05	34	4	200
			32	16	320
—	4·0	—	20	32	240

The best temperatures for extrusion vary with the composition. Alloys containing copper alone are found to extrude best at 200°–240° C., at which, though the pressure is very high, a greater speed can be used than in lower ranges. Those containing aluminium are best worked above this, at between 270° and 320° C., at which, as the table above shows, the properties are not inferior, while the ease of extrusion is improved by working above the transition temperature of the cubic β solid solution. These alloys provide one further example in which the speed of extrusion limits the rate of output, and this, combined with the necessity for small drafts in later drawing operations, goes a long way to offset the lower metal cost as compared with the brasses they are designed to replace. Kastner gives the following figures to compare one of them with other commonly extruded materials, in terms of their extrusion pressure and permissible speeds of working

TABLE 17

Material	Extrusion Speed from Die (ft./min.) for Tubes as under (in.)			Extrusion Pressure (tons/sq. in.) for Tubes $1\frac{1}{2}'' \times \frac{1}{8}''$	
	$1 \times \frac{5}{64}$	$1\frac{1}{2} \times \frac{1}{8}$	$3\frac{1}{4} \times \frac{5}{32}$	Beginning	End
Brass (63 per cent) . . .	500	250	250	29	38
Aluminium	300	250	250	19	19
Al-Mg-Si alloy	33	50	50	33	38
Zinc alloy with 4 per cent Cu	40*	16	16	48	24

* Refers to a pre-extruded billet.

It will be seen that the pressures for extrusion are considerably higher than for brass of the composition indicated: they are in general roughly the same as for duralumin.

Owing to the adverse effect which cold-working has on the properties of these zinc-base alloys, hot methods of deformation are much to be preferred. However, since in extrusion the limiting wall-thickness which can be made is about $\frac{1}{16}$ in., any further reduction must be obtained by drawing. In this connection it may be remarked that the effect on the properties produced by cold work is quite different from that which it has on most materials, and although the response of the different alloys is not identical, it may be said that, in general, in the initial stages of drawing, the tensile strength increases slightly, but this is followed, as more work is done, by a fall in strength, while the elongation values increase. If large reductions are attempted at each pass, therefore, there is danger of stretching or tearing the tube; moreover, as the number of passes increases the permissible reduction at each diminishes.

Extrusion of the Rarer Metals

The rarer metals, such as titanium, zirconium, molybdenum and uranium, now being increasingly used for nuclear power and other high-temperature applications, can be fabricated by extrusion. Indeed, this is frequently the most attractive method of working because either the crystal structure of the metal or the impurities which it contains tend to make it behave in a brittle manner if the working process imposes complex tensional stresses. The predominantly compressive nature of the forces involved in extrusion render the fabrication of such metals relatively easy, although frequently there are other difficulties which operate to complicate even this method of fabrication. Thus, the attraction of many of these new metals often arises from their strength in high-temperature service, a property which mitigates against ease of extrusion and necessitates the use of high unit pressures, temperatures and speeds in press operation. The high temperatures, coupled with the inherently reactive nature of many of these metals towards either the constituents of the atmosphere or the tools with which they come into contact, make it necessary to adopt special techniques for satisfactory extrusions. For instance, where glass lubrication has not proved entirely satisfactory, the billet has been sealed in a sheath of some inert ductile metal prior to extrusion, so that the atmosphere does not come into contact with the metal which is also separated from the working tools.

Sufficient experience in the extrusion of titanium has now been acquired for this to be a method of fabrication which is not only important but reasonably well understood. The pressures involved are rather greater than those employed in the extrusion of steel but temperatures, in the range 850°–1000° C., are somewhat lower because of the dangers of gas contamination and loss of ductility at higher temperatures.[39] The prevention of contact between the titanium and the die, to eliminate galling and seizing, is one of the most important factors[40] and the simplest method, which is being used with some success, is the oxidation of the surface of the billet. Glass and molybdenum disulphide have also been used as lubricants and sheathing with copper, or other ductile metal, has been employed with success, although the extrusion temperature has then to be kept low enough to prevent undesirable alloying between the sheath and billet materials. The sheath is usually removed by cutting and stripping followed by acid pickling.

Wilhelm and Moudry[41] have shown that the properties of extruded titanium alloys are dependent upon the extrusion ratio, the U.T.S. and Y.S. being increased by as much as 15 per cent for an increase in extrusion ratio from 10 : 1 to 100 : 1 with a 3 per cent aluminium, 5 per cent chromium alloy. This is considered to be surprising in view of the fact that extrusion takes place close to the $\beta \rightarrow \alpha$ transformation temperature and strains resulting from the extrusion process may be expected to be relieved by the precipitation of the α phase during cooling. It has been suggested[40] that the effect may be explained by a greater degree of preferred orientation resulting from the higher extrusion ratios. Alternatively it has been shown[41] that the structures of extruded bars, and therefore possibly mechanical properties, are dependent upon the rate of cooling from the extrusion temperature and rate of cooling will be determined by extrusion ratio and resulting section size. Low extrusion ratios result in a coarse precipitate of the α-phase within the grains and as a grain boundary network, while high ratios yield a less continuous and finer grain boundary network and much finer α within the grains. Irrespective of the reason for this effect of extrusion ratio the advantage of large diameter containers is apparent and the need for heavy presses obvious. It is interesting to note that the Curtiss-Wright Corporation, Buffalo, N.Y., are using a 12,000-ton press with a maximum container diameter of 24 in. for titanium extrusion.

The problems associated with the extrusion of zirconium are similar to those experienced with titanium. Temperatures as far apart as 800° and 1650° C. have been employed,[42] but in general a much narrower range of 800–1100° C. should suffice for all alloys in which there is current interest if adequate press capacity is available. Zirconium readily welds to the die during extrusion if adequate lubrication is not provided and this problem has been tackled with the same methods as have been used with titanium. Salt-bath heating of the billet combined with glass lubrication have met with some success, although Miller[43] has pointed out that some reaction would be expected between glass and hot zirconium. There is some advantage to be gained from the use of dies having a conical lead-in (140°-90°) which, together with adequate lubrication, has so far permitted the satisfactory extrusion of rod and tube from billets up to 7 in. in diameter at extrusion ratios greater than 30 : 1.

Arc-cast molybdenum ingots are usually broken down by extrusion prior to rolling,[44] extrusion ratios of 4 to 1 being usual for unalloyed material and 3 to 1 for alloys. Ingots up to $8\frac{3}{4}$ in. diameter have been extruded using glass lubrication, although the small reduction is not conducive to a good surface finish and there is a marked tendency for cracking at the front end of the bar. With salt-bath heating extrusion is satisfactory at 1250° C., but with gas-heated billets lowest extrusion pressures are observed at temperatures in excess of 1400° C., an effect which is suggested as being due to better adhesion of the glass on the salt-coated surface. There are some indications that induction heating is associated with lower ram pressures and less tendency for cracking at the front end of the extruded molybdenum than is the case with the other methods of heating. The extrusion of tubes in molybdenum has so far been achieved only from drilled ingots.

Uranium is another metal which, at least in some alloyed forms, is not easily deformed under tension and its extrusion is now extensively practised.[45] The metal rapidly attacks normal tool steels if the temperature exceeds 735° C. and for extrusion of the γ-form zirconium sheaths can be used. Carbide dies and mandrels are not attacked, but require care in use because of their brittleness. Ordinary steel tools are sufficient for extrusion of the α-form, but the reduced temperature (less than 600° C.) demands higher unit pressures. The extruded rod, whether in the γ or α form, must be protected from atmospheric oxidation and this can be achieved either by directing the rod into an argon-filled container attached to the die-block or by water quenching.

A special application of extrusion to uranium is the ' integral ' canning of fuel elements for nuclear reactors.[46] The extrusion of a composite billet of sheathed uranium results in bonding of the can and fuel and eliminates fusion welding except for the end caps. Full integral canning has been achieved from a billet composed of alternate layers of fuel and sheath material, all fitted into a container of the sheath material. After extrusion, the rod consists of sheathed fuel separated at appropriate intervals by sheath material over the whole cross-section, at which points the extruded bar can be parted.

The difficulties which have been overcome in successfully extruding these metals have provided a fund of experience, particularly with regard to lubrication and high working temperatures, which should make easier the solution of problems associated with other new metals in the future. Indeed there are some indications that some of these metals, such as plutonium[47] and beryllium[48], have already been successfully extruded in small quantities.

The Extrusion of Metal Powders

Extrusion is an obvious method of working raw material, such as chips from machining operations or metals which are initially produced in powder form, where compacting is necessary before the further consolidation of the metal in the working process. In recent years, however, this particular application of extrusion has received considerable attention as the result of the realization that it affords a method of fabricating mixtures of powdered metals and non-metals having unique properties.

The discovery by Von Zeerleder and his colleagues[49] of the remarkable properties of extruded aluminium powder (SAP) has received most attention in this new field. Conventional powder metallurgy of aluminium, involving only pressing and sintering, has not appeared promising[50] because of the presence of the stable oxide film on the surface of the particles. However, hot-working of the compacted powder breaks up these films and results in a material having mechanical properties similar at room temperature but better at elevated temperatures than those obtained with highly alloyed material made by conventional methods. The properties obtained are a function of the size of the powder particles since this influences the oxide content of the compact,[51] which frequently runs at about 13 per cent in the milled flake powders employed. SAP containing alloying elements, such as copper and magnesium, has also been prepared and shown to have useful properties.[52]

Macdonald and Ramsey[53] have used the method of extruding

mixed powders for improving the Young's Modulus of aluminium. Here the technique is invaluable since the modulus is raised either by alloying additions which form intermetallic compounds that would render the alloy brittle and unworkable if prepared by casting, or by the addition of an ' inert ' second phase such as titanium carbide which could not be dispersed other than by the method of mixing powders.

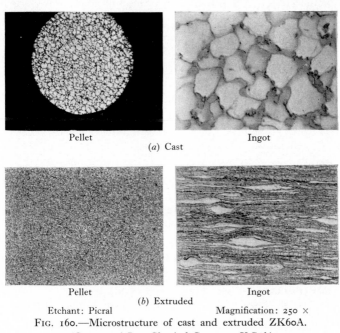

Pellet   Ingot

(a) Cast

Pellet   Ingot

(b) Extruded

Etchant: Picral   Magnification: 250 ×

FIG. 160.—Microstructure of cast and extruded ZK60A.

(*Courtesy of Dow Chemical Company, U.S.A.*)

Since magnesium oxide has a refractoriness similar to that of alumina it is not surprising to find that the extrusion of magnesium powder can also result in a material having relatively high tensile strength.   Two types of powder have been studied, one atomized to spherical particles (pellets) averaging 0·016 in. diameter[54] and the other scratched from slabs to produce lamellar particles having various sizes.[55]   Both gave material having good mechanical properties after extrusion, the greatest improvement being in the compressive yield strength as the result of a considerable improvement in the grain structure (Fig. 160).[56]   As with SAP, the properties of magnesium powder extrusions depend upon the particle size, the alloy content and the conditions of extrusion. Cole[57] has studied the effects of extrusion temperature and speed in the laboratory and has shown that extrusions of good appearance can be made at slow extrusion speeds (0·0006–0·036 in./sec. ram speed, 25 : 1 reduction) provided the temperature exceeds 470° C. for pure magnesium. Brown[55] has reported obtaining good extrusions at temperatures as low as 300° C. with higher speeds (0·03–0·3 in./sec.), although Cole[57] has suggested that the heat generated at these speeds would raise the temperature at the die beyond the minimum satisfactory temperature of 470° C. indicated by his work. This effect of temperature is the reverse of that experienced with cast billets, where hot shortness is experienced if the temperature exceeds about 420° C. A further contradiction in the behaviour of powder as compared with solid billets is that the higher the temperature the greater is the increase in extrusion speed for a given increase in pressure. The reason for these differences would appear to be concerned with the fact that, in the case of powders, pressure is required for purposes other than that of simply altering the shape of the billet and Cole has suggested that a high proportion of the work of extrusion is used in breaking up the oxide films. Once these are broken, and cohesion of adjacent oxide films and of exposed metal surfaces has taken place, the metal deforms easily, a small increase in pressure giving a large increase in flow rate.

Many of the rarer metals now being increasingly used to meet the requirements of the nuclear power industry, emerge from the ore-extraction process in powder form. In some cases the powder is melted and cast into ingots, in other cases it is more convenient to process the powder by pressing and sintering, before mechanical working. In these latter cases consolidation of the powder by extrusion is frequently employed. The powder may be cold compacted and possibly sintered before extrusion, but use is frequently made of the advantages of hot-compacting and especially since this can be performed within the extrusion press itself, so reducing compacting and extrusion to a one-stage process.

Consolidated beryllium powder can be extruded over the temperature range from 400° to 1100° C., sheathing being necessary at the higher temperatures because of the tendency of the beryllium to weld to the die materials.[48]   At low temperatures, high pressures (40 tons/sq. in.) are necessary even with low extrusion ratios (less than 8 : 1).   It is essential also to use a die with a cone angle of about 90°, so that normal metal dies have a very short life.   This problem has been overcome by the use of a metal shear die and a graphite lead-in cone,[58] the latter assisting in the lubrication.   The sheaths used in high-temperature extrusion are usually of mild steel, sometimes with copper plated on the outside to act as a lubricant.   At about 1000° C. pressures are about half those required at 450° C. and modern high-speed presses can be used.   The correct choice of sheath thickness is most important and is related to the packing density of the powder.   This is because of the tendency of the sheath to fold-in when upset under the ram pressure, a tendency which is increased with low packing densities and small reductions of area.   Beryllium tubes have been produced from powder billets having a sheathed bore and using a floating mandrel.   Difficulties may arise if account is not taken of the fact that the thermal expansion of mild steel is less than that of beryllium, so that large thicknesses of steel left within an extruded beryllium tube may cause cracking.

Beryllium extruded from powder shows appreciably higher mechanical properties than extruded cast material, as the figures in Table 18 show.

TABLE 18

(from data given in Reference 48)

Condition	U.T.S. tons/sq. in.	Lt. Proportionality tons/sq. in.	Elongation per cent
Cast	10	—	0
Hot pressed . . .	20	—	2–4
Extruded cast billets .	20–25	8–10	2–3
Extruded powder . .	40–50	10–15	12–20

This improvement in properties results from the development of a fibre texture in which the basal planes align themselves in the direction of extrusion, the $(10\bar{1}0)$ direction being parallel to the extrusion direction.   The results shown in Table 18 were obtained from tests on specimens cut in the longitudinal direction from extruded rod: there are indications that the transverse properties, as would be expected, are inferior. The properties are dependent upon the extrusion temperature and ratio and, to a lesser extent, upon the initial powder particle size.[59]

Thorium metal is usually produced in powder form, at least in the U.K., and has been successfully consolidated by extrusion in the temperature range 500°–1000° C.[45] Heating and hot working can be carried out on the bare metal, but the use of a copper sheath, about ⅛ in. thick, in which the powder is cold-compacted, is usually preferred. Extrusion ratios of 10 or 20 to 1 are suitable at temperatures between 500° and 800° C., for bars of ½ in. to 2 in. diameter. The extruded product has near-theoretical density but tends to have low ductility, possibly due to the presence of hydrogen. Vacuum annealing at 1000° C. removes this and elongations of 30 per cent may then be obtained with tensile strengths of 20 tons/sq. in.

The extrusion of powders has not been restricted to the metals and alloys mentioned, the method having been applied also, for instance, to zirconium[43] and uranium.[45] Indeed, there is no reason why the method should not be applied to other metals also should the need arise.

REFERENCES

[1] C. Smith and N. Swindells. Inst. Metals Monograph and Report Series No. 16, *The Control of Quality in Working Operations*, 1954, p. 47.

[2] M. Cook and E. Davis. *J. Inst. Metals*, 1949–50, **76**, 501.

[3] D. K. Crampton. *Trans. A.S.M.*, 1937, **25**, 55.

[4] P. Bernhreft. *Z. für Metallkunde*, 1932, **24**, 210–13, 261–3.

[5] W. W. Cotter and W. R. Clark. Metals Technology T.P. 1850, *Trans. Amer. Inst. Min. & Met. Eng.*, 1946, **166**, 447.

[6] A Wragg. *Met. Ind. (London)*, 1936, **48**, 73–7.

[7] Non-Ferrous Heavy Metal Fabrication in the U.S.A. Technical Assistance Mission No. 79. Organization for European Economic Co-operation, p. 163.

[8] D. W. D. Showell. *J. Inst. Metals*, 1949–50, **76**, 527.

[9] H. Lepp. *Tech. Pub. Internat. Tin. Res. Dev. Council*, Series D, 1937 (3).

[10] H. Lepp. Discussion. *J. Inst. Metals*, 1939, **64**, 364.

[11] A. B. Graham. *J. Inst. Eng. and Shipbuilders of Scotland*, 1938–9, **82**, 188.

[12] G. Evans. *Iron and Steel Industry*, 1938, **11**, 169.

[13] S. O. Evans. *Metal Progress*, April 1955, **67**, 91.

[14] —— *Machinery*, 20 April and 4 May 1956.

[15] P. J. Sukolski. B.I.S.R.A. Report No. MW/G/58/57.

[16] R. T. Staples and H. J. Hurst. Inst. Metals Monograph and Report Series No. 15. *The Control of Quality in Melting and Casting*, p. 51.

[17] —— *Metal Treatment*, Spring 1948, **15**, 27.

[18] C. Smith. *J. Inst. Metals*, 1949–50, **76**, 429.

[19] C. A. Colombel. *Rolling Mill Journal*, 1931, **5**, 479.

[20] British Patent No. 689,051.

[21] J. F. W. Bishop. *Quart. J. Mechanics Appl. Math.*, 1956, **9**, 236.

[22] H. A. Unckel, *Met. Ind.*, 1946, **69**, 423 and 445.

[23] H. W. D. Pugh and D. Green. Mechanical Engineering Research Laboratory, Plasticity Report No. 147, April 1958.

[24] A. v. Zeerleder. *Technology of Light Metals*. Elsevier Publishing Co., London, 1949, p. 193.

[25] T. L. Fritzlen. Metals Technology, T.P. 1851. *Trans. Amer. Inst. Min. & Met. Eng.*, 1946, **166**, 458.

[26] A. v. Zeerleder. *Aluminium*, 1937, **19** (10), 634.

[27] B.I.O.S. Report 127,144, 981, 1366, 1656, 1947–8.

[28] R. Worsdale. *Metallurgia*, 1940, **21**, 117.

[29] R. G. Wilkinson and F. A. Fox. *J. Inst. Metals*, 1949–50, **76**, 473.

[30] —— *Modern Metals*, 1957, **13** (4).

[31] F. A. Fox. *Met. Ind.* (*London*), 1941, **59**, 2.

[32] R. G. Wilkinson and S. B. Hirst. Inst. Metals Monograph and Report Series No. 15. *The Control of Quality in Melting and Casting*, p. 66.

[33] H. G. Warrington. *Modern Metals*, 1951, **7** (10), 23.

[34] H. Altwicker. *Tech. of Magnesium and its Alloys*. Published by F. A. Hughes and Co., Ltd.

[35] C. W. Roberts and B. Walters. Inst. Metals Monograph and Report Series No. 15. *The Control of Quality in Melting and Casting*, p. 40.

[36] H. Kastner. *Metallwirtschaft*, 1939, **50/51**, 1010.

[37] H. Löhberg. *Z. für Metallkunde*, 1939, **31**, 133–4, 279–83.

[38] W. Wolf. *Ibid.*, 1939, **31**, 64.

[39] Extruding Titanium. *Met. Ind.* (*London*), 1958, **92**, 445–6.

[40] A. D. McQuillan and M. K. McQuillan. *Titanium*, Butterworth, London, 1956, pp. 89–90.

[41] K. A. Wilhelm and G. A. Mandry. Titanium Successfully Hot Extruded. *Iron Age*, 1954, **173**, 126–9.

[42] R. B. Gordon and W. J. Hurford. Fabrication of Zirconium. *Zirconium and Zirconium Alloys*. Amer. Soc. Metals, Cleveland, 1953.

[43] G. L. Miller. *Zirconium*. Butterworth, London, 2nd Edn. 1957, p. 459.

[44] N. L. Deuble. Arc-Cast Molybdenum—Ingot to Bar, Sheet or Wire. *Metal Progress*, 1955, **67** (5), 89–92.

[45] L. Grainger. *Uranium and Thorium.* George Newnes, London, 1958, pp. 107-8.

[46] J. G. Ball. Metallurgical Research in Nuclear Power Production. *J. Inst. Metals,* 1955-6, **84,** 239–50.

[47] J. G. Ball and W. B. H. Lord. A History of the Early British Work on Plutonium Metallurgy. *Ibid.,* 1957-8, **86,** 369–79.

[48] J. Williams. The Fabrication and Properties of Commercially Pure Beryllium. *Metallurgical Reviews,* 1958, **3,** 1–44.

[49] A. v. Zeerleder. *Z. für Metallkunde,* 1950, **41,** 228.

[50] —— Sintered Aluminium Powder, the Development of SAP. *Met. Ind. (London),* 1952, **81,** 143-6.

[51] R. Irmann. Sintered Aluminium with High Strength at Elevated Temperatures. *Metallurgia,* 1952, **46,** 125–33.

[52] R. Irmann. Sintered Aluminium Powder. *Symposium on Powder Metallurgy, Iron and Steel Institute,* London, 1954, pp. 236-41.

[53] N. F. Macdonald and C. E. Ransey. Preparation of High-Modulus Aluminium Alloys by Powder Metallurgy. *Symposium on Powder Metallurgy, Iron and Steel Institute,* London, 1954, pp. 242-8.

[54] R. S. Busk and T. E. Leontis. The Extrusion of Powdered Magnesium Alloys. *Trans. Amer. Inst. Min. & Met. Eng.,* 1950, **188,** 297–306.

[55] D. J. Brown. Powder Metallurgy of Magnesium. *Symposium on Powder Metallurgy, Iron and Steel Institute,* London, 1954, pp. 248-52.

[56] G. S. Foerster and H. A. Johnson. Private communication from the Dow Chemical Company Ltd., Midland, Michigan.

[57] H. G. Cole. Some Experiments on the Extrusion of Magnesium and Aluminium Powders. *J. Inst. Metals,* 1957-8, **86,** 29-35.

[58] P. Loewenstein, A. R. Kaufmann and S. V. Arnold. The Metal Beryllium. *Amer. Soc. Metals,* Cleveland, 1955.

[59] J. L. Klein, V. G. Macres, D. H. Woodward and J. Greenspan. The Metal Beryllium. *Ibid.,* Cleveland, 1955.

[60] P. J. Sukolski and G. Hoyle. B.I.S.R.A. Report No. MW/G/25/58.

[61] P. J. Sukolski. B.I.S.R.A. Report No. MW/G/26/57.

CHAPTER IX

The Properties of Extruded Metals

In the main, extruded metals enjoy a high reputation both in regard to their standard of quality and for their good physical properties: the latter, indeed, are commonly superior to those obtained in other wrought forms. All the same, it has to be acknowledged that they are not always entirely homogeneous, being subject, just as are metals fashioned in other ways, to a number of aberrations which are liable to impinge to some extent on certain of their applications. It is important to avoid exaggerating these unduly, and to get them in their right perspective by seeing in what they consist and how they come about. In any examination of the consistency and uniformity of quality and properties there are two main aspects to consider. The first concerns the presence of definite flaws and defects arising from the inclusion of impurities, gas, oxide, etc., which takes place either during the casting of the billets or, as has been seen may occur, as the outcome of the mode of deformation of the metal during extrusion. The second arises from the manner in which the properties are affected according to the amount of the deformation, its distribution over the length and cross-section of the extruded part, the temperature at which the working is carried out, and so forth.

Extrusion billets may be cast in water-cooled moulds, in cast-iron moulds, or by a continuous process, the technique used depending on the characteristics of the alloy being cast and the quantity and size of billets required. Without entering upon a discussion of melting and casting practice, concerning which there is nowadays no lack of authoritative information,[1] reference can be made to some of the chief sources of extrusion faults traceable to the billets. Enough has been said about flow during extrusion to show the importance of the surface condition of the billet; it must be as clean, smooth, and regular as possible. Casting procedure must therefore be adapted to this end to

273

avoid wrinkling or roughness of the skin, splashes and laps, and the entraining of oxide membranes. Subcutaneous gas cavities, due to blowing, or from the mould dressing, are most undesirable. Gas is also an important form of unsoundness in the ingots generally, and has, of course, several sources beyond those just mentioned. Much depends on the melting conditions with the opportunity which is given for the absorption of gas, especially hydrogen, from the furnace atmosphere or the fluxes. Gas is also formed in some instances by reaction between dissolved oxide and the mould dressings, and between oxides and gases dissolved in the molten metal. In addition, air may be entrained during pouring. To all of these must be adjoined the possibility of the retention of gas originally in the metal. From whichever of these potential causes they arise, gas inclusions can be trouble-some in extruded material, particularly when they are situated near to the surface, for then they are liable to open out as blisters. These sometimes appear immediately on extrusion, or do so often when material is reheated, as, for instance, during the heat-treatment of aluminium alloys.

Other forms of unsoundness are associated with shrinkage, arising out of unsuitable pouring conditions or as the result of failure to obtain satisfactory feeding. A discard is made from the casting head, and sometimes too a rejection is made from the bottom of the ingot in the interests of soundness. It is often convenient to cast long ingots which are sawn into billets of the required length. This gives a proportionate reduction in the amount of scrap, but their production requires care in regulating the teeming to secure that freezing occurs from the bottom, so that these long castings of relatively small diameter are free from axial porosity.

Inhomogeneity, due to inverse segregation, occurs to a serious extent in extrusion billets of some alloys, as, for example, in duralumin. It has a special significance in regard to the satis-factory extrusion of tin bronzes.

The presence of inclusions of dross, and oxide, is mainly con-nected with the melting and pouring conditions. Protection from oxidation during pouring can be obtained in the case of metals such as brass, bronze, and deoxidized copper by the use of oily dressings on the moulds which give off volatile hydrocarbons.

Aluminium alloys on the other hand, and copper alloys containing aluminium, which form tough, irreducible oxide skins that are liable to become entangled in the metal, are difficult to cast satisfactorily by ordinary methods. To deal with these without turbulence and churning special casting processes are used. These include the well-known Durville method, and others such as that in which the metal is slowly poured into an almost horizontal mould which is gradually turned up into the vertical position. In another the book type of mould, with a false side which is built up as filling proceeds, thus allowing metal to be run in quietly with absence of splashing from a spout at low level, is used.

Opinion is divided as to whether it is better to insert the billet into the container with its upper end next to the die, or vice versa. From the point of view of possible unsoundness at the cast head, which may not be entirely eliminated by cropping, there is something to be said for the former because defective material then passes at once into the front end of the bar and is confined to a short length, whereas, as consideration of the flow has shown, the same material situated at the rear central part of the billet travels forward rapidly and enters the die at an early stage, continuing present in a drawn-out form over the greater part of the length of the bar. This is rather well exemplified by an experiment made by Newson[2] with composite brass billets. Two of these, of different composition but similar extrusion properties, had discs parted off one end and bored out centrally. These were then fitted on to a spigot machined on each billet, the disc of one brass going on to the opposite billet in each case, as shown in Fig. 161. The two brasses could be differentiated by etching sections taken after extrusion. In bars 13 ft. 6 in. in length extruded from these, the discs, placed next the pressure disc, were found to constitute part of the bar only 4 ft. from the front end, and extended over the rest of the length. Zeerleder,[3] on the other hand, firmly favours extruding with the head of the billet to the rear with aluminium alloys which show inverse segregation.

Those extrusion defects which have their origin in the flow sequence have already been mentioned in Chapter V, and will not be referred to again here.

Section of the Extruded Rod at

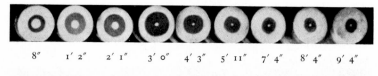

8″   1′ 2″   2′ 1″   3′ 0″   4′ 3″   5′ 11″   7′ 4″   8′ 4″   9′ 4″

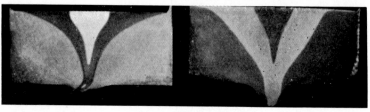

Section through billet.

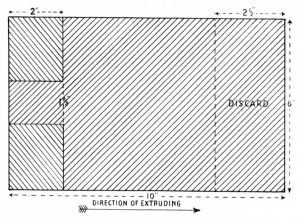

Flow of metals during extrusion of composite billet.

FIG. 161.

The Dependence of the Properties on the Degree of Deformation

The fact is familiar that the properties of most metals can be improved by working, and that while the extent of the improvement bears a relation to the amount of the deformation undergone, some metals require more than others to produce the maximum effect. For pure metals and uniform solid solutions possessed of high malleability in the cast state, the benefit produced is not very great and is fully realized without need for very extensive

276

working: it is due mainly to the elimination of the ingot structure by the breaking up of columnar and other unfavourable crystal arrangements which give a predisposition towards weakness in particular planes and directions. Metals which do not belong to the cubic system, like magnesium and zinc, are affected much more by working and show some peculiar effects due to their crystallographic anisotropy. The case of bismuth is interesting: extremely brittle in the cast state, breaking readily to expose large cleavage faces, it can nevertheless be extruded without difficulty at 40° C. or above, and is then found to have acquired a high measure of pliability. In alloys of more complex structure changes other than that of mere grain refinement are required to bring them into a fully wrought condition. The high-strength aluminium and magnesium alloys, for example, contain appreciable amounts of hard compounds in eutectic colonies or as groups of coarse particles rather unevenly distributed through the matrix of the alloy. Many of these are brittle and do not deform much during extrusion but are broken down into smaller fragments. The reduction required to do this and to distribute them uniformly in order to obtain the highest benefit from working, is high and seems to increase roughly with the amount of the hard phases and with the evenness of their occurrence in the first place. Sachs considers that for duralumin the reduction in cross-sectional area from the billet to the bar should preferably be not less than 85 per cent. Sections ought therefore to be extruded from a container large enough to allow an extrusion ratio of 7 at least.

Table 19 shows the variation in properties with increasing reduction in the case of a high-tensile brass containing Cu 59·0 per cent, Sn 1·0 per cent, Pb 0·65 per cent, Fe 0·85 per cent, Al 1·3 per cent, Mn 1·0 per cent. The figures refer to test-pieces taken axially from the extruded bars at corresponding positions.

The fact that deformation is greater in the outer zones of a bar than it is at the centre may result in differences between the properties at these places. The variation is greatest when the extrusion ratio is low, for then the centre receives only light deformation: in smaller sections, involving heavier reductions, both central and outer regions are sufficiently, even though not equally, worked to bring them into a fully wrought condition and the properties become more uniform.

TABLE 19

Reduction by Extrusion per cent	Extrusion Ratio	Yield Point tons/sq. in.	Ultimate Tensile Stress tons/sq. in.	Elongation per cent
75	4	17	35	30
86	7	18	36	30
94	16	19	37	27
97	36	22	40	25

The importance of doing enough work on the metal, and the effect of not doing so, is well illustrated by the figures in Fig. 162, relating to Schmidt's work on the alloy Electron VIw, quoted by Fiedler.[4]   These allow it to be seen that, given a certain minimum

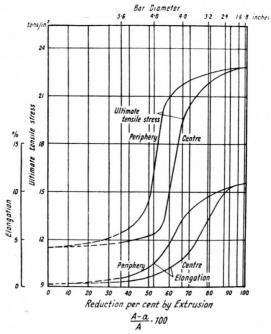

Fig. 162.—The tensile strength and elongation of extruded Elektron (*VIw*) in relation to the percentage of extrusion.   Starting from 7 inches diameter cast billet.

(*Courtesy of F. A. Hughes Ltd.*)

degree of reduction, there should be no great disparity in properties. Cook and Duddridge[5] have explored the hardness across
the sections of several sizes of rod, representing different reductions
in 60/40, free-cutting, and a high-tensile brass, finding only small
variations to exist. The highest hardness, just below the surface
of the bars, was only 2–6 per cent above that in the middle. Some
of their results are reproduced in Fig. 163, being included for

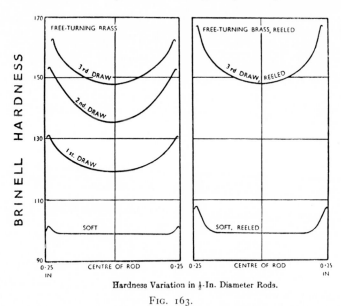

Hardness Variation in ½-In. Diameter Rods.

Fig. 163.

their interest in showing the effect of reeling and drawing on the
hardness distribution in extruded bars. No appreciable change
in diameter resulted from reeling. The curves for the drawn
condition represent successive drafts of 3·7, 5·7, and 5·9 per cent.
In further tests, on rods of a manganeze bronze for which the
extrusion ratio had been 31, the ultimate tensile strength of the
outer layers was 35·5 tons per square inch, compared with 32·6
tons per square inch at the centre.

Changes in Properties along the Extruded Length

From end to end of extruded lengths there are usually to be
found progressive changes in structure and in the associated

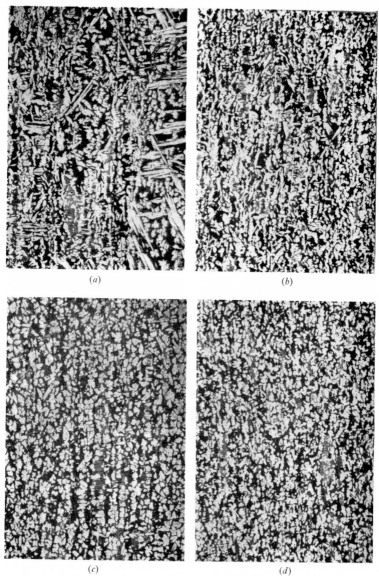

(a)   (b)

(c)   (d)

FIG. 164.—Micro-structures at different positions along $2\frac{1}{4}$-in. extruded bar (92 per cent reduction by extrusion) of brass with 58 per cent Cu, 2 per cent Pb.

 (a) Front end, centre of bar.   (c) Back end, centre of bar.
 (b) Front end, outside of bar.   (d) Back end, outside of bar.

All at 50 diameters.

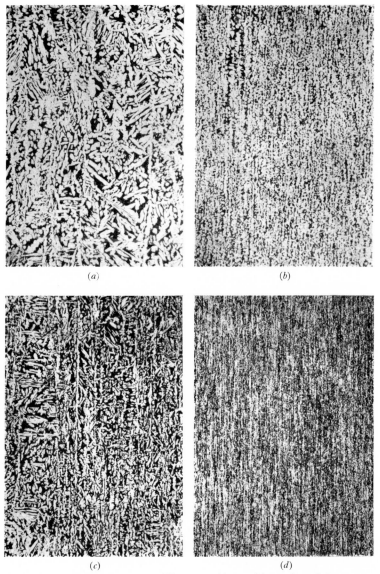

(a)	(b)
(c)	(d)

FIG. 165.—Micro-structures at different positions of brass bars (58 per cent Cu, 2 per cent Pb).

(a) 1·6 in. diam. (96 per cent reduction), front end.
(b) ,,   ,,   ,,   ,, back end.
(c) 0·5 in. diam. (99·6 per cent reduction), front end.
(d) ,,   ,,   ,,   ,, back end.
All at 50 diameters.

mechanical properties. While this is the case with most materials, it is more pronounced in those having a heterogeneous structure. The figures in the following table refer to test-pieces taken axially from the first and final thirds of extruded brass bar containing Cu 58 per cent, Pb 2 per cent.

The photomicrographs in Figs. 164 and 165 indicate the front and back end structures typically found in bars of different sizes in such material.

TABLE 20

	Proof Stress (0·1 per cent) tons/sq. in.	Ultimate Tensile Stress tons/sq. in.	Elongation per cent	H_B
Front end . .	12·8	27·9	40	88
Back end . . .	14·6	29·2	32	96

From an examination of duralumin, in which were included tests made on pieces cut eccentrically so as to include the highly worked peripheral zones seen in Fig. 166, as well as those taken axially

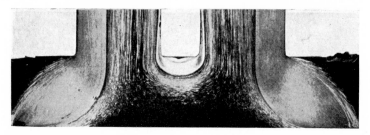

FIG. 166.—Etched residue of duralumin billet extruded through a two-hole die.

from the middle of the bars, Walbert[6] obtained the results below, from which it will be observed that the lateral differences are slight in comparison with the longitudinal.

Several factors contribute in causing these variations. In part they are attributable to the varying deformation sustained in different parts along the length which, as shown above, can exercise a considerable effect. In this respect it would be expected by reason of the flow distribution that material extruded by the

TABLE 21

Position of Test-piece	Elastic Limit tons/sq. in.	Ultimate Stress tons/sq. in.	Elongation per cent
Front end	19·0	29·1	15·2
Middle of Length . . .	19·6	30·6	14·1
Back end:			
(a) fine grained outer zone	21·0	32·7	17·6
(b) centre of bar . . .	21·5	32·1	13·5

inverted method would be more uniform in its properties than that from the direct process, and this is generally conceded to be the case. However, it is the latter process which is of greatest practical concern. In this, as already shown, after the immediate leading end which, having received only slight working, is coarse in structure and poor in properties, there follows over 60–70 per cent of the length metal that has received fairly uniform deformation in a longitudinal sense. Finally, as the back end is approached the metal has been subject to increasingly complex flow in the course of which it undergoes very severe working.

In the case, especially, of copper alloys and others requiring a high initial billet temperature there is superimposed on this variable working a progressive fall in the temperature at which the actual extrusion through the die occurs. The extent of this fall naturally depends on several factors, such as the actual temperature, the speed of extrusion, etc., and the range covered is generally greater when small sections are being made. It will be appreciated that the effects produced over the extruded length from this cause will be somewhat similar to those which would be brought about in hot rolled material from the use of different finishing temperatures, and will lead, if the temperature is high, to an overheated structure, or, if low enough, will give rise to some work-hardening. An example of the extent to which the properties are influenced by the extrusion temperature alone is given, for the case of a simple metal, in Fig. 170.

The structural variations encountered in brasses of the type referred to above are broadly as follows: starting with a high extrusion temperature, the front end tends to consist of large equi-axed β grains containing acicular masses of the α constituent.

The corresponding tensile properties are rather low, improving, however, as the grain-size diminishes. Behind this in the bar, or replacing it if the billet temperature to begin with was rather lower, the β grains possess an elongated character with the α phase preserving the Widmannstätten arrangement within these at first but changing gradually to assume a banded form lying parallel to the rod axis. This change is accompanied, both as regards tensile strength and elongation, by an improvement in properties. As the back end of the bar is approached, the directional character becomes more marked, especially in bars of small diameter. Finally, the tendency arises for the elongated α particles to change into chains of more or less rounded pieces, and this coincides, owing to the resulting continuity of the β phase, in a sharp rise in strength and fall in the elongation value.

Exaggerated Grain Growth

Structural heterogeneity of this kind is often of importance in relation to the further processing of extruded material, particularly where this involves reheating. Two instances of this may be given. Several investigations[7, 8, 9] have been made covering the structures found in extruded brass bars used for forging stock, with about 58 per cent of copper and 2 per cent of lead. For this material, extruded at 725° C. at approximately 0·5 in. per second, Hinzmann,[7] for example, found that the first third of a bar consisted of equi-axed β grains with long acicular pieces of the α constituent in a Widmannstätten arrangement. The temperature had been high enough to maintain an entirely β structure during its extrusion, and separation of the α phase had only taken place after the metal had passed through the die. About halfway along the bar the β grains had an elongated character and the α occurred partly in a rounded form as a result of having begun to separate before and during extrusion. The last 30 per cent or so of the bar, formed at a lower temperature, possessed a strongly marked fibre structure, consisting of a background of elongated β crystals embodying rounded masses of α linearly arranged. These changes took place first in the outer parts of the bar. When a bar with these features is cut into blanks, which are then reheated for forging, those from the first two-thirds of the bar behave satisfactorily, but those from the back end are unstable, showing pronounced grain growth which leads them to crack or split when they are pressed.

There is a general similarity between the above and the case of extruded duralumin reheated for forging or heat treatment. Here the rod, at first, has both its core and more-worked exterior consisting of long, spindly crystals. Continuing along the length, the highly worked outer zone increases in width until, at the back end, it extends well towards the middle; at the same time it becomes extremely fine-grained, as seen in Fig. 166, for a two-

FIG. 167.—Transverse section of extruded bar showing annulus of coarse crystals at the surface.

hole die. Often the fine-grained zones contain concentric rings of larger crystals which form in the extremely heavily worked metal coming in from the sides of the billet, where their origin can frequently be seen in sections of billet residues; in other cases they appear close to the die surface where the metal, already subjected to severe deformation, is further worked at the entrance to the die, where high local temperatures also tend to occur. Zones of this kind are shown in the section of bar in Fig. 167. On reheating, excessively large grains are liable to develop in the fine-grained areas at the back end of the bars, and this is the more marked the lower the rate at which they are heated. It is generally observed that liability to this gross crystallization extends over a greater length from the back end and further into the bar the lower the temperature at which extrusion is carried out. This is apparent in Fig. 168 which shows the structures of two discards extruded at different temperatures and subsequently heat-treated at 505° C. In Fig. 168 (*b*), which is of the discard extruded at the lower temperature, the metal has recrystallized and extremely large grains have developed, whereas in Fig. 168 (*a*) the metal has not recrystallized during heat-treatment and has retained its fine grain. Smith,[10] to whom this work is due, has stated that the examination of discards in this way may not reveal exactly the type of structure obtained in the extruded product from the particular billet being examined, although cross sections of the actual extrusions produced from the same billets, and also shown in Fig. 168, illustrate the same effects, after heat-treatment, as the discards.

The above phenomena appear to be related to other instances in which abnormally large grains are produced in worked metals. The best-known cases are those brought about in many metals when slight cold-working at the ordinary temperature is followed by annealing in an appropriate range: a critical degree of strain hardening is necessary, for which the deformation required is usually quite small, and larger deformations result in a much finer grain-size. Now the deformation in extrusion is, on the contrary, extremely heavy, and moreover is performed in the hot-working range in which strain hardening is absent. Thus the conditions are quite dissimilar. If, however, the temperature of extrusion is low, or falls to a low value during the operation, there is a possibility that some of the metal becomes cold-worked to some extent. It is perhaps significant, in this connection, that the *degree* of strain hardening as the result of cold-work depends on the temperature at which the work is applied and is less the nearer the approach to the true hot-working range. Thus it may well occur, in extrusion, that the degree of strain hardening requisite to the development of very large crystal grains is only attained in regions of very heavy deformation. The fact that temperature and deformation gradients exist in extrusion will favour the critical concurrence of these two factors, and it would seem possible to have, in different parts, (*a*) zones in which conditions favoured recrystallization with the development of

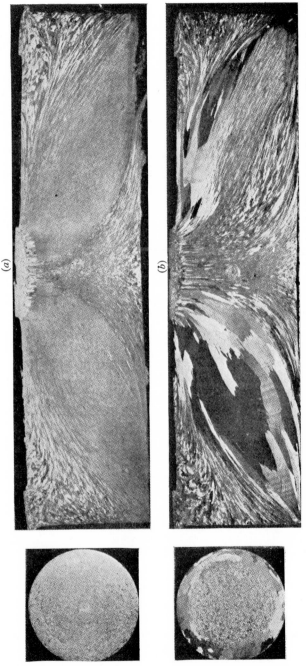

FIG. 168.—Extrusions and discards of D.T.D. 364B alloy heat-treated at 505° C. showing (a) fine grain of unrecrystallized metal and (b) coarse grain after recrystallization. × 1.

(Smith, 'J. Inst. Metals'.)

fine-grained structure, (b) places at which the deformation and temperature coincided to cause abnormal grain growth, and (c) other zones where the work was insufficient or the temperature too low for recrystallization of the elongated grains, though later, if these were heated, they might become the seat of grain growth. Gow[11] has suggested that exaggerated grain growth involves the same mechanisms as secondary recrystallization, by virtue of the fact that both processes occur in the same regions in aluminium extrusions. Textural analyses have indicated the probable importance of preferred orientations in these mechanisms and have lead to the suggestion that methods designed to modify the nature of the flow of metal during extrusion, with the idea of preventing critical strain, will be successful only if they are effective in altering the texture.

The methods available for controlling grain growth in extrusions have been summarized and discussed by Locke.[12] The techniques, already mentioned, of raising the extrusion temperature, so as to ensure complete recrystallization during extrusion, or of quenching at the die, so as to restrict recrystallization, may both be used in some circumstances, although both are of limited application. Certain alloying elements, such as manganese, chromium and zirconium, have the effect of raising the recrystallization temperatures of aluminium alloys, so that on heat-treatment the bar may remain in the work-hardened condition. However, Smith has shown that such additions are not always effective in preventing grain growth and even when they do result in fine-grained material they may give rise to deficiencies in mechanical properties.

Locke considers that the most rewarding methods for overcoming excessive grain growth are likely to be those in which the mode of flow is altered to reduce the strain effects below that of the critical value. In Germany[13] the technique has been tried of making apertures in the die additional to those of the particular shape required, and so relieving the strain in critical parts of the metal during its flow in extrusion. The method met with some success, but Smith is doubtful of its economic feasibility. Modification of the flow by the use of dies with a conical lead-in has been tried also, but again with only limited success. However, Singer and Ball[14] have indicated some improvement from simplifying the flow in a duralumin billet by the use of an aluminium sheath as a lubricant.

Subjecting the extrusion to a controlled amount of cold work before heat-treatment, has been suggested as a possible method of preventing grain growth. Smith has shown this process to be unreliable also, since large grains developed in some cold-worked, heat-treated products, which in the absence of cold-work would have retained a fine grain on heat-treatment. Additionally, this method would have the disadvantage that it would remove the ' extrusion effect ' (see page 290). Low-temperature annealing prior to solution-treatment, so as to remove by recovery the strain energy necessary for grain growth, has been shown to be successful on some occasions but to be so unpredictable as to be of little practical value. In the case of stamping brass, Smith and Swindells[15] have indicated the value of extruding at a relatively low temperature, thereby inducing considerable strain in the extrusion which would result in a fine grain size on heat-treatment. The method requires considerable increases in the loads required for extrusion and may be impracticable in the cases of some light alloys.

It is apparent that, as yet, there is no complete solution to the problem of exaggerated grain growth. The satisfactory production of a particular extrusion can only be achieved by careful study of the characteristics of the alloy and of the changes in size and shape effected by the deformation in each case, and by close regulation of the temperature and speed of extrusion.

Mechanical Anisotropy

Extrusion readily gives rise to directional properties due to the formation of a fibre structure in the direction of working. This may originate in several ways, as by the stringing out of inclusions or particles of hard constituents, by the linear distortion of cored dendrites to give a banded structure, and by the development of preferred orientations in the crystals.[11, 16] The properties in various directions relative to the axis for a manganese bronze rod, the extrusion ratio for which was 7·8, and of composition Cu 57·6 per cent, Sn 0·98 per cent, Mn 1·14 per cent, Fe 0·60 per cent, Pb 0·46 per cent, Zn rem., have been reported by Cook and Duddridge as follows:

TABLE 22

Position of Test-piece	U.T.S. tons/sq. in.	Elongation per cent	Izod Impact ft.-lb.
Longitudinal	31·5	41	28
45° to axis	30·3	29	26
Transverse	28·5	20	22

The transverse strength is almost invariably lower than in the longitudinal direction, the difference being most pronounced with heterogeneous materials which show a well-marked fibre. This has no great significance in the majority of applications since the applied stresses in service are generally such as to make the longitudinal properties of most importance.

A very low transverse strength is sometimes found in the back ends of extrusions in the strong aluminium alloys containing high alloying additions. Sachs associates this with the occurrence of minute longitudinal cracks, and puts out the suggestion that the intense shearing deformation in certain zones, combined with the presence in the flowing metal of stringers of particles of hard compounds, can cause loss of cohesion and the development of fissures. The transverse strength is most affected when the extrusion is done at a low temperature.

It has been suggested that the ' extrusion effect ', observed in certain aluminium alloys, is due to preferred orientation, although other factors exercise some influence on the phenomenon. The effect appears to have been first noted by Matthaes,[17] who observed that extruded rods and other sections in certain aluminium alloys are considerably harder and stronger than the same materials in the rolled or forged conditions. The following figures, due to Smith,[10] give some indication of the magnitude of the effect in a duralumin-type alloy after heat-treatment.

These higher properties persist after annealing or ageing treatments but come down to normal if heat-treatment is preceded by cold drawing by about 15 per cent. Further drawing produces an increase towards the original high properties.[18] X-ray and metallographic examination shows that the preferred orientation produced by extrusion persists after heat-treatment but is des-

TABLE 23

Form of Material	0·1 per cent P.S. tons/sq. in.	Ultimate Stress tons/sq. in.	Elongation per cent on 2 in.
(a) Rolled sheet, 0·064 in. thick	15·5	27·5	16
(b) Forged bar, ¾ in. dia., forged from (c) . . .	14·2	25·8	20
(c) Extruded bar, 2 in. dia. .	20·6	33·5	15

troyed if recrystallization is induced by drawing. Unckel associates the initial decrease in properties with the destruction of this texture, and the subsequent increase with further drawing is associated with a decrease in grain size.

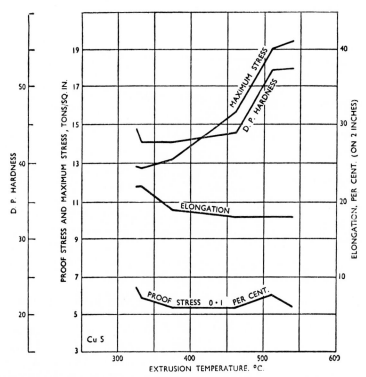

FIG. 169.—The mechanical properties of 5 per cent copper-aluminium alloy extruded at different temperatures.

The 'extrusion effect' is most marked in material extruded at a temperature approaching the upper practical limit, though it is then accompanied by a lower elongation. Even so, by using a high extrusion temperature and maintaining it uniform, the alloy can be regularly produced with a tensile strength 10–15 per cent above the normal specification. Low extrusion temperatures give lower and less regular properties. The effect is not

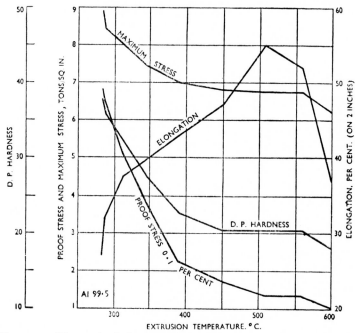

Fig. 170.—The mechanical properties of aluminium extruded at different temperatures.

an isolated one, and is strongly shown by other alloys.[19] For example, Fig. 169 shows, for a 5 per cent copper-aluminium alloy, the result of tests on bars extruded at different temperatures. Compared with Fig. 170, for aluminium in which the hardness and strength are lower the higher the working temperature, the results for the former are in the opposite direction.

The presence of small quantities of manganese or chromium is essential for the 'extrusion effect' to be observed in certain alloys. Fig. 171, from results obtained by Dreyer and Hansen,[20] shows the effect of increasing manganese content in a duralumin-type alloy on the tensile properties of extruded, extruded and drawn, and sheet material. A similar effect is observed with aluminium-zinc-magnesium alloys, in which chromium additions are also helpful. Dreyer and Hansen consider that the influence

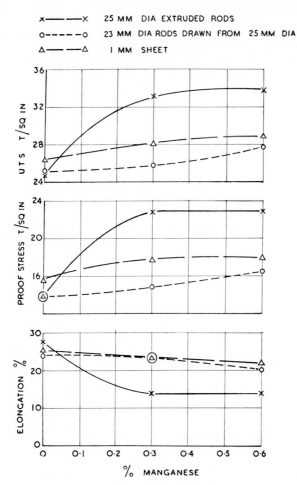

FIG. 171.—Influence of manganese content of duralumin type alloy on the ' extrusion effect '.

(*Hardy*, ' *Metallurgia* '.)

293

of these additions is due to their effect upon recrystallization, since they were able to show that recrystallization occurred at lower temperatures in a manganese-free alloy than in the same alloy containing 0·3 or 0·6 per cent manganese.

Hardy[19] considers that the evidence is fairly strongly in favour of Unckel's theory of preferred orientation, as being the cause of the high properties of extruded alloys in the longitudinal direction. Certainly the later evidence presented by Unckel[21, 22] lends considerable support to his earlier suggestion in this direction. In this later work he determined the mechanical properties in different directions on rods in the extruded and in the extruded, drawn and heat-treated conditions. The higher longitudinal properties in the extruded material were brought down to the same values as those in the transverse direction in the drawn and heat-treated material. Moreover, Unckel calculated the differences in mechanical properties to be expected from the different textures observed in extruded and drawn materials and showed that these were of the same order as those he obtained experimentally.

Preferred orientation is not without its effects upon the properties of magnesium alloys, as may well be expected from the fact that magnesium crystallizes in the hexagonal system, in which preferred orientation is likely to develop to a greater extent than in cubic materials. In extruded bars the grains are oriented so that the base of the hexagonal prism in each case lies approximately in the direction of extrusion, the main axes of the crystals having random orientation. This occasions a difference between the values of the proof stress in compression and tension, the former being only half to two-thirds the latter. This is a serious disadvantage for many technical purposes, and attempts have been made to remedy it.* Schmidt[23] puts the low compressive yield-point down to twin formation, which does not occur under tensional stress, and has shown that if it can be arranged to produce a fine-grained structure, in which twinning is much more difficult, a marked improvement can be obtained. This can be done either by extruding at a speed much below the maximum possible, and using a low temperature, or by extruding at a normal temperature and full permissible speed and quenching

* British Patent No. 337,706.

the metal immediately it leaves the die to suppress the growth of the grains. The figures in Table 24 show the effect of these methods.

TABLE 24

Extrusion Temperature ° C.	Proof Stress tons/sq. in.	Speed of Extrusion, in. per second on ram		
		0·08	0·25–0·3	0·6
250	in tension	15·5	15·2	15·2
	in compression	14·0	11·4	10·8
350	in tension	14·6	14·6	—
	in compression	8·3	7·9	—
350 followed by quenching	in tension	—	15·5	—
	in compression	—	14·9	—

REFERENCES

[1] *The Control of Quality in Melting and Casting.* Inst. Metals Monograph and Report Series No. 15.

[2] J. E. Newson. Discussion. *J. Inst. Metals*, 1931, **45**, 378.

[3] A. v. Zeerleder. *Tech. des Aluminiums*, 265.

[4] R. Fiedler. *Tech. of Magnesium and Its Alloys*, 370.

[5] M. Cook and G. K. Duddridge. The Effect of Drawing on the Hardness and Tensile Strength of Brass Rod. *J. Inst. Metals*, 1939, **64**, 311-29.

[6] H. Walbert. The Process of Flow in Light Alloys Extruded through Single and Multiple Dies. *Aluminium*, 1938, **6**, 379-85.

[7] R. Hinzmann. The Heat Treatment and Structure of $(\alpha + \beta)$ Brass. *Z. für Metallkunde*, 1927, **19**, 297-303; 1933, **25**, 67-70.

[8] W. Koster. The Technological Behaviour of Drawn Brass Rods. *Z. Anorg. Chem.*, 1926, **154**, 197-208.

[9] G. Sachs and W. Eisbein. The Power Consumption and Mechanism of Flow in Extrusion Presses. *Mitt. Material*, S. **16**, 1931, 67–96.

[10] C. Smith. *J. Inst. Metals*, 1949-50, **76**, 429.

[11] K. V. Gow. *Acta Metallurgica*, 1954, **2**, 396.

[12] D. H. Locke. *Metallurgia*, 1954, **50**, 268.

[13] F.I.A.T. Final Report, 1011.

[14] A. R. E. Singer and C. S. Ball. Golden Jubilee Issue, *J. Birmingham Met. Soc.*, 1954, p. 153.

[15] C. Smith and N. Swindells. Inst. Metals Monograph and Report Series No. 16. *The Control of Quality in Working Operations*, 1954, p. 47.

[16] J. F. W. Bishop. *Metallurgical Reviews*, 1957, **2**, 361.
[17] K. Matthaes. *Metallwirts.*, 1932, **11**, 176.
[18] H. Unckel. *Ibid.*, 1940, **19**, 37.
[19] H. K. Hardy. *Metallurgia*, 1944, **30**, 240.
[20] K. L. Dreyer and M. Hansen. *Z. für Metallkunde*, 1941, **33**, 193.
[21] H. Unckel. *Metallwirts.*, 1942, **21**, 185.
[22] —— *Ibid.*, 1942, **21**, 531.
[23] W. Schmidt. Crystal Structure and the Working of Metals, with Special Reference to Elektron. *Z. für Metallkunde*, 1933, **25**, 229–36.

CHAPTER X

The Impact Methods of Extrusion

The Manufacture of Collapsible Tubes

THE production of collapsible metal tubes has its origin in a patent taken in 1841 by John Rand for the making of 'vessels so constructed as to collapse under slight pressure and thus force out the fluid contained therein through proper openings for that purpose'. A simple form of screw-down press (Fig. 172) was used to begin with, and the method was applied to make lead tubes to contain artist's colours. Tubes made of tin were introduced some years later. According to Askew, the method was in operation in France in 1855, where Richard exhibited tubes at the Paris Exhibition in that year. It does not appear to have been actively taken up in America until about 1870, being introduced there by Wirtz from Austria. The industry has developed an ever-widening field of usefulness in the packing of such toilet preparations as tooth paste, shaving cream, cosmetics, etc.; and a diversity of other commodities like adhesives and cements, mustard, shoe polish, and so forth.

FIG. 172.—The first tube-making press used in 1841 by John Rand, inventor of collapsible tubes.

(*Courtesy of International Tin Research and Development Council.*)

Essentially the process consists in placing an unheated slug of metal, of thickness suitable for the length and wall thickness of the required tube, in a shallow die and subjecting it to a percussive blow by a punch or former to cause the metal to flow up over the punch through the annular orifice between it and the sides of the die. Normally the punch is undercut above a narrow shoulder so that the tubes fit loosely upon it and can be readily stripped off. Conical punches, which aid centring in the die and thus in giving concentric tubes, are preferable to those with flat ends. Meticulous polishing of the working surfaces of the tools over which the metal flows is required. A diagram of the arrangement is shown in Fig. 173. The base of the die in which the projecting nozzle of the tube is formed may be threaded so as to form an external thread on the nozzle ready to receive the screw-cap. In this case the die is either made in halves to open in removing the tube, an arrangement which lacks robustness in

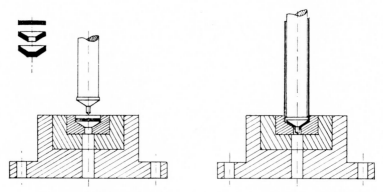

FIG. 173.—Formation of collapsible tubes by impact extrusion.

meeting the heavy stresses entailed in the process, or that part of the die containing the thread may be made to revolve to unscrew the tube. Generally, however, the nozzle is threaded in a subsequent operation. The die, which takes the form of an insert in a heavy steel holder, and the punch, are of fully hardened tool steel and have an average life of 300,000–400,000 tubes. Excellent service has been obtained in some instances by the use of cemented carbide tools, though particular care is needed with this material, owing to its rigidity, in ensuring that the die ring is fitted with extreme accuracy into the holder.

According to the purpose to which they are to be put, collapsible tubes are made of tin, lead or tin-lined lead, and also of aluminium. In the U.S.A. the Federal Food Laws disallow the employment of lead containers for food products, tooth paste, etc., and the use of tin tubes preponderates; in Europe, on the other hand, the cheaper tin-coated tube is very commonly resorted to. The tin used is not, as a rule, in the pure form, but is alloyed with 0·4–0·5 per cent of copper to increase the stiffness of the tubes; for the same reason lead tubes generally contain 0·6 per cent of antimony. Where, owing to the nature of the contents, corrosive action may be anticipated, it is by no means infrequent for the tubes to be sprayed internally with lacquer, or flushed out with hot wax. Alternatively, since corrosion is especially liable to occur at the nozzle where there is exposure to the atmosphere, a method has been evolved in which a pure tin nozzle is welded on in a later operation.

In the preparation of blanks for extrusion, the metal after melting and alloying in gas or electric furnaces, is cast in vertical or open chill moulds into the form of slabs $\frac{1}{2}$–1 in. thick, which are rolled out into sheets of the required gauge. These are fed into automatic blanking machines which cut out a number of circular discs at each stroke which are then rumbled in batches to detach adherent rags of metal. At this stage a measured quantity of lubricant is added to each batch. The question of lubrication is one of special importance in promoting even flow of the metal over the punch. Johnson[4] has indicated the comparative behaviour of a number of different lubricants and concluded that those which are liquid, and usually based on lubricating oils, are unsuitable. This seems to be due to the comparative ease with which they can be squeezed out under the very high pressures and at the elevated temperatures developed during the extrusion. Tallow, soaps, solid lubricants and lanolin generally behaved satisfactorily.

For the tin-coated tubes the blanks are cut from sandwich plates prepared by rolling a sheet of lead between two thin tin sheets, the relative thicknesses of the tin coating on each surface of the blanks being of the order of $2\frac{1}{2}$ per cent. In another method a sandwich ribbon, from which blanks are cut, is prepared by the extrusion of a composite billet of lead and tin from a small hydraulic press. In the blanking of tin-coated material it is desirable to contrive that the tin is drawn over the sheared edges of the blank, otherwise difficulty is met in securing a continuous coating over the tube. The making of extrusion blanks by die-casting has attracted attention, but, except in the case of zinc, has not proved yet to be economically feasible.

Mechanical presses of the crank, eccentric or toggle types are used to carry out the extrusion. Modern practice calls for machines of rugged construction in order to give the rigidity

FIG. 174.—Modern 80-ton semi-automatic tube extrusion press of Danish manufacture.

(*Courtesy of International Tin Research and Development Council.*)

needed to meet the precision required of the product. An illustration of one of these is given in Fig. 174. In some designs the stroke of the press is more than double the maximum length of tube produced to allow the latter to be stripped off the punch, but more usually a very short stroke is made and the punch, on withdrawal from the die, is tilted forward for stripping either by hand or by means of compressed air directed through the punch. A type of press has been introduced embodying a modified motion in which the punch comes almost to rest touching the blank and then accelerates to perform the extrusion, thus regulating the speed of the working stroke and easing the flow, whilst avoiding the shock of impact. It has still to be proved whether the advantages claimed for this modification in working are sufficiently real to warrant the additional cost involved in construction.

An interesting recent development by the Convair Division of General Dynamics Corporation[15] makes possible the impact extrusion of tough and brittle alloys by the use of high-velocity, high-energy forces developed from compressed air. By arranging for a piston, which acts as the impact tool, to be held in a state of equilibrium by a high air pressure acting on a small area of one end of the piston and a low pressure acting on a large area of the opposite end of the piston, the machine is set for firing. If the high pressure is now increased so as to cause the piston to move and arrangements made, through an appropriate valve, for the effective area over which the high-pressure air is acting to be increased by a small movement of the piston, then the piston can be made to move forward at energies up to 1,500,000 ft. lb. with velocities exceeding 2,000 ft./sec. Such forces, of explosive, or near-explosive, intensity, make it possible to form metals which would rupture during fabrication by normal methods. This would appear to be a field worthy of further detailed study.

While blanks may be fed into the machine by hand, in the latest methods this is done through coin or hopper feeds, and by employing these in conjunction with air stripping and a conveyor system, the operation of the presses can be rendered entirely automatic. Semi-automatic presses operate at speeds of 20–30 strokes per minute, and those which are fully automatic at about 60 s.p.m., giving an output of 200 gross per day.

After extrusion, the nozzles of the tubes are pierced, and screw threaded, and the open ends are trimmed to length by removing the flash; these operations being done in small high-speed lathes. They are then ready to receive a base coat of cellulose paint, after which they pass by conveyor through thermostatically regulated drying ovens and thence to a two or more colour printing machine where they receive a design appropriate to their intended purpose. They finally travel through a drying oven, and, after undergoing inspection, proceed to the packing stage.

At the present time, collapsible tubes can be made in sizes up to a maximum of 3 in. in diameter and 12 in. in length, with wall thicknesses varying according to the other dimensions from 0·005 in. to 0·010 in. Larger tubes than these could doubtless be made by the use of more powerful presses.

Possibly on account of the inherent experimental difficulties, there is very little published information on impact extrusion regarding the effect of such factors as the composition and structure of the metals employed; form of punch, speed of operation, etc. Derge and Warren Stewart,[1] in a study of the process in an experimental apparatus, have investigated the form of pressure curves obtained at different speeds of extrusion for alloys of tin containing small amounts of copper, and for various grades of pure tin. Their results confirm those found by Pearson and Smythe[2] for the extrusion of rods from long billets in that the pressures required are found to vary exponentially with the extrusion speed. In neither case did the rates of straining even approach those encountered in impact extrusion and any attempt to extrapolate the results to the very much higher rates resulting from impact is likely to be unsafe because of

(a) The effect of rate of strain on the stress/strain properties of the extruding metal.

(b) The effect of inertia and resilience of the tools.

These two factors have been referred to by Johnson[3] as those which exert the major influence in distinguishing impact from slow-speed extrusion.

A systematic research into impact extrusion has been conducted by a group of workers guided by Professor H. W. Swift in the University of Sheffield during recent years.[4] They have studied the cold extrusion of different metals at various strain rates up to those encountered in impact extrusion, which they have simulated with the aid of a drop hammer.[5] In certain respects the basic characteristics of extrusion under impact are similar to those at slow speed. Thus, Wallace[5] has shown that while lead slugs of various thicknesses may require slightly different pressures for their successful extrusion the results are not essentially different when the rate of straining is varied between those limits normally met in slow extrusion and impact extrusion. Similarly, the effect of the extent of the reduction upon extrusion pressure is only slightly different under impactive conditions from the semi-logarithmic relationship observed at slow speeds. Johnson[4] has given the results of tests made to study the effect on the extrusion pressure of the profile on punch heads and compression discs used in the manufacture of collapsible tubes. In the extrusion of lead and aluminium, tools with circular profiles, as shown in Fig. 175, with $R_1 = 10$ in. and $R_2 = 7$ or $12 \cdot 5$ in. or $R_1 = 5 \cdot 7$ in. and $R_2 = 7$ in., gave the lowest maximum pressure during successful tube forming.

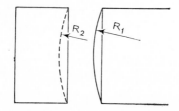

FIG. 175.—Tool profiles for impact extrusion.
(*Courtesy of British Iron and Steel Research Assoc.*)

Undoubtedly of the greatest importance in impact extrusion is the effect of speed and its relation to temperature effects. It has been shown[5] that some 90 per cent of the work done on the slug appears as heat, which is frequently sufficient to raise the temperature of the newly formed tubes over 100° C. The Sheffield workers have investigated the effect of this heating in an indirect way by comparing the pressure-distance curves of an interrupted extrusion with that of a straight-through extrusion. The purpose of the interruption was to allow sufficient time for the heat generated during the previous extrusion to dissipate before the next stage of extrusion began. The envelope of the interrupted extrusions therefore approximates to the curve that would have been obtained if the slug had remained cold during the whole process of extrusion. The results indicated, for both lead and aluminium, that temperature effects were negligible at speeds of the order of 0·05 in. per minute. At the speed of 8 in. per minute the envelopes of the interrupted extrusions were greater than those of the straight-through extrusions, indicative of heat being liberated at a rate sufficient to depress the yield strength of the metal. This effect may be expected to be even more marked at the higher speeds employed in industrial impact extrusion.

Under isothermal conditions, increasing rates of straining, in general, raise the yield strength of metals.[6] Since strain heating has the opposite effect, it may be expected that the effect of different speeds of impact extrusion, compared by their influence upon pressure requirements, may not follow a simple law, but will vary from one metal to another and with the geometry of the extrusion. Such behaviour is indeed observed.[4]

The flow of the metal during the forming of collapsible tubes has been the subject of some study by the Sheffield Group.[4] This has shown that the zone of deformation lies very close to the punch, on the face of which there is considerable sliding of the metal, discouraging the formation of dead metal zones. As may be expected, the severest distortion occurs at the punch corners. Varying the speed of extrusion produced no differences in the flow patterns for lead and aluminium, although studies of the flow resulting from the use of tools of various profiles showed interesting differences. Thus flat punch heads and compression discs cause specially severe deformation of the metal in the vicinity of the die orifice. The same is true of a punch head having a spherical depression. Radii or chamfers at the edges of tools help to ease the deformation at the orifice, but a spherical profile seems to make the deformation still more uniform, which probably accounts for the lower pressures required with such tools.

The Impact Extrusion of Aluminium

Following upon pioneer work in the U.S.A. and Germany, the extrusion of aluminium by impact methods started as a commercial proposition in 1920. Besides being concerned with the manufacture of collapsible tubes, such as those in Fig. 176, many other articles in the form of deep shells are also made, and the process enters into competition with methods involving deep drawing sequences. Such additional outlets include cans and capsules for food products, radio condensers and shielding pots, electric torch cases, etc.; there are also applications in the textile and aircraft industries.

Although as compared with cold drawing, the call made upon the tools is very heavy, the advantages of extrusion are numerous. A single operation in the latter replaces several drawing stages with intermediate annealing treatment, so that fewer machines are required and production is more rapid. In addition, the

FIG. 176.—Collapsible tubes in aluminium.
(*Courtesy of H. G. Sanders & Son, and British Aluminium Company.*)

higher strength of the extruded product often permits a reduction in the thickness of the article to be made. The point at which extrusion can economically replace drawing depends not only on the depth of the shell required, but also on other factors such as shape. For instance, rectangular shells which present difficulty in drawing, are readily extruded. For plain round shells with a flat base it may be taken that extrusion becomes profitable when the length exceeds $1\frac{1}{2}$ times the diameter. Other special advantages are that the thickness of the base is not related to that of the wall, but may be regulated by adjustment of the stroke of the press; the base can be made flat or conical and may include integral lugs, which need not be centrally placed. Holes in projecting lugs or nozzles can be pierced during extrusion only if they are coaxial with the shell. The sides of shells, on the other hand, must usually be straight and of even thickness, although external and internal axial fins are possible: fluting of the walls, for example, must be done subsequently if it is required. Embossed lettering can only be formed on the base, by engraving the bottom of the die.

Though they are generally rival processes, impact extrusion and drawing can often be combined with advantage, shells made in a preliminary stage by the former being later increased in depth by drawing.

The grade of aluminium for impact work is of very considerable importance, for while metal of a purity of 99·5 per cent can be used, it imposes arduous conditions on the tools, causing wear to be heavy, and a purer metal of 99·75 per cent is much to be preferred. Following the introduction in 1936 of the refined product containing 99·9–99·99 per cent of aluminium, it has been used in increasing amounts, possessing distinct advantages on account of its high ductility. Its physical properties are shown in Table 25.

TABLE 25

Al per cent	H_B	Maximum Stress tons/sq. in.	Elongation per cent
99·5	22	5 –5·5	35–40
99·99	14	2·3–3·0	40–50

Despite the movement towards the softer grades of aluminium for most purposes, where superior strength is required there is a tendency to look in the direction of the more easily worked aluminium alloys, and the production of shells in several of these has been achieved.

As a general rule aluminium is extruded cold in impact methods, although by heating the blanks to 175°–250° C., an advantage is obtained both in the diminution of pressure on the tools, and in increasing the depth of shell which it is possible to form. The following figures, quoted by Zeerleder,[7] show the relative resistance to extrusion offered by aluminium and some of its alloys at 20° C. and at 250° C., from which it will be inferred that many of them do not lend themselves to impact extrusion.

TABLE 26

Material	H_B at 20° C.	Specific Extrusion Pressure Kg./sq. mm.	
		At 20° C.	At 250° C.
Refined aluminium (99·99 per cent)	14	81	–
Aluminium (99·5 per cent) . .	23	114	42
Aluman	32	120	–
Anticorodal	34	152	83
R.R.56	52	194	–
R.R.59	58	204	–
Avional D	58	230	162
Peraluman 2	58	240	–

After the blanks have been cut, they must be annealed to make them as soft as possible for extruding. In this connection the grain-size is of some importance, for while slightly lower hardness is associated with a coarse-grained structure, such a structure is most undesirable in other respects. In a series of tests on aluminium made by Stelljes,[8] blanks having grain-sizes varying from 150 per sq. mm. to 0·04 per sq. mm., with hardnesses ranging from 20·4 to 18·6, were extruded. A coarse grain in the blank was found to persist in the shell, giving rise to a rough, orange-peel effect on the surface. Photographs illustrating this also serve to give an insight into the manner and distribution of the deformation, and are reproduced in Fig. 177. The material which first passes over the punch to form the top of the shell suffers least deformation, but this increases as extrusion proceeds, and finally, towards the base, a zone of equi-axed crystals may be seen. From this it would seem that increasingly severe work, coupled with a rise in temperature, has brought the metal to a point where recrystallization has taken place locally.

A few of the blank shapes which are used are shown in Fig. 173.

The cupped form, with an angle of 45°, is of benefit in securing a deep shell. When a nozzle is to be formed on the base, the blanks are pierced to allow the passage of the projection on the end of the punch. Rectangular shells are formed from similarly shaped blanks.

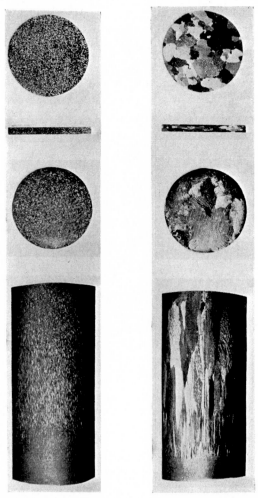

FIG. 177.—Impact extruded aluminium shells from blanks with different grain-size. The macro-etchings show, starting from the top, the surface and section of the blanks, and the base and side of the extruded shells.

The work-hardened condition in which the shells leave the press is retained where stiffness is desirable; on the other hand, for collapsible tubes, or in cases where further working remains to be done, complete or, possibly, local annealing is carried out.

Aluminium is much stiffer to work than lead or tin, so that it

FIG. 178.—350-ton Bliss press for impact extrusion of aluminium.

is necessary to have much heavier presses than for the latter. One of these is illustrated in Fig. 178. The extruded shells are stripped by compressed air, as with the softer metals, or, in the case of tubes with perforated ends, by means of spring stripper plates which push them off the punch on its upstroke.

The range of impact extruded shells in aluminium is from 0·5 in. up to 5 in. in diameter, with a maximum length for the widest of these of about 10 in., the thickness to which the walls can be made varying with the size from 0·004 in. to 0·06 in.

The Production of Zinc Shells

The purity of zinc affects its successful working to an extent even greater than with aluminium, and practice is confined almost wholly to the use of the special grades containing 99·99 per cent of the metal, though restricted use is made of an alloy with 0·6 per cent of cadmium for dry battery cells. In addition to their application in this direction, extruded zinc parts find outlets in the radio industry and for small electrical units, having one advantage over aluminium in the ease with which they can be soldered. Production is mainly confined to cylindrical parts. The metal is unsuitable for making collapsible tubes.

The blanks are preheated prior to extrusion to bring them into the range from 150° to 180° C. in which the metal possesses considerable plasticity. Chase[9] gives the limiting sizes which come within practical operation as being from 0·437 in. outside diameter to a maximum of 2·125 in., with a lower limit for the wall thickness of 0·014 in. for the smallest shells, to 0·020 in. for the largest. These dimensions can be held to 0·003 in., while the thickness of the base can be controlled to 0·007 in. The longest shells, obtainable with the greatest width, are 8 in., and the smallest $2\frac{1}{2}$ in.

The Impact Extrusion of Magnesium

Impact extrusions have been made from pure magnesium and most of its commercial alloys.[10] The extrusions made have been of the sizes and shapes used in dry-cell batteries, consisting mainly of round cans varying in diameter from about $\frac{7}{16}$ in. to $1\frac{1}{4}$ in. and from 1 in. to 6 in. in height. The process for magnesium impact extrusions is basically the same as for other metals, the main difference being the temperature of operation, which may vary from 175° C. to 390° C. depending on the alloy and speed of operation. Slugs may be made from cast, powder compact, extruded bar or plate material, a graphite dispersion, applied in a carefully controlled quantity by tumbling, being used as lubricant.

The Hooker Process of Impact Extrusion

The impact extrusion of soft metals had long been established when, in 1903, George W. Lee stumbled across an interesting modification which has proved valuable in making thin tubes in the harder metals. While he was engaged at Binghampton, N.Y., U.S.A., in the manufacture of collar-studs, Lee conceived the idea of the bachelor button type of fastener consisting of two parts, a stud and a press fastener. As it was made at first, the stud was pressed from an aluminium blank to the form shown at *a*, Fig. 179. It occurred to him that by a slight modification of the tools, a stud of improved appearance, as seen at *b*, could be produced without additional cost. This seemed to require that the punch should have a small projection at the end; one made with the projection somewhat longer than had been the intention was found, surprisingly, to give, when it was tried, a short length of tube attached to the flanged part of the stud, as at *c*. This result led him to make further experiments on the same lines, and, finally, to seek patent protection for a method of producing tubular bodies by extrusion in this way. Considerable difficulties were encountered in obtaining this, since the Patent Office at Washington could not be convinced from the drawings that the method was feasible, and only agreed to grant a patent after arrangements had been made for the process to be witnessed.

(*a*)   (*b*)

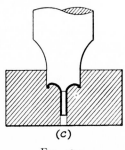

(*c*)

Fig. 179.

Despite all his efforts, Lee was unable to make a commercial success of his idea, and after a few years of endeavour, he sold the rights to a patent lawyer, Leslie Hooker, who had been following the process, and from whom it derives its present name. Hooker and his associates formed a company with a factory at Pawtucket, R.I., where, when some improvements in detail had been effected, they were able to bring it to the productive stage.

The Hooker process as it is run to-day remains fundamentally

the same as when Lee developed it. Briefly, it consists in introducing a cold blank into a strongly supported cylinder containing
a die bush, into which is entered a punch made to fit the die
closely so as to prevent the escape of metal round its sides. The
pressure exerted by the shoulder of the punch upon impact first
squeezes up the blank, and then as the punch continues to descend,
causes it to extrude through the annulus formed by the projection

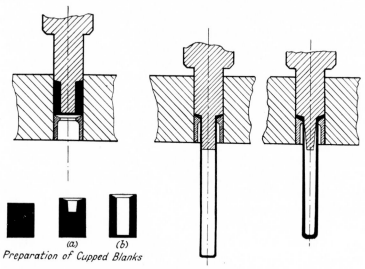

Preparation of Cupped Blanks

FIG. 180.—Hooker impact process for tubes.

on the punch and the die bush. The diagram in Fig. 180 shows
the principal features of the method. The close resemblance
which the arrangement bears to that used in the production of
tubes by direct extrusion of hot billets in hydraulic presses may
be remarked.

While the Hooker method is applicable to lead and tin, it is
chiefly utilized in fabricating metals which undergo work-
hardening during deformation. The metals which are most
suitable are those possessing a good degree of ductility, such as
copper, 70/30 brass and aluminium. For these materials Hooker
extrusion has the advantage over the other impact method that
the pressure required in forcing a thick-walled blank down into
a thin shell is less intense than in making the metal flow up round

the punch; thus the tools, which are necessarily subjected to extremely arduous duties in bringing about large deformations in a single blow on such stiff metals, are relieved to some extent.

Flat blanks are occasionally used in Hooker working, but the cupped type, despite the additional coining which they entail, are preferable and economically worth while, since by leaving a lower degree of reduction to be effected by extrusion, thin tubes are more readily made. Open-ended or closed tubes can be made at will. If a heavy base is required, as for cartridge-cases, the blank is cupped so as to leave the bottom thick; tubes in which the base is to have the same thickness as the walls are made from blanks which, after cupping, are stamped to thin the base to the extent required, while for open-ended tubes a thickness of only a few thousandths of an inch is left in the base after blanking. By tapering the end of the punch, so that, as it descends into the die during the extruding motion, the annulus diminishes, tubes with a tapered wall thickness can be produced. The sketches in Fig. 180 show some of these variations.

Used at one time extensively in the U.S.A. for forming brass cartridge-cases, the process is utilized chiefly at present for the manufacture of copper tubes for the radiators of liquid-cooled aircraft engines, and for heat exchangers. The following is an outline of the sequence of operations for this purpose. In the first place, high-grade copper of at least 99·9 per cent purity must be selected, and it is usual to employ the electrolytic product. Lightly drawn rod is cut in a shearing machine into cylinders $\frac{7}{16}$ in. in length, and these are formed into blanks for extrusion in two operations in heavy draw presses. After a preliminary anneal at 600° C., they are indented in the first stage to the form shown at a in Fig. 180, and are then re-annealed before being fully indented as at b into cups $\frac{9}{16}$ in. in length, $\frac{7}{16}$ in. in diameter, with a wall $\frac{1}{10}$ in. thick. These are once again annealed before being extruded directly into tubes 10 in. long, 0·265 in. diameter, having a thickness of 0·006 in. $\pm$ 0·0005. If necessary, the wall thickness can be reduced to as little as 0·004 in. The tubes are produced in a severely work-hardened state, so that before the ends can be pressed into the final hexagonal form, local annealing must be carried out.

The presses which have been found most satisfactory for the

process are straight-sided crank presses of the geared or plain type, with a stroke of only about 2 in. One of these is shown in Fig. 181. Each press carries two sets of dies, above which the punch-holders are mounted on slides to which a transverse reciprocating motion is given, travelling at half the speed of the

FIG. 181.—40-ton Bliss press used for the Hooker process.

press. Each slide carries two punches, one for extrusion, the other for trimming. Taking the sequence of events for one of these sets: a pin-ring hopper feeds the cup blanks on to a friction dial-plate, and, as the cross-head of the press descends, the extrusion punch picks up one of the cups, while at the same time the trimming punch enters the die and severs the tube previously extruded from the residual flange or discard which it lifts out of

314

the die on its nose, the released tube dropping out on to a tray below the press. The slide now moves across, and on the next down-stroke the extrusion punch, carrying the blank, enters the die and, after compressing the blank, extrudes it into a tube. Simultaneously the trimming punch enters a spring stripper which pulls off the discard on the upward stroke. The other slide with its two punches is meanwhile carrying out the same sequence over its particular die, but on the opposite stroke, so that tubes are extruded alternately from each die at every revolution of the press, which operates at 120 s.p.m., giving a production of about 45,000 tubes in an 8-hour day. Crane refers to a modification of the process by which, instead of using the reciprocal motion and trimming punch, a single punch is fixed to the cross-head. One blank follows another in succession without clearing the discard out of the die; each new blank forcing out the remnant of the previous one. The consecutive tubes, separated by a film of lubricant, are said to be easily broken apart for trimming.

The die assembly consists of a soft steel holder plate shrunk round a die-ring of hardened high-speed steel. Within the die-ring is fitted a die-bush, also of high-speed steel, which is replaceable when it becomes worn. The average life of this part, working on copper, is about 60,000 operations. The upper surface of the bush, forming the step in the die with a bevel of about 30°, is highly polished and is given a small radius at the inner edge. The aperture of the bush, which, of course, controls the outside diameter of the tubes, is ground and lapped to size. The extrusion punch is made in two parts, so that the projecting nose which serves as a mandrel and suffers the heaviest wear, can be renewed, usually after making about 15,000 to 20,000 tubes. The extruding shoulder on the punch is tapered to 20°; actually extrusion takes place most readily with a flat punch and steep die, but a compromise is effected on this to reduce the amount of discard.

The astonishing reductions which it is possible to effect on copper and brass in what is apparently a cold-forming process would probably repay fuller investigation than it has hitherto received. The reduction of 95–97 per cent imposed in the extrusion of the copper tubes described above, is far in excess of that which can be given in other forming processes without the introduction of annealing stages. The case of 70/30 brass is similar, though the reduction by extrusion does not usually exceed 75 per cent. Attempts to carry out the extrusion operation slowly instead of under impact invariably results in the breaking of the tools under the excessive pressure, and the success of the impact method is, therefore, related to the speed of deformation. Considerable heat is, of course, generated during the interval of about $\frac{1}{15}$ of a second, during which compression and extrusion of the blank takes place. Foisy[11] states that during production of copper blanks of the size given, weighing 7·5 gm., the initial pressure on the punch is 50,000 lb., falling to 10,000 lb. when flow has started. Taking the mean pressure as 20,000 lb., and neglecting friction losses in the machine, and transfer of heat to the tools, the heat developed would be sufficient to raise the copper to 360° C., at which self-annealing would be possible. It is certainly the case that unless the tools are kept cool by copious lubrication, the tubes produced are in the soft condition. Ordinarily, however, the dies are flooded with oil, and the tubes leave the press at 150°–200° C., showing work-hardening. An explanation which may be offered for the unusual plasticity under impact, lies in the well-known fact that the extent of hardening as the result of deformation is dependent on the temperature, being less at high than at low temperatures in the cold-working range; hence the heating up of the blank as it is upset and begins to flow allows greater subsequent deformation than would ordinarily be possible without ductility becoming exhausted or the pressure becoming excessive. Jevons[12] has put forward the interesting suggestion that, as indicated by high-speed tensile tests, hardening as the result of deformation is not instantaneous, but takes an appreciable, though small, time to manifest itself, so that work done under impact may be complete before hardening has asserted itself. It may be pointed out that indications of the existence of a stage of momentary fluidity in metals during straining are not lacking, and if a phenomenon of this kind was definitely established it might well prove to be of importance in cold-forming processes generally.

The Cold Extrusion of Steel

The cold impact extrusion of steel was initiated in Germany in the late 1930's, since when it has undergone considerable development, particularly in the United States. The process is not practicable, due to the excessive pressures required, if the bare steel is simply coated with one of the usual types of lubricant, and its successful exploitation has stemmed from the discovery, in Germany, of the value of phosphate coating applied to the steel prior to the lubricant. Holden[13] has reviewed the effect of phosphate coatings in assisting cold extrusion and, while stating that the mechanism whereby they operate is not completely understood, has indicated the importance of some of their properties. The coatings consist of aggregates of tertiary zinc-phosphate crystals which are strongly adherent to, and completely cover, the steel surface. Due to their capilliarity, phosphated surfaces retain more lubricant than bare steel surfaces, and the fact that the coating is most effective when used in conjunction with a soap, vegetable oil or animal fat, suggests that this property is of some importance. However, it is clear that this is not the only function of the phosphate coating, since there is some evidence that such coatings possess plastic properties and behave like a high-viscosity lubricant under the conditions of cold extrusion. Additionally, it has been suggested that there is some reaction, as well as adsorption, of the lubricant upon the phosphate and this assists in the reduction of friction between the steel and tools.

The technique of impact extrusion in the case of steel is not essentially different from that described previously for aluminium, and the subjects of die and press design with particular regard to steel have been discussed in a series of papers presented at a conference on the subject.[13] Wilson[13] has considered the metallurgical requirements of steels for cold extrusion and the properties of extruded components. Most of the steel to which cold extrusion is applied is of low-carbon, deep-drawing, quality, although the technique is being extended to low-alloy and other steels.[14] The microstructural condition of a steel for impact extrusion should be such as to render the material as soft as possible in order to limit extrusion pressures; coarse spheroidized carbide particles, uniformly dispersed, may be expected to give the lowest pressures. In general, the effects of the rate of straining and of the heat generated by the deformation will be the same in the case of steels as in the case, previously discussed, of non-ferrous metals, but with the additional complication of strain-ageing effects with certain steels. The surface quality of the blanks is likely to be of particular importance where there is an increase in external diameter during extrusion, since surface defects may then open up and give rise to longitudinal defects on the external surface of the pressing.

REFERENCES

[1] G. Derge and J. Warren Stewart. *Trans. Amer. Inst. Min. & Met. Eng.*, 1940, **137**, 389.

[2] C. E. Pearson and J. A. Smythe. *J. Inst. Metals*, 1931, **45**, 345-69.

[3] W. Johnson. *Ibid.*, 1955-6, **84**, 165-79.

[4] —— B.I.S.R.A. Report, MW/E/55/54.

[5] J. F. Wallace. B.I.S.R.A. Report, MW/E/66/54.

[6] D. S. Clark and G. Datwyler. *Amer. Soc. Test. Mat.*, 1948, **38**, 98.

[7] A. v. Zeerleder. *Tech. des Aluminiums* (published by Akademische Verlagsgesellschaft Leipzig) 1938, p. 265.

[8] H. A. J. Stelljes. *Aluminium*, 1939, **21**, 279-300.

[9] H. Chase. *Product. Eng.*, 1937, **8**, 214-15.

[10] T. L. Patton. *Modern Metals*, 1951, **7** (10), 54-8.

[11] G. A. Foisy. *Trans. Amer. Soc. Mech. Eng.*, 1927 **50** (9) 93.

[12] J. D. Jevons. *Metal Industry*, 1938, **53**, 615-18.

[13] Conference on the Cold Extrusion of Steel. *Sheet Metal Industries*, 1953, **30**, 445-524.

[14] T. E. Lloyd and E. S. Kopicki, *Iron Age*, 1949, **164**, 90.

[15] ——. High Pressure Impact Extrusion and Press-Forming Process. *Met. Ind.*, 1959, **94**, 109.

CHAPTER XI

Some Special Applications
of Extrusion

Extrusion Forging

AN example of a combined forging and extrusion process is to
be found in the manufacture of poppet valves for internal-
combustion engines. These are made in one operation from a

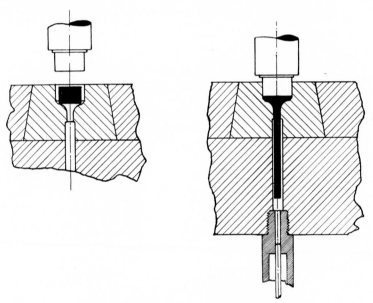

FIG. 182.—The extrusion of steel poppet valves.

heated steel blank which is partly extruded through a die to
form the shank, leaving the remainder of the metal to form the
head. The general arrangement of the punch and die used for
this is shown in elevation in Fig. 182. The die is lubricated
before the operation with a high-flash oil. In the method used

319

at the Chevrolet works[1] slugs $1\frac{1}{4}$ in. diameter and $\frac{15}{16}$ in. long are sheared off steel bars which have been heated to 850° C. These slugs are then smoothed and descaled in tumbling barrels before being reheated to 1100° C. in a gas-fired furnace. Extrusion is performed in a 300-ton punch press, in which the blanks are fed directly into the die, where they are struck by the descending punch. The metal is squeezed up to fill out the die and is then forced, in part, through the aperture in the base to form the valve stem. The base of the die is so shaped that the material remaining unextruded when the punch has made its full stroke forms the head and shoulders of the valve. After extrusion the valves are tumbled again, cut to length in a punch press, and finally annealed. A chrome steel with the following composition is typically used for the valves: 0·4–0·5 per cent carbon, 0·3–0·5 per cent manganese, 3·0–3·5 per cent silicon, 8–10 per cent chromium, 0·025 per cent sulphur and phosphorus.

A method* of forming projectile shells from steel billets by a continuous operation in which a forging stage in a closed die is followed by extrusion is illustrated in Fig. 183. To begin with a hot billet, 1, inserted in a press container, 2, is acted upon by a ram, 3, with attached mandrel, 4, so as to force the metal into the die-chamber formed by the die-ring, 5. During this the lower end of the die-ring is closed by a plug, 6, to permit the base of the shell to be formed and consolidated. The completion of this stage is shown at (a). In one method of operation, the plug is held in its operative position by a hydraulic ram, 7, the pressure on which becomes released when the pressure on the plug exceeds a predetermined value. When this is reached, and the plug is free to be displaced, the operation is completed by the further descent of the press ram causing the extrusion of the remaining portion of the billet through the die-ring and so giving rise to the hollow shell as seen at (b).

The production of hollow forgings includes many examples in which extrusion is a factor in that the dies are only semi-enclosed, and have an opening at the top through which the punch is entered, leaving an annulus through which the metal, while going partly to take up the special configuration of the die cavity, is also forced out to form part of the object. These really result

* British Patent No. 469,550.

from an out-growth of processes for making shells and projectiles by piercing methods. Cone[2] has described the practice in America of the Bethlehem Steel Corporation in making speciality forgings in nickel-chrome, chrome-molybdenum, nickel-chrome-molybdenum, and corrosion-resisting steels, as well as in ordinary carbon steels. Billets broken off long steel bars are preheated to suitable temperatures in the range 1150°–1260° C. These are

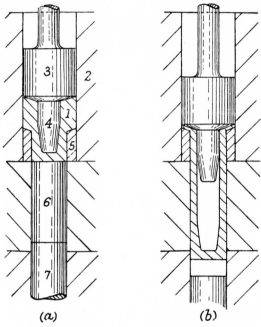

FIG. 183.—A forging-extrusion operation.

inserted in the die where they are pierced by the descending punch, causing the die to be filled out and the extrusion of part of the metal. The hollow pressings so derived are then often push-drawn by being placed on the end of a long mandrel and forced through a series of drawing rings. In this way they are elongated and have their wall thickness reduced. Instances of the above kinds of forgings are illustrated in Fig. 184, which include those for such applications as cylinder sleeves for aero-motors, trunk pistons for loco-boosters, valve bodies, and short lengths of tube for bearing races.

A further interesting adaptation of extrusion is in the production of turbine blades. It is possible to form a turbine blade with an integral root from a round or flat billet, much after the manner described above in making poppet valves, by extruding part of the metal to form the blade section and leaving enough of the billet in the container to form the foot. In the case where a round billet is used, the root section can be flattened while the metal is still hot after removal from the press. A method* devised by Henry Wiggin & Co., however, gives the advantage that several

FIG. 184.—Examples of hollow extrusion-forgings.
(*Courtesy of ' Steel '.*)

blades, each with integral root, are extruded simultaneously from one billet, and that the roof portion receives more adequate working. The essential feature of this process lies in the use of a specially shaped container, or die, the inner wall of which is formed with a number of recesses each shaped to correspond with a turbine blade of the required form. In Fig. 185, (*a*) and (*b*) show the sectional elevation and plan respectively of such a container designed to make four blades at the same time. The bottom of each recessed opening, 1, is shaped as indicated at 2, so as to conform with the desired shape of the root of the blades. The container, which is mounted in a 400-ton vertical hydraulic

* British Patent No. 459,742.

press, has a closure block at its lower end during the extrusion stroke. The extrusion ram has an approximately squared end, indicated by the lines 3. A hot cylindrical billet having been inserted, the extrusion ram enters the container and forces the metal to flow outwards into the recesses, whence it extrudes

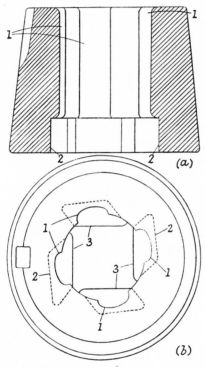

Fig. 185.—Sketch of the special ram and die used in the extrusion of turbine blades.

upwards into the space between each recess and the exterior of the ram.

On completion of the working stroke, the article consists of a thin residual disc in the base of the container with four rooted blades extending from it at right angles. By moving the closure block laterally to a position where a large opening in it coincides with the bottom of the container, the extruded assembly can be ejected by the ram and removed from the press.

The process can be applied to produce blades of different section and length in such materials as monel, austenitic heat-resisting steels, stainless steel, as well as in brass or copper. As extruded, the blades in some of these metals tend to be somewhat soft and, with the object both of bringing up the physical properties and of finishing the blade profile to very accurate dimensions, they are subsequently subjected to a cold rolling or swaging process which increases their hardness.

Fig. 186.—Drilled billet $3\frac{3}{8}''$ diameter $\times$ 6" long, in Nimonic 90.

The extrusion process lends itself particularly well to the manufacture of turbine blades and the like when these are required to have one or more longitudinal passages. Cylindrical billets of the alloy (the Nimonic Series may be so treated) are drilled to a predetermined pattern (Fig. 186) and the holes are filled with mild steel rods or other suitable fillers which can be removed from the component at the end of the forming operations. The filled billet is then extruded directly under glass lubrication just as though a solid bar was being made, with the exception that it is first located in the container so that the hole pattern is in a desired orientation with respect to the die orifice. After the discard has been removed and the product deglassed, it may then be subjected to a further reduction in area or change in form by hot-rolling or forging and the filler is retained for these operations. At the end of the forming processes, the filler is removed before machining is begun. Fig. 187 typifies this type of product and illustrates three alternative hole patterns in a constant section aerofoil suitable for nozzle guide vanes.

FIG. 187.—Extruded Wiggin cooled blade sections.

In such cases the design must be such as to allow the use of constant section bar, but in most forms of moving blade this is not possible. Here again, blades with an integral root may be produced with internal cooling channels from filled billets. A rectangular billet is usually the starting point and the leading portion is extruded to aerofoil form, the stroke being limited so that the unextruded portion is of sufficient length to allow the fir-tree root to be machined therefrom, as in the cases mentioned earlier. The filler is removed before machining usually, but not until any further forming operations, such as imparting twist or changes in profile along the length of the blade, have been completed. Fig. 188 shows a partial extrusion sectioned to show the interior of one of the passages.

FIG. 188.—Part extrusion in Nimonic 90.

The Extrusion of Cathode Copper

An interesting technique which deserves attention is that developed in the U.S.A. for the conversion of electro-deposited copper cathodes into commercial products in the form of tubes, rod, wire and strip without the necessity for remelting it in the first place.[3, 4] In the result a material of very high purity is obtained, free from all but the merest traces of oxide, which compares favourably in its analysis and electrical characteristics, with O.F.H.C. copper. It also meets the usual hydrogen-anneal bend test for the latter. The principle of the process depends on the fact that if particles of cathode copper are subjected to a stream of reducing gas at a high temperature and the clean surfaces are then brought together under pressure, they cohere. Perfect metallic union occurs, with crystal intergrowth between the surfaces so as to produce a homogeneous mass. The process is covered by the term ' coalescence '.

The operations which are involved are: (*a*) the production of the cathodes in a brittle condition to allow them to be broken up, (*b*) cold briquetting, (*c*) heating and cleaning in a reducing atmosphere, (*d*) simultaneous coalescing and extrusion. The practice followed in the deposition of the brittle cathodes has been adapted to that of the standard multiple tankhouse, with precautions against entry of dust. Blanks similar to the ordinary starting sheets, but attached by soldered contact to the cathode bars, are dipped, before immersion in the depositing tanks, in a bath of embrittling agent. This consists of a solution of corn oil and asphaltum in petrol and carbon tetrachloride. During deposition the film of reagent prevents close adherence of the metal to the blank, and also between the deposited crystals themselves. After washing, the brittle deposit is stripped by rapping it with a hammer. It is then passed through 4-in. openings in a harddrawn copper grizzly, and after automatic weighing, is conveyed to the briquetting press. This is a hydraulic press in which cylindrical billets approximately 300 lb. in weight, $9\frac{3}{4}$ in. in diameter, and 16 in. in length are pressed up cold under a pressure of 15 tons per square inch. A density of 83 ± 2 per cent of that of massive copper is aimed at so as to give the necessary bonding strength and at the same time allow gas penetration in the next stage.

Gas purification is carried out in a ' pusher ' type of gas or electrically heated furnace. The briquetted billets rest on carriers, and are kept isolated to prevent them sticking to one another. They remain in the furnace for 3 hours and are brought up to about 850° C. The reducing gas mixture, which must contain hydrogen and/or carbon monoxide and be freed from sulphur, has a high proportion of water-vapour. Its action is to reduce any surface oxide and to eliminate most of the sulphur in the metal, as well as removing about 15 per cent of the arsenic and antimony.

Special measures are required to transfer the hot billets from the furnace to the extrusion press in the same atmosphere in order to avoid reoxidation of the copper aggregate. Each billet is pushed by a hydraulic ram through a gas-tight metal housing into a sealed loading chamber in front of the press container. The extrusion ram then pushes it into the container. Apart from this the extrusion press is of the conventional horizontal type. The container used is 10¼ in. in diameter, and extrusion pressures from 10 to 30 tons per square inch are required, the latter for products down to 0·6 sq. in. in cross-sectional area. As in standard practice, flats and small rods are coiled hot as they come from the press. Table 27 shows the average composition of the coalesced copper product in comparison with that of wire-bar from the same anode source, and with that of O.F.H.C. copper.

TABLE 27

	Wire-bar from Tough Cathodes	Coalesced Copper	Oxygen-free, High-conductivity Copper
Cu . . .	99·9534	99·9871	99·9800
O . . .	0·0372	0·0035	0·0000
S . . .	0·0014	0·0008	0·0025
As . . .	0·0008	0·0007	0·0008
Sb . . .	0·0016	0·0013	0·0028
Se, Te . .	0·0002	0·0003	0·0031
Ni, CO . .	0·0005	0·0005	0·0016
Fe . . .	0·0005	0·0005	0·0015
Pb . . .	0·0004	0·0005	0·0004
Ag . . .	0·0016	0·0020	0·0016
Au . . .	0·000026	0·000033	—

It will be apparent that, in principle, the foregoing process has a near resemblance to those methods by which powdered metal aggregates are consolidated and shaped into serviceable forms by the application of pressure and heat. The differences lie chiefly in the much smaller sizes of particles used in ordinary powder-metallurgy practice and in the means adopted for shaping, which in the latter case is usually carried out in a cold pressing operation followed by sintering. The existence of definite limitations in regard to the size, and especially the length, of product that can be made in pressed powder compacts has caused some attention to be given to the practicability of extruding the powders. Though the idea has attractions from more than one point of view, there may be difficulties in its application. These are discussed in a survey of the question by Jones.[5] The above refers to dry powders, but in other directions extrusion has for long found application in connection with metal powders, for it formed the basis of one of the early methods of manufacturing metal lamp filaments. In this, tungsten powder admixed with a binder to give plasticity was extruded into threads which were then rendered strong and tenacious by sintering. More recently, the commercial production of rods, tubes, nozzles and other shapes, consisting of hard carbides of metals such as tungsten, tantalum, and titanium, has been undertaken. Here again a plastic binder, such as starch or gum arabic, is mixed with the carbide powder for the extrusion process, the products being subsequently baked, and finally sintered at a high temperature in a protective atmosphere. An application of a similar kind lies in the preparation of special rods for arc welding. An interesting feature of this is that a small amount of flux is incorporated with the comminuted metals, besides the usual binder to facilitate extrusion. An instance of such a mixture is one consisting of 38 per cent copper, 53 per cent phosphor-copper (15 per cent P), 8 per cent tin, and 1 per cent borax. The rods are sintered at 235° C.

REFERENCES

[1] J. B. Nealey. The Extrusion and Annealing of Chevrolet Motor Valves. *Heat Treating and Forging*, 1936, **22**, 523–4.

[2] E. F. Cone. Extruded Steel Forgings. *Steel*, 1934, **94**, 25–7.

[3] H. H. Stout. Coalesced Copper: Its History, Production and Characteristics. *Amer. Inst. Min. and Met.*, Tech. Pubn. 1238, 1940.

[4] J. Tyssowski. The Coalescence Process for Producing Oxygen-free Copper. *Amer. Inst. Min. and Met.*, Techn. Pubn. 1217, 1940.

[5] W. D. Jones. The Extrusion of Metal Powders. *Met. Ind. (London)*, 1940, **57**, 27–30.

Index

331

Johnson, *see* Dodeja
Johnson & Collins, 205
Jones, 26, 328
Jordan & Thomson, 220
Judge cable-sheathing press, 51

KASTNER, 261
K–monel, 237
Körber, 182
Krupp yoke-frame press, 100

LEAD ALLOYS, age hardening of, 61
for cable sheaths, 59
for impact extrusion, 298
for pipe, 28
Lead and alloys, continuous extrusion of pipe, 26
melting and casting of, 45
pipe, 2, 21, 26
pipe bend presses, 9
slug extrusion, 57
Lee, 311
Lee, *see* Northcott
Lepp, 234, 235
Lindner, 134
Locke, 288
Loewy, 110, 123
Logan, 137
Löhberg, 198, 261
Lorant, 91
Lubrication, 163, 171, 242, 246, 263
in impact extrusion, 299, 316, 317

MACDONALD & RAMSEY, 266
McKeown & Hopkin, 60, 61
McLean, *see* Northcott
Magnesium alloys, 255
properties of, 257, 295
powder, extrusion of, 267
Malthaes, 290
Mandrels, steels for, 110
types of, 86, 91
Manganese bronze, 229, 230
Mechanical presses, 78, 300, 314

Mechanical properties, brass, 230, 231, 282
dependence on work, 276
duralumin, 283
in transverse direction, 290
lateral variation in, 279
longitudinal variation in, 279
magnesium, 257, 278
zinc, 261
Metal powders, extrusion of, 266, 326
Miller, 264
Molybdenum, 265
Moudry, *see* Wilhelm
Monel metal, 237, 324
Multi-hole extrusion, 173, 178, 199
Muntz metal, 230

NAVAL BRASS, 230
Newson, 164, 275
Nickel alloys, 237
-aluminium bronze, 230, 232
-silver, 230, 232, 236
Nimonic alloys, 324
Northcott, McLean & Lee, 173
Nozzle-swirl process, 48
Nuclear reactor fuel elements, 265

OXIDE FILMS, entrained in extrusion, 23, 37, 157, 164, 170, 171
prevention of, 26, 42, 161

PEARSON & SMYTHE, 64, 145, 183, 302
Peters, 29
Phosphate coatings, for impact extrusion of steel, 317
Phosphor-bronze, 235
Pickling, of steel extrusions, 241
Pick-up, of aluminium alloys, 249
Piercey, 46
Piercing, of billets, 87
Piping, 157
Pirelli cable-sheathing press, 53
Plane strain extrusion, 207

335